艾略特詩選

〈荒原〉、〈四重奏〉
及其他觀察

艾略特　著

杜國清　譯

T. S. Eliot

出版弁言

　　艾略特無疑是二十世紀最具代表性的詩人之一，其詩作、詩劇、評論等等，不僅在歐美引起龐大的討論和研究，連帶輻射到亞洲，擴散到全球，於文學創作和批評都有相當顯著的影響。

　　《荒原》迄今猶被認為是英美現代詩歌的領航者，時值出版一百周年，遂邀請杜國清先生對這部經典詩篇重新譯釋。杜國清先生是臺灣最早接觸並譯介艾略特著述的先行者之一，於六〇年代起便有相關譯作發表，尤其是譯著《艾略特文學評論選集》（田園出版社，1969）的出版，既為臺灣最早系統性整理艾略特詩觀的專書，亦開啟了彼時認識艾略特的便捷通道。

　　本書最初的構想是從編排〈荒原〉為獨立詩集出發，然而身兼詩人、學者、譯者等多重身分的杜國清先生提出了更理想的建議，既然要向艾略特致敬，何不精心嚴選其重要的代表詩作集結成冊，不僅梳理艾略特在詩創作上的脈絡，也能夠一窺艾略特文字對現世關懷的面向。因此，便將全書定調成求質不求量，也不求全的「艾略特詩選」，輯錄詩人於 1917 至 1936 年間創作的傳世作品。

　　所有艾略特的詩作皆採中英對照，其間出現的希臘文、拉丁文、德文、法文、義大利文、梵文等均如實呈現，詩句則編入行碼，以利讀者參閱。書中亦保留艾略特的原註，同時加入杜國清先生自己的譯註，讓部分內容相對晦澀的詩作較容易親近。在

翻譯上，杜國清先生沿用過去的古典用字與時代語境，並與現代詞彙取得平衡，充分詮釋出艾略特詩的背景氛圍，卻又不致顯得突兀。

　　書末的附錄，除整理艾略特生平之外，特將艾略特的文學論及《荒原》的翻譯版本等重要研究一併集中，使其書寫面貌更為完整。而基於尊重發表時間，文章內容除將體例調整一致，盡量維持原貌不再更動。

　　在紛擾動盪的時局下，由〈荒原〉揭櫫問世以來，艾略特不朽詩作深刻且前瞻的預示，無疑仍為人們提供了一盞照亮前途的明燈，進而走入其精神領域，探究深奧卻也最真切的世界觀，使心靈飽足滋潤，視野開闊清澈，繼續迎向下一個世紀。

陳逸華　謹誌
2022 年　冬日

CONTENTS

Prufrock and Other Observations

普魯佛洛克及
其他觀察

·1917·

Prufrock and Other Observations
1917

The Love Song of J. Alfred Prufrock

S'io credesse che mia risposta fosse
A persona che mai tornasse al mondo,
Questa fiamma staria senza piu scosse.
Ma perciocche giammai di questo fondo
5. *Non torno vivo alcun, s'i'odo il vero,*
Senza tema d'infamia ti rispondo.

Let us go then, you and I,
When the evening is spread out against the sky
Like a patient etherized upon a table;
10. Let us go, through certain half-deserted streets,
The muttering retreats
Of restless nights in one-night cheap hotels
And sawdust restaurants with oyster-shells:
Streets that follow like a tedious argument
15. Of insidious intent
To lead you to an overwhelming question…

普魯佛洛克及其他觀察
1917

普魯佛洛克的戀歌

假如我的回話是向著
可以回返陽世的人，
我這團火焰就不再搖晃；
既然沒人能從地獄活著回去，
5. 假如這句話當真，就是
回答你我也不怕染上惡名。

那麼我們走吧，你我
當黃昏擴展在天邊
像麻醉在手術台上的病人；
10. 我們走吧，走過半荒涼的街道
走過不眠的夜在細語的偏僻地帶
那些只住一晚的下等旅館，以及
蠔殼散亂的鋸屑的餐館：
背後的街道像一場冗長的議論
15. 帶著詭譎的意向
把你引向無可逃避的問題……

Prufrock and Other Observations
1917

Oh, do not ask, "What is it?"
Let us go and make our visit.

In the room the women come and go
20. Talking of Michelangelo.

The yellow fog that rubs its back upon the window-panes,
The yellow smoke that rubs its muzzle on the window-panes
Licked its tongue into the corners of the evening,
Lingered upon the pools that stand in drains,
25. Let fall upon its back the soot that falls from chimneys,
Slipped by the terrace, made a sudden leap,
And seeing that it was a soft October night,
Curled once about the house, and fell asleep.

And indeed there will be time
30. For the yellow smoke that slides along the street,
Rubbing its back upon the window-panes;
There will be time, there will be time
To prepare a face to meet the faces that you meet;
There will be time to murder and create,
35. And time for all the works and days of hands
That lift and drop a question on your plate;

普魯佛洛克及其他觀察
1917

哦，別問我「那是什麼？」
我們走吧，我們拜訪去。

　　婦人們在客廳來回走著
20. 談論著米開蘭基羅。

　　暮色的煙霧在窗玻璃上摩擦背脊，
暮色的煙霧在窗玻璃上摩擦鼻尖
在黃昏的每個角落，伸著舌頭，
在汪著汙水的池塘上逡巡著，
25. 背上承載著煙囪飄落的煤煙，
溜過了陽台邊，突然下跳，
看出這是十月柔謐的夜晚，又在
屋子附近捲起旋渦，然後沉沉入睡。

　　真的啊還有時間
30. 讓暮色的煙霧在街上蹓躂，
在窗玻璃上摩擦背脊；
還有時間，還有時間
準備一張臉會見你所會見的臉；
還有謀殺與創造的時間
35. 還有從事每日所有工作的手
抬起的疑問掉落在你的餐盤上的時間；

Time for you and time for me,

And time yet for a hundred indecisions,

And for a hundred visions and revisions,

40. Before the taking of a toast and tea.

In the room the women come and go

Talking of Michelangelo.

And indeed there will be time

To wonder, "Do I dare?" and, "Do I dare?"

45. Time to turn back and descend the stair,

With a bald spot in the middle of my hair—

[They will say: "How his hair is growing thin!"]

My morning coat, my collar mounting firmly to the chin,

My necktie rich and modest, but asserted by a simple pin—

50. [They will say: "But how his arms and legs are thin!"]

Do I dare

Disturb the universe?

In a minute there is time

For decisions and revisions which a minute will reverse.

55. For I have known them all already, known them all—

Have known the evenings, mornings, afternoons,

普魯佛洛克及其他觀察
1917

你有你的，我還有我的時間啊，
還有躊躇百次猶在躊躇，
幻見千回尚且幻見的時間，
40. 在拿起土司喝茶之前。

　　婦人們在客廳來回走著
談論著米開蘭基羅。

　　真的啊還有時間
懷疑：「我敢嗎？」「我真的敢嗎？」
45. 還有回身走下樓梯
看見我頭上禿出中間一塊的時間——
（她們會說：「他的頭髮長得好稀喲！」）
我的晨禮服，我的硬領穩穩地架在下顎，
我的領結華美而優雅，以一枚樸素的飾針扣住——
50. （她們會說：「可是他的手臂和腿好瘦喲！」）
我敢嗎
我敢擾亂宇宙嗎？
在一瞬間還有決定和修訂的時間
卻讓另一瞬間完全加以否定。

55. 　　因我早就熟識了那一切，那所有的一切——
熟識了那些黃昏，早晨，午後

I have measured out my life with coffee spoons;

I know the voices dying with a dying fall

Beneath the music from a farther room.

60.　　So how should I presume?

And I have known the eyes already, known them all—

The eyes that fix you in a formulated phrase,

And when I am formulated, sprawling on a pin,

When I am pinned and wriggling on the wall,

65.　Then how should I begin

To spit out all the butt-ends of my days and ways?

And how should I presume?

And I have known the arms already, known them all—

Arms that are braceleted and white and bare

70.　[But in the lamplight, downed with light brown hair!]

Is it perfume from a dress

That makes me so digress?

Arms that lie along a table, or wrap about a shawl.

And should I then presume?

75.　And how should I begin?

普魯佛洛克及其他觀察
1917

我用咖啡匙量出了我的人生；
我熟悉從那房間傳來的音樂底下
餘音裊裊而終於消逝的聲音。
60.　　　現在，我該怎麼表示呢？

　　　而且我早已熟識了那些眼睛，熟識了那一切——
那些把你們安釘在公式化的套語裡的眼睛，
當我被公式化地套住，趴在釘針上，
當我被釘在牆上掙扎時
65.　到底，我該怎樣開始
吐掉我日常生活的菸蒂？
　　　現在，我該怎麼表示呢？

　　　而且我早已熟識了那些手臂，熟識了那一切——
那些戴著手鐲露出的雪白的手臂
70.　（但在燈光下，有著淺棕色的茸茸細毛！）
一時使我心慌意亂的
是衣飾裡的香氣嗎？
在餐桌上伸直或捲著圍巾的那些手臂。
　　　現在，我就得表示了嗎？
75.　　　我該怎麼開始呢？

Shall I say, I have gone at dusk through narrow streets
And watched the smoke that rises from the pipes
Of lonely men in shirt-sleeves, leaning out of windows? …

　　I should have been a pair of ragged claws
80. Scuttling across the floors of silent seas.

And the afternoon, the evening, sleeps so peacefully!
Smoothed by long fingers,
Asleep… tired… or it malingers,
Stretched on the floor, here beside you and me.
85. Should I, after tea and cakes and ices,
Have the strength to force the moment to its crisis?
But though I have wept and fasted, wept and prayed,
Though I have seen my head [grown slightly bald] brought in
upon a platter,
I am no prophet—and here's no great matter;
90. I have seen the moment of my greatness flicker,
And I have seen the eternal Footman hold my coat, and

普魯佛洛克及其他觀察
1917

我得說嗎，我曾在黃昏穿過狹窄的街道
望見了穿著襯衫探出窗外的寂寞男人
從他們的煙斗冒起的紫煙？……

　　我無寧該是一對粗糙的蟹螯
80.　在沉靜的海底急急橫行。

午後，黃昏，如此安寧地沉睡！
長長的纖指愛撫著的，
酣睡的……疲倦的……或許它在裝病，
四肢伸躺在地板上，就在你我的身旁。
85.　到底在吃過午茶與點心與冰水之後
我有力量將這緊張的瞬間推進高潮嗎？
雖然我曾痛哭絕食，我曾痛哭禱告，
雖然我曾見過我的頭（微禿的）被放在大盤上帶進來，
我可不是先知──何況這兒沒有重大的事情；
90.　我曾見過自己偉大的瞬間閃耀，
而且我曾見過永恆的僕人拿著我的外衣吃吃地笑，

snicker,

And in short, I was afraid.

And would it have been worth it, after all,

After the cups, the marmalade, the tea,

95. Among the porcelain, among some talk of you and me,

Would it have been worth while,

To have bitten off the matter with a smile,

To have squeezed the universe into a ball

To roll it toward some overwhelming question,

100. To say: "I am Lazarus, come from the dead,

Come back to tell you all, I shall tell you all"—

If one, settling a pillow by her head,

Should say: "That is not what I meant at all.

That is not it, at all."

105. And would it have been worth it, after all,

Would it have been worth while,

After the sunsets and the dooryards and the sprinkled streets,

After the novels, after the teacups, after the skirts that trail

along the floor—

And this, and so much more?—

110. It is impossible to say just what I mean!

普魯佛洛克及其他觀察
1917

總而言之，我真是害怕喲。

　　　到底是不是值得呢
　　在咖啡，果醬，午茶之後，
95.　是不是真的值得：
　　在瓷杯之間，在你我的談話間，
　　露出微笑就將事情咬掉？
　　是不是值得將宇宙捏壓成球
　　滾到那個無可逃避的問題？
100.　是不是值得說：「我是拉撒路，我從死裡復活，
　　我回來做見證，向你們訴說一切」——？
　　要是有人在她的頸邊放個枕頭：
　　　「我可沒那個意思，一點也
　　　沒有那個意思。」——這麼說也是值得的嗎？

　　　到底是不是值得呢
105.　是不是真的值得：
　　在日暮，在前庭，在灑了水的街道之後，
　　在小說之後，杯茶之後，長裙曳過地板之後——
　　這個，以及其他種種之後？——
110.　我沒法說出我真正的意思！

But as if a magic lantern threw the nerves in patterns on a
screen:
Would it have been worth while
If one, settling a pillow or throwing off a shawl,
And turning toward the window, should say:
115.   "That is not it at all,
        That is not what I meant, at all."

No! I am not Prince Hamlet, nor was meant to be;
Am an attendant lord, one that will do
To swell a progress, start a scene or two,
120. Advise the prince; no doubt, an easy tool,
Deferential, glad to be of use,
Politic, cautious, and meticulous;
Full of high sentence, but a bit obtuse;
At times, indeed, almost ridiculous—
125. Almost, at times, the Fool.

        I grow old… I grow old…
I shall wear the bottoms of my trousers rolled.

普魯佛洛克及其他觀察
1917

就像幻燈將神經做成種種模樣放映在銀幕上吧：
是不是真的值得呢
要是有人放好枕頭或扔下披肩，
然後轉身向著窗口：
115. 　「我可沒那個意思哪，一點也
　　沒有那個意思。」這麼說也是值得嗎？

不！我不是哈姆雷特王子，也無意是他；
我只是隨侍的貴族吧了，一個只能
推動情節的進展，客串一二場面，
120. 對王子進諫的隨臣吧了；無疑的，爽手的用具
卑遜且樂於被用，
足智多謀，深思熟慮而且小心翼翼的；
能夠高談闊論，但有點遲鈍；
有時，實實在在是個笑柄——
125. 有時，完完全全是個「小丑」。

　　我老了……我老了……
我該穿上捲起褲腳的長褲了吧。

Shall I part my hair behind? Do I dare to eat a peach?
I shall wear white flannel trousers, and walk upon the beach.
130. I have heard the mermaids singing, each to each.

I do not think that they will sing to me.

I have seen them riding seaward on the waves
Combing the white hair of the waves blown back
When the wind blows the water white and black.

135. We have lingered in the chambers of the sea
By sea-girls wreathed with seaweed red and brown
Till human voices wake us, and we drown.

普魯佛洛克及其他觀察
1917

　　我的頭髮該往後梳開了吧？我還敢吃桃子嗎？
我該穿上白法蘭絨長褲到海濱散步了吧。
130. 我聽到了人魚在互相歌唱。

　　我想她們不會再為我歌唱了吧。

　　風吹著，海水一黑一白晃蕩著
我看到了她們向海上凌波而去
梳著隨波披散的白髮。

135. 　　我們留戀在海底深宮，身邊
海女裝飾著紅色棕色海草的花圈
直到人類的聲音驚醒我們，我們沉溺。

Portrait of a Lady

Thou hast committed —
Fornication: but that was in another country,
And besides, the wench is dead.

—— *The Jew of Malta*

I

5. Among the smoke and fog of a December afternoon
You have the scene arrange itself — as it will seem to do—
With "I have saved this afternoon for you";
And four wax candles in the darkened room,
Four rings of light upon the ceiling overhead,
10. An atmosphere of Juliet's tomb
Prepared for all the things to be said, or left unsaid.
We have been, let us say, to hear the latest Pole
Transmit the Preludes, through his hair and finger-tips.
"So intimate, this Chopin, that I think his soul
15. Should be resurrected only among friends

普魯佛洛克及其他觀察
1917

一位婦人的肖像

你曾經犯罪——

私通：但那是在別的國度，

此外，那位淫婦已死了。

——《馬爾他島的猶太人》

I

5. 在十二月煙霧瀰漫的午後

你有了現成的場景——像似有意安排的——

當你說，「我為你留下了這個下午呢」；

四根蠟燭在幽暗了的房間裡，

四圈光輪在頭頂的天花板上，

10. 準備將一切事情說出或留著不說

那種朱麗葉的墳墓的氣氛。

告訴你吧，我們剛去聽了波蘭的新進鋼琴家

從髮梢與指尖彈出來的序曲。

「這蕭邦，真令人貼心感動，我想他的靈魂

15. 能在心中復活的，不過是兩三個知音而已

Some two or three, who will not touch the bloom

That is rubbed and questioned in the concert room."

— And so the conversation slips

Among velleities and carefully caught regrets

20. Through attenuated tones of violins

Mingled with remote cornets

And begins.

"You do not know how much they mean to me, my friends,

And how, how rare and strange it is, to find

25. In a life composed so much, so much of odds and ends,

(For indeed I do not love it ... you knew? you are not blind!

How keen you are!)

To find a friend who has these qualities,

Who has, and gives

30. Those qualities upon which friendship lives.

How much it means that I say this to you —

Without these friendships — life, what cauchemar!"

 Among the winding of the violins

And the ariettes

35. Of cracked cornets

Inside my brain a dull tom-tom begins

Absurdly hammering a prelude of its own,

普魯佛洛克及其他觀察
1917

他們才不會去碰觸在音樂廳裡

被揉弄和疑問的花朵。」

──這麼地，會話溜進了

未表現為行動的欲望與煞費苦心的奉承話裡

20. 透過逐漸屛弱的梵哦玲調子

滲雜著遠方的樂號

而又開始。

「我的朋友，你不知道他們對我的意義有多大，

而且那是多麼，多麼難得和不可思議啊

25. 要在這麼多零碎雜湊而成的人生中找到他們，

（真的，人生我並不喜愛……你知道？你可不愚昧啊！

你是多麼的伶俐！）

要找到具有這些氣質的一個朋友，

不但具有，而且給予

30. 友情所寄託的那些氣質的朋友。

我對你這麼說，用意有多深──

沒有這些友情──人生，好一個惡夢喲！」

在梵哦玲的繚繞

以及樂號破裂的

35. 小抒情曲中

我腦裡鈍重的咚咚開始

胡亂地敲著它自己的序曲，

Capricious monotone

That is at least one definite "false note."

40. Let us take the air, in a tobacco trance,

Admire the monuments,

Discuss the late events,

Correct our watches by the public clocks.

Then sit for half an hour and drink our bocks.

II

45. Now that lilacs are in bloom

She has a bowl of lilacs in her room

And twists one in her fingers while she talks.

"Ah, my friend, you do not know, you do not know

What life is, you who hold it in your hands";

50. (Slowly twisting the lilac stalks)

"You let it flow from you, you let it flow,

And youth is cruel, and has no remorse

And smiles at situations which it cannot see."

I smile, of course,

55. And go on drinking tea.

"Yet with these April sunsets, that somehow recall

My buried life, and Paris in the Spring,

普魯佛洛克及其他觀察
1917

令人心煩意亂的單調

至少那是一個決定性的「錯誤音符」。

40.　菸草燻得頭昏昏的，讓我們出去散步吧，

稱讚些紀念碑，

討論些最近的事件，

把我們的錶對準公眾時鐘吧。

然後坐上半個鐘頭，喝喝黑啤酒吧。

II

45.　現在紫丁香盛開，因此

她的房裡有一盆紫丁香

她邊說著話，邊捻著一朵。

「我的朋友啊，你可不知道

人生是什麼，手中緊握著它的你呀可不知道；

50.　（慢慢捻著紫丁香的花枝）

「它從你手中溜去，消逝了，

青春是殘酷的，不知後悔

卻對著它看不見的情境微笑。」

當然，我微笑了，

55.　且繼續飲茶。

「然而這些四月的傍晚，多少使我想起

已被埋葬的人生，以及春天的巴黎，

I feel immeasurably at peace, and find the world
To be wonderful and youthful, after all."

60.   The voice returns like the insistent out-of-tune
Of a broken violin on an August afternoon:
"I am always sure that you understand
My feelings, always sure that you feel,
Sure that across the gulf you reach your hand.

65.   You are invulnerable, you have no Achilles' heel.
You will go on, and when you have prevailed
You can say: at this point many a one has failed.
But what have I, but what have I, my friend,
To give you, what can you receive from me?
70. Only the friendship and the sympathy
Of one about to reach her journey's end.

    I shall sit here, serving tea to friends ...."

    I take my hat: how can I make a cowardly amends
For what she has said to me?
75. You will see me any morning in the park
Reading the comics and the sporting page.

普魯佛洛克及其他觀察
1917

因此我心中感到無限寧靜，我發現，畢竟
這世界充滿美好和青春。」

60.　　　那聲音像八月午後斷斷續續的梵哦玲
如一再反復的不和諧調子，又再回來：
「我總相信，你了解
我的感情，總相信你會感覺到，
相信你會跨過鴻溝伸出手來。

65.　　　你沒有致命的弱點，你沒有亞吉利的腳踵呀。
你將繼續求進，當你得到勝利時
你一定會說：在這點許多人挫敗了。
可是啊，朋友，我必須，我必須
給你什麼呢？你能從我這裡得到什麼呢？
70.　只是即將到達旅程終點的
一個女人的友情和同情吧了。

　　　我將坐在這兒，給朋友們倒茶……」

　　　我拿起帽子：我怎能給予怯懦的補償呢
對她向我說的話？
75.　早上你隨時會在公園裡見到我
看著漫畫和體育版的消息。

Particularly I remark.

An English countess goes upon the stage.

A Greek was murdered at a Polish dance,

80. Another bank defaulter has confessed.

I keep my countenance,

I remain self-possessed

Except when a street-piano, mechanical and tired

Reiterates some worn-out common song

85. With the smell of hyacinths across the garden

Recalling things that other people have desired.

Are these ideas right or wrong?

III

The October night comes down; returning as before

Except for a slight sensation of being ill at ease

90. I mount the stairs and turn the handle of the door

And feel as if I had mounted on my hands and knees.

"And so you are going abroad; and when do you return?

But that's a useless question.

You hardly know when you are coming back,

95. You will find so much to learn."

My smile falls heavily among the bric-à-brac.

普魯佛洛克及其他觀察
1917

我特別注意的是
英國的伯爵夫人走上了舞台。
希臘人跳著波蘭舞時被謀殺了，
80. 另一個虧空公款的銀行員認罪了。
我不露臉色，
我泰然自若。
除非當街上那自鳴鋼琴，機械地疲倦地
反覆著一首唱濫了的通俗歌曲
85. 除非風信子的氣味橫過花壇
而想起別人所欲望的事情。
這些想法對嗎？錯了嗎？

III

十月的夜晚落下來；一如往常歸來
只是稍有心緒不寧的感覺，
90. 我上了樓梯，轉動門把
感到似乎是用自己的手和膝蓋爬上來一般。
「所以你想到外國去吧；什麼時候回來呢？
但那是個無濟於事的問題。
什麼時候回來你自己也不知道呀，
95. 你將發現要學的事情太多了吧。」
我的微笑沉重地落在裝飾的古董間。

"Perhaps you can write to me."
My self-possession flares up for a second;
This is as I had reckoned.
100. "I have been wondering frequently of late
(But our beginnings never know our ends!)
Why we have not developed into friends."
I feel like one who smiles, and turning shall remark
Suddenly, his expression in a glass.
105. My self-possession gutters; we are really in the dark.

"For everybody said so, all our friends,
They all were sure our feelings would relate
So closely! I myself can hardly understand.
We must leave it now to fate.
110. You will write, at any rate.
Perhaps it is not too late.
I shall sit here, serving tea to friends."

And I must borrow every changing shape
To find expression ... dance, dance
115. Like a dancing bear,
Cry like a parrot, chatter like an ape.

普魯佛洛克及其他觀察
1917

　　「也許你會寫信給我。」
我自制的鎮靜瞬間動搖起來；
這，正如我所預料的啊。
100.「我最近時常感覺到奇怪
（但開始時誰知道結局！）
為什麼我們不能成為朋友呢？」
我面帶笑容，一回頭感到似乎
在鏡中突然看到自己的表情。
105.我自制的鎮靜動搖了；我們的確在黑暗中。

　　「因為大家都這麼說，所有的朋友，
他們都以為我倆的感情一定很
親密！我自己也難以了解。
如今我們只好歸於命運了。
110.無論怎樣，你會寫信吧。
說不定還不太遲呢。
我將坐在這兒，給朋友們倒茶。」

　　我必須借用每種變化的形體
以求得表現……跳吧，舞吧
115.像熊那麼跳吧，
像鸚鵡那麼叫吧，像猿猴那樣饒舌吧。

Let us take the air, in a tobacco trance—

Well! and what if she should die some afternoon,
Afternoon grey and smoky, evening yellow and rose;
120. Should die and leave me sitting pen in hand
With the smoke coming down above the housetops;
Doubtful, for quite a while
Not knowing what to feel or if I understand
Or whether wise or foolish, tardy or too soon ...
125. Would she not have the advantage, after all?
This music is successful with a "dying fall"
Now that we talk of dying—
And should I have the right to smile?

普魯佛洛克及其他觀察
1917

菸草燻得頭昏昏的，讓我們出去散散步吧──

　　可是！要是有天下午她突然死掉，那又怎樣呢
陰沉沉煙茫茫的午後，黃昏昏玫瑰色的夕暮；
120.　假如她死去，留下握筆獨坐的我
當煙靄從屋頂上落下來；
疑神不定地，我有好久
不知道該怎麼說，或者我是否了解，
到底是聰明還是愚蠢，太遲或是太快……
125.　總之，她不是獲得好處了嗎？
這音樂是成功的以「嬝嬝餘音」而終了
現在我們既然談到死的終極問題──
到底我有微笑的權利嗎？

Preludes

I

The winter evening settles down
With smell of steaks in passageways.
Six o'clock.
The burnt-out ends of smoky days.
5. And now a gusty shower wraps
The grimy scraps
Of withered leaves about your feet
And newspapers from vacant lots;
The showers beat
10. On broken blinds and chimney-pots,
And at the corner of the street
A lonely cab-horse steams and stamps.

And then the lighting of the lamps.

普魯佛洛克及其他觀察
1917

序曲集

I

冬天的黃昏安定下來
帶著走廊下牛排的氣味。
六點鐘。
燃盡了的日子的菸蒂。
5. 這時一陣驟雨捲起
骯髒的碎片
你腳邊的枯葉
以及空地上的報紙；
驟雨打在
10. 損壞了的百葉窗和煙囪管上，
在街道的角落，孤零零的
一匹載客的馬冒著熱氣，在跺腳。

於是燈光亮了。

II

    The morning comes to consciousness
15. Of faint stale smells of beer
    From the sawdust-trampled street
    With all its muddy feet that press
    To early coffee-stands.
    With the other masquerades
20. That time resumes,
    One thinks of all the hands
    That are raising dingy shades
    In a thousand furnished rooms.

III

    You tossed a blanket from the bed,
25. You lay upon your back, and waited;
    You dozed, and watched the night revealing
    The thousand sordid images
    Of which your soul was constituted;
    They flickered against the ceiling.
30. And when all the world came back
    And the light crept up between the shutters

普魯佛洛克及其他觀察
1917

II

　　早晨蘇醒了
15.　帶著啤酒微微發酸的味道
　　從踩踏鋸屑的街道
　　以沾滿街泥的腳，急急地
　　向清晨的咖啡攤走去。
　　憶及時間所又開始的
20.　其他化裝舞會，
　　令人想到所有的手
　　在帶家具的上千公寓房間
　　拉起燻黃了的遮陽棚。

III

　　你從床上扔開絨被
25.　你躺著，等待著；
　　你昏昏打盹，望著夜浮現出
　　成千汙穢的形象
　　以此構成你的靈魂；
　　這些形象閃晃在天花板上。
30.　而當整個世界又再回來
　　當陽光從百葉窗的間縫鑽進來

And you heard the sparrows in the gutters,

You had such a vision of the street

As the street hardly understands;

35. Sitting along the bed's edge, where

You curled the papers from your hair,

Or clasped the yellow soles of feet

In the palms of both soiled hands.

IV

His soul stretched tight across the skies

40. That fade behind a city block,

Or trampled by insistent feet

At four and five and six o'clock;

And short square fingers stuffing pipes,

And evening newspapers, and eyes

45. Assured of certain certainties,

The conscience of a blackened street

Impatient to assume the world.

I am moved by fancies that are curled

Around these images, and cling:

50. The notion of some infinitely gentle

普魯佛洛克及其他觀察
1917

當你聽到麻雀在簷槽上，
你看到了街衢也難以理解的
街衢的景象。
35. 沿著床緣坐著，
你捲下頭上的捲髮紙
或是緊扣著黃黃的腳底
以弄髒了的兩隻手掌。

IV

他的靈魂緊繃著橫過的天空
40. 在都市建築物背後黯然褪色，
或被堅持的腳步踐踏著
在四點五點六點鐘的時候；
以及填塞煙斗的短粗手指
以及晚報，以及
45. 確實了某些確信的眼睛，
黑暗了的街衢的良心
急於想要擁有這世界。

捲繞著這些形象的
幻想令我感動，我緊纏著：
50. 無限溫柔而又

Infinitely suffering thing.

Wipe your hand across your mouth, and laugh;
The worlds revolve like ancient women
Gathering fuel in vacant lots.

普魯佛洛克及其他觀察
1917

無限苦惱的某種事物的觀念。

　　用你的手擦擦嘴邊，笑吧；
世界一再迴轉，有如古代女人
在空地收集燃料。

Rhapsody
on a Windy Night

Twelve o'clock.

Along the reaches of the street

Held in a lunar synthesis,

Whispering lunar incantations

5. Dissolve the floors of memory

And all its clear relations,

Its divisions and precisions,

Every street lamp that I pass

Beats like a fatalistic drum,

10. And through the spaces of the dark

Midnight shakes the memory

As a madman shakes a dead geranium.

   Half-past one,

The street lamp sputtered,

15. The street lamp muttered,

The street lamp said, "Regard that woman

Who hesitates towards you in the light of the door

普魯佛洛克及其他觀察
1917

風夜狂想曲

十二點。
沿著街首延伸的地方走去
被囚在月青冷的綜合裡,
月悄悄聲的咒語
5. 溶解了記憶的地板
及其一切明朗的關係,
其區分處與精確度,
我所經過的每盞街燈
像宿命的鼓敲響著,
10. 而通過黑暗的空間
午夜搖蕩著記憶
像瘋子搖蕩著枯死的天竺葵。

　　一點半,
街燈吐著唾沫,
15. 街燈嘟嘟喃喃,
街燈說:「看哪,那個女人,
她躊躇地向你走來,你在門亮光的地方

Which opens on her like a grin.

You see the border of her dress

20. Is torn and stained with sand,

And you see the corner of her eye

Twists like a crooked pin."

The memory throws up high and dry

A crowd of twisted things;

25. A twisted branch upon the beach

Eaten smooth, and polished

As if the world gave up

The secret of its skeleton,

Stiff and white.

30. A broken spring in a factory yard,

Rust that clings to the form that the strength has left

Hard and curled and ready to snap.

Half-past two,

The street lamp said,

35. "Remark the cat which flattens itself in the gutter,

Slips out its tongue

And devours a morsel of rancid butter."

So the hand of a child, automatic,

普魯佛洛克及其他觀察
1917

門在她臉上開著，笑嘻嘻似地，
你看到了吧，她的衣服貼邊
20. 撕裂了且有沙子弄髒，
你看到了吧，她的眼角
像彎曲的扣針皺扭著。」

記憶將一群歪歪扭扭的東西
高高地拋棄不理；
25. 海灘上被扭斷了的枝條
被啃磨得平滑而光亮
有如這世界放棄了
它那僵硬白色的
骸骨的秘密。
30. 壞掉了的彈簧在工廠的圍場裡，
鐵鏽粘纏著已經失去彈力的彈簧，
那形狀僵硬而彎曲，隨時可能斷折。

兩點半，
街燈說：
35. 「看哪，貓匍匐在街溝裡
伸出舌頭
貪吃一口腐臭的奶油。」
如此，小孩的手，自動地

Slipped out and pocketed a toy that was running along the

quay.

40. I could see nothing behind that child's eye.

I have seen eyes in the street

Trying to peer through lighted shutters,

And a crab one afternoon in a pool,

An old crab with barnacles on his back,

45. Gripped the end of a stick which I held him.

Half-past three,

The lamp sputtered,

The lamp muttered in the dark.

The lamp hummed:

50. "Regard the moon,

La lune ne garde aucune rancune,

She winks a feeble eye,

She smiles into corners.

She smoothes the hair of the grass.

55. The moon has lost her memory.

A washed-out smallpox cracks her face,

Her hand twists a paper rose,

That smells of dust and old Cologne,

She is alone

普魯佛洛克及其他觀察
1917

伸出，將沿著碼頭跑的玩具裝進衣袋。

40.　那個小孩的眼後我什麼也看不見。

我在街上看到了許多眼睛

試圖透過燈光亮的百葉窗窺探，

以及有天下午水池裡的一隻毛蟹，

一隻背上附著藤壺的老毛蟹

45.　咬上了我逮住牠的手杖的尖端。

　　　三點半，

街燈吐著唾沫，

街燈在黑暗中嘟喃著。

街燈哼著說：

50.　「看看月亮吧，

月亮什麼抱怨也沒有，

她眨著纖弱的眼睛，

她含笑在每個角落，

她撫摩著草的毛髮。

55.　月亮失去了她的記憶。

洗掉的疱瘡使她的臉輝裂，

她手中捻著一朵人造玫瑰

有著塵埃與奧德嘉濃香水的氣味，

她孤單單的

60. With all the old nocturnal smells

That cross and cross across her brain."

The reminiscence comes

Of sunless dry geraniums

And dust in crevices,

65. Smells of chestnuts in the streets,

And female smells in shuttered rooms,

And cigarettes in corridors

And cocktail smells in bars.

    The lamp said,

70. "Four o'clock,

Here is the number on the door.

Memory!

You have the key,

The little lamp spreads a ring on the stair,

75. Mount.

The bed is open; the tooth-brush hangs on the wall,

Put your shoes at the door, sleep, prepare for life."

    The last twist of the knife.

普魯佛洛克及其他觀察
1917

60. 雖有夜的古色古香繚繞
穿過且交錯在她的腦子裡。」
回憶想起了
背日而枯槁的天竺葵
以及裂縫裡的塵埃，
65. 街上栗子的香味，
以及拉下窗簾的房間裡女人的氣味，
以及走廊裡的紙菸
以及酒吧裡雞尾酒的氣味。

　　　街燈說：
70. 「四點了，
這是門房的號碼。
回憶！
你有鑰匙，
小洋燈將光輪投在梯階上，
75. 上去吧。
睡床展開著；牙刷掛在牆上，
把鞋子放在門口，睡吧，準備明天吧。」

　　　刀子最後的一扭。

Morning
at the Window

They are rattling breakfast plates in basement kitchens,
And along the trampled edges of the street
I am aware of the damp souls of housemaids
Sprouting despondently at area gates.

5.   The brown waves of fog toss up to me
Twisted faces from the bottom of the street,
And tear from a passer-by with muddy skirts
An aimless smile that hovers in the air
And vanishes along the level of the roofs.

普魯佛洛克及其他觀察
1917

窗邊晨景

她們在地下廚房響出早餐嘩喇嘩喇的盤聲，
而沿著被踐踏的街道邊緣
我發覺女僕們濕潤的靈魂
在地下室的便門邊頹然萌芽。

5.　　褐色的晨霧從街底
將一些歪扭的臉容向我波晃上來，
且將穿著骯髒裙子的路人
飄浮在空中毫無主意的微笑撕破了
而沿著屋頂的平面消逝。

Prufrock and Other Observations
1917

The Boston
Evening Transcript

The readers of the Boston Evening Transcript
Sway in the wind like a field of ripe corn.

When evening quickens faintly in the street,
Wakening the appetites of life in some
5. And to others bringing the Boston Evening Transcript,
I mount the steps and ring the bell, turning
Wearily, as one would turn to nod good-bye to Rochefoucauld,
If the street were time and he at the end of the street,
And I say, "Cousin Harriet, here is the Boston Evening
Transcript."

普魯佛洛克及其他觀察
1917

波斯頓晚報

波斯頓晚報的讀者們
像一片成熟的麥田在風中搖晃。

　　當黃昏在街上微弱地復蘇過來，
覺醒了有些人的生存欲望，
5.　而將波斯頓晚報拿給別人，
我登上梯階，按了鈴，疲倦地
轉身，向羅什福克[1]點頭再見一般，
假如街道是時間而他就在街道的尾端，
我轉身說：「哈利葉表姐，波斯頓晚報在這兒。」

1　譯註：羅什福克（François de La Rochefoucauld, 1613-1680），《箴言集》
（*Maximes*, 1665）的作者。

Prufrock and Other Observations
1917

Aunt Helen

Miss Helen Slingsby was my maiden aunt,

And lived in a small house near a fashionable square

Cared for by servants to the number of four.

Now when she died there was silence in heaven

5. And silence at her end of the street.

The shutters were drawn and the undertaker wiped his feet —

He was aware that this sort of thing had occurred before.

The dogs were handsomely provided for,

But shortly afterwards the parrot died too.

10. The Dresden clock continued ticking on the mantelpiece,

And the footman sat upon the dining-table

Holding the second housemaid on his knees —

Who had always been so careful while her mistress lived.

普魯佛洛克及其他觀察
1917

海倫阿姨

海倫・斯列斯比小姐是我未婚的阿姨。
住在時髦的廣場附近的小屋裡
服侍她的僕人數達四個。
且說她死的時候天國靜悄悄的
5. 而她在街尾的家也是靜悄悄的
窗簾垂下來而殯儀館的人擦著腳——
他明白這種事情從前也曾有過。
狗漂漂亮亮地被豢養著,
但不久鸚鵡也死了。
10. 德累斯頓製的鐘仍舊在壁爐架上滴答著,
僕人坐在餐桌上
膝上抱著第二位的女用人——
女主人活著的時候,她一直就這麼小心呢。

Cousin Nancy

Miss Nancy Ellicott
Strode across the hills and broke them,
Rode across the hills and broke them —
The barren New England hills —
5. Riding to hounds
Over the cow-pasture.

  Miss Nancy Ellicott smoked
And danced all the modern dances;
And her aunts were not quite sure how they felt about it,
10. But they knew that it was modern.

  Upon the glazen shelves kept watch
Matthew and Waldo, guardians of the faith,
The army of unalterable law.

普魯佛洛克及其他觀察
1917

南希表妹

南希‧艾理克特小姐
大步走過山崗而踏破了山崗，
騎馬橫過山崗而踏破了山崗——
新英格蘭那些荒涼的山崗——
5. 帶著獵狗騎在馬上
奔過母牛的牧場。

南希‧艾理克特會抽菸
什麼現代舞也都會跳；
她的伯母們對這可不知怎麼說好，
10. 她們只知道那是很現代的。

在鑲玻璃的擱板上睜睜注視的是
馬太和華都，信仰的守護者，
不可變的律法的兵團。

Mr. Apollinax

'What novelty! What marvellous paradoxes!
How inventive he is!'

When Mr. Apollinax visited the United States
His laughter tinkled among the teacups.

5. I thought of Fragilion, that shy figure among the birch-trees,
And of Priapus in the shrubbery
Gaping at the lady in the swing.
In the palace of Mrs. Phlaccus, at Professor Channing-
Cheetah's
He laughed like an irresponsible foetus.

10. His laughter was submarine and profound
Like the old man of the sea's
Hidden under coral islands
Where worried bodies of drowned men drift down in the
green silence,
Dropping from fingers of surf.

15. I looked for the head of Mr. Apollinax rolling under a chair

普魯佛洛克及其他觀察
1917

阿保里奈克斯先生

多麼新奇！多麼匪夷所思！
好一個富有創意的人哪！

阿保里奈克斯先生訪問美國時
他的笑聲在茶杯間玎玲噹啷響。
5. 我想到福瑞基龍，在樺樹間那靦腆的樣子，
以及坡瑞帕斯，在灌木中
張口望著鞦韆上的婦人。
在福烈卡斯夫人的公館或在千尼‧啟塔教授的邸宅
他笑得像個不負責任的胎兒。
10. 他的笑，潛水而深沉
像那位海底老人
隱藏在珊瑚島下
那兒，溺死者苦惱的軀體，在綠色的沉靜中隨流捲入，
當他們從波浪的手指間掉落。
15. 我尋找著阿保里奈克斯先生在椅子下滾轉的頭，

    Or grinning over a screen

With seaweed in its hair.

I heard the beat of centaur's hoofs over the hard turf

As his dry and passionate talk devoured the afternoon.

20.   "He is a charming man"—"But after all what did he mean?"—

"His pointed ears... He must be unbalanced,"—

"There was something he said that I might have challenged."

Of dowager Mrs. Phlaccus, and Professor and Mrs. Cheetah

I remember a slice of lemon, and a bitten macaroon.

普魯佛洛克及其他觀察
1917

　　或在屏風那邊笑嘻嘻的，

頭髮上纏著海草。

我聽到了仙駝（半人半馬）在硬固的草場上踏蹄，

當他那乾澀而熱情的談話吞下了午後。

20. 「他是個有趣的人哪」──「可是到底他說的是什麼意

思？」──

「他那尖尖的耳朵……他一定感到不平衡吧！」──

「他所說的有些事情我可會抗議的。」

想到遺孀福烈卡斯夫人與啟塔教授夫婦，

我記起了一片檸檬和咬了一口的瑪卡宏小甜餅。

Hysteria

As she laughed I was aware of becoming involved in her laughter and being part of it, until her teeth were only accidental stars with a talent for squad-drill. I was drawn in by short gasps, inhaled at each momentary recovery, lost finally in the dark caverns of her throat, bruised by the ripple of unseen muscles. An elderly waiter with trembling hands was hurriedly spreading a pink and white checked cloth over the rusty green iron table, saying: "If the lady and gentleman wish to take their tea in the garden, if the lady and gentleman wish to take their tea in the garden ..." I decided that if the shaking of her breasts could be stopped, some of the fragments of the afternoon might be collected, and I concentrated my attention with careful subtlety to this end.

普魯佛洛克及其他觀察
1917

歇斯底里症

她一笑，我就有被捲進她的笑裡而成為其中一部分的感覺，直到她的牙齒只是一些偶爾具有班教練才能的星子。我被那短促的喘息所引誘，被每一瞬間的回復所吸進，最後迷失在她的咽喉那黑暗的洞穴裡，因那看不見的筋肉的小波浪而瘀傷了。一位上了年紀的侍者在生鏽的綠鐵桌上，以顫抖的手鋪著一張粉紅間白的方格桌巾，說：「要是小姐和先生想在庭園裡喝茶，要是小姐和先生想在庭園園裡喝茶……」要是她胸乳的顫動能被中止，我確定午後的一些片斷可以被收集起來，而我細心入微地將我的注意力集中在這個目的上。

Conversation Galante

I observe: "Our sentimental friend the moon!
Or possibly (fantastic, I confess)
It may be Prester John's balloon
Or an old battered lantern hung aloft
5. To light poor travellers to their distress."
She then: "How you digress!"

   And I then: "Some one frames upon the keys
That exquisite nocturne, with which we explain
The night and moonshine; music which we seize
10. To body forth our own vacuity."
She then: "Does this refer to me?"
"Oh no, it is I who am inane."

   "You, madam, are the eternal humorist,
The eternal enemy of the absolute,
15. Giving our vagrant moods the slightest twist!
With your air indifferent and imperious

普魯佛洛克及其他觀察
1917

風流的會話

我的觀察：「我們感傷的朋友，月亮喲！
那或許就是（異想天開，我承認）
普瑞斯特·約翰的氣球吧
或許就是一盞高掛空中七凸八凹的舊燈籠
5.　照著那些可憐旅人心上的哀愁吧。
於是她：「你別胡扯！」

　　接著我：「有人敲響琴鍵
構成那優美的夜色，讓我們用來說明
夜和月光；我們所抓住的音樂
10.　用來表現我們自己的空虛。」
於是她：「這是指我而說的嗎？」
「噢，不，我才是空洞的。」

　　「夫人，妳是個永恆的幽默家，
絕對者永恆的敵人，
15.　給我們游移不定的情緒最輕的一摔！
以妳那漠不關心和無比專橫的態度

Prufrock and Other Observations
1917

At a stroke our mad poetics to confute—"

And—"Are we then so serious?"

普魯佛洛克及其他觀察
1917

一擊之下我們的瘋狂詩學就被駁倒啦——」
　於是——「我們就這麼認真嗎？」

La Figlia che Piange

O quam te memorem virgo ...

Stand on the highest pavement of the stair—
Lean on a garden urn—
Weave, weave the sunlight in your hair—
5. Clasp your flowers to you with a pained surprise—
Fling them to the ground and turn
With a fugitive resentment in your eyes:
But weave, weave the sunlight in your hair.

So I would have had him leave,
10. So I would have had her stand and grieve,
So he would have left
As the soul leaves the body torn and bruised,
As the mind deserts the body it has used.
I should find
15. Some way incomparably light and deft,
Some way we both should understand,

普魯佛洛克及其他觀察
1917

悲歎的少女

噢，少女，我叫妳什麼好呢……

站在最高的樓階上吧──
斜靠著花瓶吧──
織吧，將陽光織在妳的髮鬢──
5. 以意想不到的痛苦將花束緊抱在身上吧──
將花束丟棄在地上，而回顧
以難以捉摸的怨恨的眼神：
織吧，將陽光織在你的髮鬢。

如此，我可要他離開，
10. 如此，我可要她佇立而悲哀，
如此，他可會離開了吧
像靈魂離開被撕裂和瘀傷的肉體，
像心靈遺棄了它所用過的肉體。
我該找到
15. 某種無比輕巧的方法，
某種你我都該明白的方法，

Simple and faithless as a smile and shake of the hand.

She turned away, but with the autumn weather
Compelled my imagination many days,

20. Many days and many hours:
Her hair over her arms and her arms full of flowers.
And I wonder how they should have been together!
I should have lost a gesture and a pose.
Sometimes these cogitations still amaze

25. The troubled midnight and the noon's repose.

普魯佛洛克及其他觀察
1917

有如微笑和握手那麼單純且無需信守的。

　　她背過臉去，但因秋天的氣候
　逼迫著我的想像許多日子，
20.　許多日子和許多鐘頭：
　她的長髮遮在手臂，她的手臂抱滿了花。
　我奇怪，他們兩人怎會在一起！
　我該會失去平常的體態和姿勢。
　有時這些思緒仍然驚擾著
25.　失眠的半夜和中午的歇息。

Poems

詩集

·1920·

Gerontion

Thou hast nor youth nor age
But as it were an after dinner sleep
Dreaming of both.

Here I am, an old man in a dry month,
5. Being read to by a boy, waiting for rain.
I was neither at the hot gates
Nor fought in the warm rain
Nor knee deep in the salt marsh, heaving a cutlass,
Bitten by flies, fought.
10. My house is a decayed house,
And the Jew squats on the window sill, the owner,
Spawned in some estaminet of Antwerp,
Blistered in Brussels, patched and peeled in London.
The goat coughs at night in the field overhead;
15. Rocks, moss, stonecrop, iron, merds.
The woman keeps the kitchen, makes tea,
Sneezes at evening, poking the peevish gutter.
                    I an old man,
A dull head among windy spaces.

詩集
1920

小老頭

你沒有青春，也沒有老年
好像那是飯後一場小睡
夢見這兩樣吧了。

我就是，在乾燥的季節裡
5. 聽著小孩念書，等待著雨的老人。
我沒上過火門關的戰場，
沒在熱雨中打過仗，
也未曾膝蓋陷在鹽沼裡，揮著短劍，
給惡蠅叮著作戰。
10. 我的住房是一個朽壞了的房子，
房東是猶太人，蹲在窗台上，
出生在叫什麼安特窩的小咖啡館裡，
在布魯塞爾燙了傷，在倫敦敷了藥脫了皮。
夜裡山羊在上頭的原野咳嗽；
15. 岩石，鮮苔，變形草，鐵，鳥糞。
婦人在廚房裡打雜，泡茶，
黃昏時打著噴嚏，捅著彆扭的排水溝。
　　　　　　　　　我一個老人，
遲鈍的腦袋兒在當風的空間。

20.   Signs are taken for wonders. 'We would see a sign!'

The word within a word, unable to speak a word,

Swaddled with darkness. In the juvescence of the year

Came Christ the tiger

    In depraved May, dogwood and chestnut, flowering judas,

25. To be eaten, to be divided, to be drunk

Among whispers; by Mr. Silvero

With caressing hands, at Limoges

Who walked all night in the next room;

    By Hakagawa, bowing among the Titians;

30. By Madame de Tornquist, in the dark room

Shifting the candles; Fräulein von Kulp

Who turned in the hall, one hand on the door.

    Vacant shuttles

Weave the wind. I have no ghosts,

35. An old man in a draughty house

Under a windy knob.

    After such knowledge, what forgiveness? Think now

History has many cunning passages, contrived corridors

And issues, deceives with whispering ambitions,

詩集
1920

20.　　　徵兆被認為神蹟。「我們會看到徵兆！」
話中的話，說不出話，
裹在黑暗的襁褓中。歲月返回青春的時候
耶穌那老虎來了

　　　在墮落的五月，山茱萸和栗子，開花的猶大木，
25.　被吃掉，被分割，被喝飲
在竊竊私語中；被施維羅先生
愛撫的手，在里摩吉
他整夜踱步在隔壁的房間；

　　　被冢川，他在梯西安畫家間鞠躬如也；
30.　被敦葛斯特夫人，她在幽暗的房間裡
更換蠟燭；被馮克普
他在大廳，一隻手握著門把，突然轉身。
　　　中空的杼梭
織著風。我沒有鬼魂，
35.　一個老人，住在通風的屋子裡
在當風的山崗下。

　　　知道這些之後，有什麼寬恕？且想一想吧
歷史有許多陰險詭詐的通道，設計巧妙的走廊
和出口，矇騙人們以竊竊私語的野心，

40. Guides us by vanities. Think now
She gives when our attention is distracted
And what she gives, gives with such supple confusions
That the giving famishes the craving. Gives too late
What's not believed in, or is still believed,
45. In memory only, reconsidered passion. Gives too soon
Into weak hands, what's thought can be dispensed with
Till the refusal propagates a fear. Think
Neither fear nor courage saves us. Unnatural vices
Are fathered by our heroism. Virtues
50. Are forced upon us by our impudent crimes.
These tears are shaken from the wrath-bearing tree.

The tiger springs in the new year. Us he devours. Think at
last
We have not reached conclusion, when I
Stiffen in a rented house. Think at last
55. I have not made this show purposelessly
And it is not by any concitation
Of the backward devils.
I would meet you upon this honestly.
I that was near your heart was removed therefrom
60. To lose beauty in terror, terror in inquisition.
I have lost my passion: why should I need to keep it

詩集
1920

40.　以浮華虛榮誘導我們。且想一想吧
　　歷史給予，當我們的注意力分散時，
　　而她所給予的，卻以如此軟弱的混亂
　　因此越給予越不能饜足欲望。給予太遲了
　　所給予的，不論是不再相信，或者仍然相信，
45.　只存在於記憶中，復燃的熱情。給予太早了
　　給予那懦弱的手中，被認為沒有也行的東西，
　　直到拒絕增加了恐懼。想一想，
　　恐懼和勇氣都救不了我們。不自然的惡德
　　生自我們的英雄主義。美德
50.　被厚顏無恥的罪惡強加在我們身上。
　　這些眼淚從盛怒的樹上搖落下來。

　　　　新年老虎跳躍著。我們被牠吞掉。最後想一想吧
　　我們還沒達到結論啊，當我
　　在租借的房裡僵硬時。最後想一想吧
55.　我不是毫無意圖地這麼表現自己
　　那也不是由於背後
　　魔鬼們的挑唆。
　　這點，我準備與你真誠面對。
　　與你心靈接近的我，被從中拉離
60.　而在恐懼中失去美，在審問中失去恐懼。
　　我已經失去熱情：我有什麼必要持有，

Since what is kept must be adulterated?

I have lost my sight, smell, hearing, taste and touch:

How should I use it for your closer contact?

65.   These with a thousand small deliberations

Protract the profit of their chilled delirium,

Excite the membrane, when the sense has cooled,

With pungent sauces, multiply variety

In a wilderness of mirrors. What will the spider do

70. Suspend its operations, will the weevil

Delay? De Bailhache, Fresca, Mrs. Cammel, whirled

Beyond the circuit of the shuddering Bear

In fractured atoms. Gull against the wind, in the windy straits

Of Belle Isle, or running on the Horn,

75. White feathers in the snow, the Gulf claims,

And an old man driven by the Trades

To a sleepy corner.

                        Tenants of the house,

Thoughts of a dry brain in a dry season.

詩集
1920

既然持有的一定被攙雜？

我已經失去視覺，嗅覺，聽覺，味覺和觸覺：

我該怎麼用這些感覺與你進一步接觸？

65.　　　這些與無數微小的顧慮

從冷卻的熱狂中抽出利益，

刺激薄膜，當感覺冷下來，

以辛辣的調味品，變化出繁複多樣，

在鏡子的原野中。蜘蛛想做什麼呢，

70.　中止作業嗎？象鼻蟲

可以遲延嗎？德貝拉琪，福瑞斯加，凱梅爾夫人旋動著。

越出顫慄的大熊星座的軌道

在破碎的原子裡。海鷗逆著風，

在風狂的貝爾島海峽[1]，或在哈恩岬角[2]上奔馳。

75.　白羽毛在雪中，海灣呼叫著，

而一個老人，被貿易風

追向昏睡的涯角。

　　　　　　這些房客們，

在乾枯季節裡乾枯頭腦的思緒。

1　譯註：貝爾島海峽，介乎紐芬蘭與拉布拉多間，聖‧羅倫斯海灣入口處。

2　譯註：哈恩岬角，在南美洲最南端。

Burbank with a Baedeker: Bleistein with a Cigar

Tra-la-la-la-la-la-laire — nil nisi divinum stabile est; caetera fumus — the gondola stopped, the old palace was there, how charming its grey and pink — goats and monkeys, with such hair too! — so the countess passed on until she came through the little park, where Niobe presented her with a cabinet, and so departed.

Burbank crossed a little bridge
   Descending at a small hotel;
Princess Volupine arrived,
5.   They were together, and he fell.

Defunctive music under sea
   Passed seaward with the passing bell
Slowly: the God Hercules
   Had left him, that had loved him well.

10. The horses, under the axletree

詩集
1920

帶旅行指南的伯本克： 抽雪茄的伯烈斯坦

　　得啦—啦—啦—啦—啦—啦—咧—非神聖的不能永恆，
其餘的是雲煙——威尼斯的平底船靠岸了，古老的宮殿在
那兒，那古灰與桃紅多美啊——山羊與猴子也有這樣的身
毛！——於是伯爵夫人走來，經過了一座小庭園，尼歐比
向她呈獻了箱子，然後離開。

伯本克在小旅館前下來
　當他經過了一座小橋；
芙露蘋尼公主到達了
5.　兩人在一起，他傾倒。

海底殯葬的音樂悠悠地
　伴著喪鐘傳過海面；
天神赫克力斯[1]遺棄了他
　雖然他很敬愛天神。

10.　轅架下的馬從伊斯翠亞

Beat up the dawn from Istria
With even feet. Her shuttered barge
Burned on the water all the day.

But this or such was Bleistein's way:
15.   A saggy bending of the knees
And elbows, with the palms turned out,
Chicago Semite Viennese.

A lustreless protrusive eye
Stares from the protozoic slime
20. At a perspective of Canaletto.
The smoky candle end of time

Declines. On the Rialto once.
The rats are underneath the piles.
The jew is underneath the lot.
25.   Money in furs. The boatman smiles,

Princess Volupine extends
A meagre, blue-nailed, phthisic hand
To climb the waterstair. Lights, lights,
She entertains Sir Ferdinand

詩集
1920

踏著齊步驚醒曙光;
她那關上百葉窗的彩船
　一整天燃燒在水上。

伯烈斯坦就是這種作風:
15.　膝蓋無力的彎曲,臂肘
攤出兩個手掌,猶太系
　維也納人,生在芝加哥。

突出的眼睛失去了光亮
　從原生動物的黏質
20.　凝視嘉納勒圖²的透視畫。
　冒煙的時間的殘燭

頹落。曾在利額圖交易所。
　老鼠在囤積的貨底下。
猶太人在分得的一份底下。
25.　錢在毛皮裡。舟夫笑啦,

肺癆的芙露蘋尼公主伸出
　指甲蒼白的纖弱手指
登上水梯。燈光,燈光,
　她歡待費迪南‧克連爵士。

30. Klein. Who clipped the lion's wings
   And flea'd his rump and pared his claws?
   Thought Burbank, meditating on
   Time's ruins, and the seven laws.

詩集
1920

30. 誰剪掉了獅子的翅膀
　　戳牠的屁股，削牠的指爪？
　　伯本克在默想，沉思著
　　時間的廢墟與那七條律法。

1　譯註：赫克力斯（Hercules），力大無比的天神，宙斯（Zeus）之子，財貨
　　的守護神。
2　譯註：嘉納勒圖（Canaletto, 1697-1768），義大利威尼斯畫家。

Sweeney Erect

And the trees about me,
Let them be dry and leafless; let the rocks
Groan with continual surges; and behind me,
Make all a desolation. Look, look, wenches!

5. PAINT me a cavernous waste shore
      Cast in the unstilled Cyclades,
    Paint me the bold anfractuous rocks
        Faced by the snarled and yelping seas.

    Display me Aeolus above
10.   Reviewing the insurgent gales
    Which tangle Ariadne's hair
        And swell with haste the perjured sails.

    Morning stirs the feet and hands
        (Nausicaa and Polypheme),
15. Gesture of orang-outang

直立的史威尼

而我周圍的樹木，
讓它們枯槁且掉光葉子吧；讓岩石
以不斷湧來的波浪呻吟吧；在我背後
讓一切荒蕪吧。看呀看呀，姑娘們！

5. 　畫給我在那浪濤滾滾的賽島
　　　洞穴遍地的荒涼海岸吧，
　　畫給我面向咆哮狂吠的海原
　　　那勇敢而曲折的奇岩吧。

　　向我展示高空風神伊歐拉斯
10. 　　檢閱叛逆的暴風吧
　　當它糾纏亞麗德妮[1]的頭髮
　　　急忙地鼓起背誓的帆。

　　清晨激起手和腳的活動
　　　（諾希嘉亞[2]以及波力費麥[3]）。
15. 以類人猿猩猩的姿態

Rises from the sheets in steam.

This withered root of knots of hair
  Slitted below and gashed with eyes,
This oval O cropped out with teeth:
20. The sickle motion from the thighs

Jackknifes upward at the knees
  Then straightens out from heel to hip
Pushing the framework of the bed
  And clawing at the pillow slip.

25. Sweeney addressed full length to shave
  Broadbottomed, pink from nape to base,
Knows the female temperament
  And wipes the suds around his face.

(The lengthened shadow of a man
30. Is history, said Emerson
Who had not seen the silhouette
  Of Sweeney straddled in the sun.)

Tests the razor on his leg

從悶熱的床單中站起來。

這個枯萎的毛髮糾結的根部
　　下面有狹長如眼的裂縫，
這個卵形的 O 突然露出牙齒：
20.　　大腿傳來鐮刀的移動

在膝蓋地方向上彎曲如折刀
　　然後伸直，從腳跟到臀部，
將床架的床頭板向前推進，
　　手爪緊抓著枕頭的套子。

25. 上下左右頸背到底部都要
　　刮得潤紅，史威尼細心叮嚀，
他很瞭解女人的性情，
　　將臉上周邊的肥皂沫擦淨。

　　（一個人的影子拉長了，
30.　　愛默生說，就是歷史
他從來就沒看過太陽底下
　　史威尼仰然大步的影子。）

史威尼在腿上試著剃刀

Waiting until the shriek subsides.

35. The epileptic on the bed

    Curves backward, clutching at her sides.

The ladies of the corridor

    Find themselves involved, disgraced,

Call witness to their principles

40.   And deprecate the lack of taste

Observing that hysteria

    Might easily be misunderstood;

Mrs. Turner intimates

    It does the house no sort of good.

45. But Doris, towelled from the bath,

    Enters padding on broad feet,

Bringing sal volatile

    And a glass of brandy neat.

詩集
1920

等著平靜下去的尖叫。
35.　倒在床上患癲癇症的病人
　　　向後扭捲，緊抓著兩腰。

走廊上那些女士們
　　發現自己被捲入，沒有面子，
要求證明自己的節操，
40.　　對缺乏品味表示抗議。

看出患了歇斯底里症
　　很有被人誤解的可能；
屠納夫人的話中暗示
　　這種家庭沒什麼好名聲。

45.　但是多麗絲，裹著毛巾，
　　　從浴室進來，光著腳底，
帶著揮發性的提神藥品
　　　以及一瓶純白蘭地。

1　亞麗德妮（Ariadne）：希臘傳說中克里特島公主，邁諾斯女兒。她愛上
　　Theseus，給他走出迷宮的線索而殺死人身牛頭的怪物 Minotaur。
2　諾希嘉亞（Nausicaä）：在《奧德賽》中 Phaeacia 公主，Alcinous 和 Arete
　　美麗的女兒。她發現奧德賽被海浪漂來，引他到她父親的宮中款待他。
3　波力費麥（Polyphemus）：囚禁奧德賽於石穴中的獨眼巨人。

A Cooking Egg

En l'an trentiesme do mon aage
Que toutes mes hontes j'ay beues...

Pipit sate upright in her chair
  Some distance from where I was sitting;
5. *Views of the Oxford Colleges*
  Lay on the table, with the knitting.

Daguerreotypes and silhouettes,
  Her grandfather and great great aunts,
Supported on the mantelpiece
10. An *Invitation to the Dance.*

I shall not want Honour in Heaven
  For I shall meet Sir Philip Sidney
And have talk with Coriolanus
  And other heroes of that kidney.

烹調用的蛋

在我三十歲
　飽嘗了自己的一切羞恥時⋯⋯

琵琵蒂挺身坐在椅上
　與我坐的地方稍隔距離；
5.　《牛津大學景觀》
　放在桌上，與編織物一起。

銀板照片與半面畫像，
　她的祖父與曾祖姑母們，
壁爐前的飾台上支撐著
10.　「舞蹈晚會招待券」。

我不想要天國的榮譽
　因我將遇到席德尼爵士[1]；
我要交談的將是一些
　英雄們像柯里歐勒納斯[2]。

15. I shall not want Capital in Heaven
     For I shall meet Sir Alfred Mond:
We two shall lie together, lapt
     In a five per cent Exchequer Bond.

I shall not want Society in Heaven,
20.   Lucretia Borgia shall be my Bride;
Her anecdotes will be more amusing
     Than Pipit's experience could provide.

I shall not want Pipit in Heaven:
     Madame Blavatsky will instruct me
25. In the Seven Sacred Trances;
     Piccarda de Donati will conduct me.

But where is the penny world I bought
     To eat with Pipit behind the screen?
The red-eyed scavengers are creeping
30.   From Kentish Town and Golder's Green;

Where are the eagles and the trumpets?

詩集
1920

15. 我不想要天國的資本
　　因我將與蒙德爵士相遇：
我們兩人將躺在一起
　　埋在五分利息的國債裡。

我不想要天國的社交會，
20. 　　因波姬[3]將是我的新娘子；
她的奇聞軼事會更有趣
　　比起琵琵蒂的各種經歷。

我不要天國的琵琵蒂：
　　貝法斯基[4]夫人會啟迪我
25. 以「七個神聖的夢境」；
　　畢加達杜納迪[5]會指引我。

我買來與琵琵蒂在屏風後
　　吃的便宜世界如今何在？
從肯提西鎮和格達格林
30. 　　紅眼的清道夫緩緩走來；

蒼鷹和喇叭在哪裡？

Poems
1920

Buried beneath some snow-deep Alps.

Over buttered scones and crumpets

Weeping, weeping multitudes

35. Droop in a hundred A. B. C.'s

埋在某個阿爾卑斯山深雪中。
對著司康餅和煎餅塗上奶油
　在哭泣，哭泣的一群人
35.　在無數大眾茶館[6]裡低垂著頭。

1　譯註：席德尼爵士（Sir. Philip Sidney, 1554-1586），英國軍人，政治家，作家，當時騎士的典型和偶像。
2　譯註：柯里歐勒納斯（Coriolanus），紀元前五世紀羅馬的將軍，因主張廢除護民官，將政治的糧穀分給窮民而被逐。
3　譯註：波姬（Borgia, 1480-1519），義大利文藝復興時代有名的人物，許多文人藝術家追求的對象。
4　譯註：貝法斯基（Helena Petrovna Blavatsky, 1831-1891），俄國見神論者和神秘學家。
5　譯註：畢加達杜納迪（Piccarda de Donati），但丁《神曲‧天國篇》裡的引導人。
6　譯註：大眾茶館（A. B. C.），倫敦 Aerated Bread Company 經營的咖啡館。

Adulterous Mix of Everything

In America, professor;
In England, journalist;
It's fast and sweaty
That you will hardly follow my trail.
5. In Yorkshire, lecturer;
In London, a bit of a banker,
You will pay my head well.
It's in Paris that I do my hair
Black jemenfoutist's helmet.
10. In Germany, philosopher
Overexcited by Emporheben
In the open air of Bergsteigleben;
I always wander here and there
At various strokes of tra la la
15. From Damascus to Omaha.
I will celebrate my feast day
In an African oasis
Dressed in a giraffe skin.

詩集
1920

一切不正當的混合

在美國，教授；
在英格蘭，新聞記者；
若要跟隨我
請跨大步流著汗來吧。

5. 在約克郡，演講者；
在倫敦，小銀行家，
充分地支付給我的頭吧。
在巴黎，戴在頭上的是
蠻不在乎的黑盔。

10. 在德國，哲學者
由於高揚而過分激動
在登山生活的大氣中；
我不斷地到處流浪
隨著嘟啦啦的音調

15. 從大馬士革到奧馬哈。
我將慶祝我的節日
在一個非洲的綠洲
穿起長頸鹿的皮。

Poems
1920

We will show my cenotaph

20. To the burning coasts of Mozambique.

詩集
1920

　　　我將展示我的紀念碑
20.　在莫桑比克灼熱的海岸。

Honeymoon

They have seen the Netherlands, they are returning to Terre
Haute;
But one summer night, here they are in Ravenna, at ease
Between two sheets in the home of two hundred bugs,
The sweat of summer, and the smell of a bitch in heat,
5. They lie on their backs and spread apart the knees
Of four sticky legs all swollen with bites.
They raise the sheet to better scratch.
Less than a league from here is Saint Apollinaire in Classe,
The basilica known to amateurs
10. For its acanthus columns which the wind batters.

   At eight o'clock they will catch the train
To prolong their miseries from Padua to Milan,
Where they will find The Last Supper, and an inexpensive
Restaurant. He will calculate the tip with a pencil.
15. They will have seen Switzerland and crossed France.
And Saint Apollinare, straight and ascetic,

詩集
1920

蜜月

他們觀光了荷蘭低地，將返回特雷霍特高地；
但是有一夏夜，他們來到拉威那，安逸地
在兩張床單之間，住有兩百隻臭蟲，
夏天的汗臭，以及母狗發情的氣味。

5.　他們仰臥著，伸開溼黏黏的
四隻腳膝蓋，因蟲咬傷而發腫。
為了更方便抓癢而掀開被單。
離此不到一里格有克拉塞的聖亞坡理納聖殿，
對愛好者，那是有名的巴西利卡建築，

10.　柱頭上的花草紋飾，隨風振動。

　　他們將乘坐八點鐘的火車
延長他們的痛苦，從帕多瓦到米蘭，
那裡他們會找到〈最後的晚餐〉和便宜的
餐館。他會計算小費，以鉛筆記下。

15.　他們想去瑞士看看，而橫過法國。
聖亞坡理納，嚴守戒律的苦行者，

Poems
1920

Old, disaffected mill of God, still keeps
In its worn stones the precise form of Byzantium.

詩集
1920

廢棄了的神的舊工廠，現在仍然
在崩塌的石堆裡，保持精準的拜占庭形式。

The Hippopotamus

And when this epistle is read among you, cause that it be
read also in the church of the Laodiceans.

The broad-backed hippopotamus
Rests on his belly in the mud;
Although he seems so firm to us
5.   He is merely flesh and blood.

   Flesh-and-blood is weak and frail,
Susceptible to nervous shock;
While the True Church can never fail
For it is based upon a rock.

10.   The hippo's feeble steps may err
In compassing material ends,
While the True Church need never stir
To gather in its dividends.

詩集
1920

河馬

你們唸了這書信，便交給老底嘉的教會，
叫他們也唸。[1]

背脊寬大的河馬
匍伏在泥淖裡休息；
雖然看來很頑健
5. 只是血肉之軀而已。

　血肉之軀虛且弱
容易感受神經震盪；
真理教會將長存
因它奠基在磐石上。

10. 　河馬無力的腳步
或有差錯追求物欲；
真理教會不必動
就能坐收它的紅利。

The 'potamus can never reach
15. The mango on the mango-tree;
But fruits of pomegranate and peach
Refresh the Church from over sea.

At mating time the hippo's voice
Betrays inflexions hoarse and odd,
20. But every week we hear rejoice
The Church, at being one with God.

The hippopotamus's day
Is passed in sleep; at night he hunts;
God works in a mysterious way —
25. The Church can sleep and feed at once.

I saw the 'potamus take wing
Ascending from the damp savannas,
And quiring angels round him sing
The praise of God, in loud hosannas.

30. Blood of the Lamb shall wash him clean
And him shall heavenly arms enfold,
Among the saints he shall be seen

詩集
1920

河馬永遠勾不到
15. 芒果樹枝上的芒果；
海外的桃子石榴
卻使教會精神振作。

河馬一到交尾期
發出奇妙的嘶啞聲；
20. 每禮拜我們聽到
與神一體教會歡騰。

河馬在白天睡覺
晚上出去尋索獵物；
神的工作很神秘──
25. 教會能夠邊睡邊吃。

眼看著河馬舉翼
從潮濕的草原升空；
合唱天使在身邊
高聲讚美上帝恩寵。

30. 羔羊的血洗淨他
天使伸手將他抱著；
看見他在聖者中

Performing on a harp of gold.

He shall be washed as white as snow,
35.   By all the martyr'd virgins kist,
While the True Church remains below
Wrapt in the old miasmal mist.

詩集
1920

彈著黃金豎琴演奏。

他將被洗得雪白，
35. 被殉教的處女吻撫；
而真理教會仍舊
籠罩著下界的瘴霧。

1　譯註：引自《新約聖經》〈歌羅西書〉第四章十六節。

Whispers of Immortality

Webster was much possessed by death
And saw the skull beneath the skin;
And breastless creatures under ground
Leaned backward with a lipless grin.

5.   Daffodil bulbs instead of balls
Stared from the sockets of the eyes!
He knew that thought clings round dead limbs
Tightening its lusts and luxuries.

Donne, I suppose, was such another
10.   Who found no substitute for sense,
To seize and clutch and penetrate;
Expert beyond experience,

He knew the anguish of the marrow
The ague of the skeleton;
15.   No contact possible to flesh
Allayed the fever of the bone.

詩集
1920

不朽的呢喃

韋伯斯特 [1] 被死亡所劫持
甚至看到了皮下的頭骨；
沒有胸脯的動物在地底下
向後傾斜露出無唇的笑。

5.   不是眼珠而是水仙的球根
在眼窩裡凝然瞪眼！
他知道，思想糾纏著死的四肢
勒緊它的欲望和奢侈。

    唐恩 [2]，我認為，也是這一夥人
10. 他發現感覺無可取代，
如要把握、抓住、和穿透；
超越經驗的行家，

    他知道骨髓的苦惱，
骸骨的突然發冷；
15. 對肉體可能的任何接觸
都不能減輕骨頭的熱病。

Grishkin is nice: her Russian eye
Is underlined for emphasis;
Uncorseted, her friendly bust
20. Gives promise of pneumatic bliss.

The couched Brazilian jaguar
Compels the scampering marmoset
With subtle effluence of cat;
Grishkin has a maisonnette;

25. The sleek Brazilian jaguar
Does not in its arboreal gloom
Distil so rank a feline smell
As Grishkin in a drawing-room.

And even the Abstract Entities
30. Circumambulate her charm;
But our lot crawls between dry ribs
To keep our metaphysics warm.

詩集
1920

格麗斯金是美：露西亞人的眼睛

勾畫眼圈使更加突顯；

脫下胸衣，她那友善的胸脯

20. 令人幻想充氣的幸福。

　　這隻蹲伏的巴西豹

將驚慌奔逃的狨猴追捕

放出貓的微妙異臭；

格麗斯金有間公寓小屋；

25. 　　條紋光滑的巴西豹

從不在幽暗的密林

撒散貓屬的惡臭氣味

像客廳裡的格麗斯金。

　　甚至「抽象的實體」

30. 也在她的魅力周邊繞轉；

而我們的命運趴在枯肋間

使我們的形上學保持溫暖。

1　譯註：韋伯斯特（John Webster, 1580?-1625?），對艾略特具有相當影響的
　　十七世紀英國文學者。

2　譯註：唐恩（John Donne, 1573-1631），對艾略特具有相當影響的十七世紀
　　英國文學者。唐恩為玄學派（metaphysical）有名的詩人。

Mr. Eliot's
Sunday Morning Service

Look, look, master, here comes two religious caterpillars.

―――― *The Jew of Malta*

Polyphiloprogenitive
The sapient sutlers of the Lord
5. Drift across the window-panes.
In the beginning was the Word.

In the beginning was the Word.
Superfetation of τὸ ἔν,
And at the mensual turn of time
10. Produced enervate Origen.

A painter of the Umbrian school
Designed upon a gesso ground
The nimbus of the Baptized God.
The wilderness is cracked and browned

詩集
1920

艾略特先生
星期日早上的禮拜

> 看哪，看哪，主人，這裡來了兩條宗教上的毛蟲。
>
> ——《馬爾他島的猶太人》

繁衍滋生不絕的
神的那些精明的小商販
5. 匆匆掠過玻璃窗前。
太初有道。

　　太初有道。
「太一」的重複受孕，
隨著歲月遞邅而產生
10. 無氣力的神學家俄利根。

　　翁卜理安派 [1] 的畫家
在石膏的地上畫著
受洗禮的神的後光。
荒野龜裂而呈褐色

15. But through the water pale and thin
Still shine the unoffending feet
And there above the painter set
The Father and the Paraclete.

The sable presbyters approach
20. The avenue of penitence;
The young are red and pustular
Clutching piaculative pence.

Under the penitential gates
Sustained by staring Seraphim
25. Where the souls of the devout
Burn invisible and dim.

Along the garden-wall the bees
With hairy bellies pass between
The staminate and pistilate,
30. Blest office of the epicene.

Sweeney shifts from ham to ham

詩集
1920

15.　　　　但透過薄薄的蒼白水面
仍然照著無罪的雙足
畫家在那上方題註
「聖靈與天父」。

穿著黑服的長老們
20.　走近懺悔的林蔭道；
緊握著贖罪的小錢
年輕人，滿臉紅疱。

　　　　懺悔的天門，凝視的
六翼天使支撐著；
25.　天門下，虔誠的靈魂
在燃燒，隱隱幽幽。

　　　　沿著花園牆壁，蜜蜂
腹部毛茸茸的，飛過
雄蕊與雌蕊之間，
30.　兩性者[2]有福的職責。

　　　史威尼移動屁股

Poems
1920

Stirring the water in his bath.

The masters of the subtle schools

Are controversial, polymath.

詩集
1920

不斷攪動洗澡水。[3]
精微學派的先生們
好議論而且博學。

1　譯註：翁卜理安派（Umbrian School），Niccolò da Foligno 所創，盛行
　　十五、六世紀。
2　譯註：兩性者，暗示僕於上帝與人類之間的耶穌。
3　譯註：史威尼潑弄洗澡水諷刺「洗禮」的儀式。

Sweeney Among
the Nightingales

omoi peplegmai kairian plegen eso!

Apeneck Sweeney spread his knees
Letting his arms hang down to laugh,
The zebra stripes along his jaw
Swelling to maculate giraffe.

The circles of the stormy moon
Slide westward toward the River Plate,
Death and the Raven drift above
And Sweeney guards the hornèd gate.

Gloomy Orion and the Dog
Are veiled; and hushed the shrunken seas;
The person in the Spanish cape
Tries to sit on Sweeney's knees

Slips and pulls the table cloth

詩集
1920

夜鶯中的史威尼

哎呀，我遭到那致命的一擊啦！

猿脖史威尼伸開膝腿
讓他的兩臂下垂笑著，
斑馬的條紋沿著下巴
5. 脹成長頸鹿的斑駁。

　　暴風雨欲來的月暈
西傾向著普烈塔河，
死神與烏鴉座在天空漂移
而史威尼把角型門 [1] 守著。

10. 　　陰鬱的獵戶和犬座罩著
面紗；退縮無聲的海浪；
穿著西班牙披肩的女人
想坐在史威尼膝腿上

　　卻滑倒，拉下桌布

15. Overturns a coffee-cup,
Reorganised upon the floor
She yawns and draws a stocking up;

The silent man in mocha brown
Sprawls at the window-sill and gapes;
20. The waiter brings in oranges
Bananas figs and hothouse grapes;

The silent vertebrate in brown
Contracts and concentrates, withdraws;
Rachel née Rabinovitch
25. Tears at the grapes with murderous paws;

She and the lady in the cape
Are suspect, thought to be in league;
Therefore the man with heavy eyes
Declines the gambit, shows fatigue,

30. Leaves the room and reappears
Outside the window, leaning in,
Branches of wisteria
Circumscribe a golden grin;

詩集
1920

15. 竟將咖啡杯打翻，
　　在地板上整頓一下
　　她拉上絲襪打個哈欠；

　　　　穿著深褐色的沉默男人
　　躺在窗台邊，張著口；
20. 侍者端來橘子香蕉
　　溫室葡萄和無花果；

　　　　穿棕色衣服的沉默脊椎動物
　　收縮、凝縮、退縮；
　　原名拉比諾維奇的雷切爾
25. 以凶殘的指爪攫取葡萄果；

　　　　她和那位穿肩衣的婦人
　　有嫌疑，看來事先約好；
　　因此那眼皮沉重的男人
　　拒絕開局，顯示疲勞，

30. 　　　走出房間，又出現
　　在窗外，向裡面窺視，
　　在紫藤枝椏蔓延範圍內
　　一個黃金的笑露出牙齒；

The host with someone indistinct

35.　Converses at the door apart,

The nightingales are singing near

The Convent of the Sacred Heart,

And sang within the bloody wood

When Agamemnon cried aloud

40.　And let their liquid siftings fall

To stain the stiff dishonoured shroud.

詩集
1920

　　主人跟不清楚的某人
35. 說話，在門口那邊，
　　夜鶯們在附近唱著
　　「聖心的修道院」，

　　也在血腥的樹林裡唱著
　　當阿伽門農 [2] 大聲叫喊時，
40. 且讓牠們的排泄物灑落
　　弄髒受辱的僵硬裹屍布。

1　譯註：角型門，死亡之門或淫逸之門，見《伊尼亞德》第六章。
2　譯註：阿伽門農，特洛伊戰爭中的希臘聯軍統帥，為妻子及其情人所謀害。

The Waste Land

荒原

· 1922 ·

The Waste Land

*"Nam Sibyllam quidem Cumis ego ipse oculis meis vidi
in ampulla pendere, et cum illi pueri dicerent: Σιβυλλα
τι θελεις; respondebat illa: αποθανειν θελω."*

*For Ezra Pound
il miglior fabbro.*

荒原

「在庫瑪耶我親眼看見那位女巫
被吊在甕中,每當孩童問她:女巫姑,妳想怎樣?
她總是回答說:我想死啊。」

　　給艾茲拉・龐德(Ezra Pound)
　　更靈巧的名手。

The Waste Land
1922

I.

The Burial of the Dead

April is the cruellest month, breeding

Lilacs out of the dead land, mixing

Memory and desire, stirring

Dull roots with spring rain.

5. Winter kept us warm, covering

Earth in forgetful snow, feeding

A little life with dried tubers.

Summer surprised us, coming over the Starnbergersee

With a shower of rain; we stopped in the colonnade,

10. And went on in sunlight, into the Hofgarten,

And drank coffee, and talked for an hour.

Bin gar keine Russin, stamm' aus Litauen, echt deutsch.

And when we were children, staying at the arch-duke's,

My cousin's, he took me out on a sled,

15. And I was frightened. He said, Marie,

Marie, hold on tight. And down we went.

In the mountains, there you feel free.

I read, much of the night, and go south in the winter.

荒原
1922

I.

埋葬

四月最是殘酷的季節，孕育著
紫丁香於死寂的土原，摻雜著
追憶與慾情，以春雨
撩撥萎頓的根莖。
5. 冬天使我們溫暖，覆蓋著
大地以遺忘的雪泥，以
枯乾的球根滋養短暫的生命。
夏天突然襲來，從史坦勃爾格‧熱湖那邊
帶來一陣驟雨；我們在柱廊裡避雨，
10. 太陽一出，又走進荷芙公園，
喝了咖啡，聊了一小時。
我不是露西亞人，立陶宛出身，我是道地的德國人。
我們幼年時，住在我的堂兄
大公的宅邸，他帶我出去坐雪橇
15. 我真的害怕。他說，瑪琍亞，
瑪琍亞，緊緊扶著呀。就這樣我們滑了下去。
在那山中，誰都感到逍遙自在。
夜裡我大半看書，冬天就到南方。

The Waste Land
1922

.

       What are the roots that clutch, what branches grow

20.   Out of this stony rubbish? Son of man,[1]

You cannot say, or guess, for you know only

A heap of broken images, where the sun beats,

And the dead tree gives no shelter, the cricket no relief,

And the dry stone no sound of water.[2] Only

25.   There is shadow under this red rock,

(Come in under the shadow of this red rock),

And I will show you something different from either

Your shadow at morning striding behind you

Or your shadow at evening rising to meet you;

30.   I will show you fear in a handful of dust.

            Frisch weht der Wind

            Der Heimat zu

            Mein Irisch Kind,

            Wo weilest du? [3]

35.   "You gave me hyacinths first a year ago;

"They called me the hyacinth girl."

—Yet when we came back, late, from the Hyacinth garden,

Your arms full, and your hair wet, I could not

Speak, and my eyes failed, I was neither

40.   Living nor dead, and I knew nothing,

荒原
1922

這些蟠纏的根鬚是什麼？從這亂石的
20. 廢堆裡生出什麼枝椏？人子喲
祢說不出，祢無從猜想，因祢知道的
只是一堆破碎的形象，曝晒在烈日下，
那裡枯木不能成蔭，蟋蟀給不了安慰，
而乾燥的岩石沒有水聲。只有
25. 影子在這紅色的岩石下，
（走進這紅色岩石的影子裡吧），
我將顯示給你某種異樣的東西，
那不是早晨在你背後大踏步的你的影子
也不是傍晚在你面前迎遇你的你的影子；
30. 我要顯示給你的只是一把骨灰的恐怖吧了。

微風清爽地吹著
吹向了家鄉，
我愛爾蘭之子喲
你停泊何方？

35. 「一年前你首先給我風信子花；
「以後人家就叫我風信子姑娘。」
——可是後來我們從風信子花園回來，
妳手臂抱滿了花，頭髮潤濕，我說不出
話來，兩眼迷茫，活著麼？
40. 死了麼？我什麼也不知道，

Looking into the heart of light, the silence.
Oed' und leer das Meer.[4]

    Madame Sosostris, famous clairvoyante,
Had a bad cold, nevertheless
45. Is known to be the wisest woman in Europe,
With a wicked pack of cards.[5] Here, said she,
Is your card, the drowned Phoenician Sailor,
(Those are pearls that were his eyes. Look!)
Here is Belladonna, the Lady of the Rocks,
50. The lady of situations.
Here is the man with three staves, and here the Wheel,
And here is the one-eyed merchant, and this card,
Which is blank, is something he carries on his back,
Which I am forbidden to see. I do not find
55. The Hanged Man. Fear death by water.
I see crowds of people, walking round in a ring.
Thank you. If you see dear Mrs. Equitone,
Tell her I bring the horoscope myself:
One must be so careful these days.

60.   Unreal City,[6]
Under the brown fog of a winter dawn,

荒原
1922

只是望著那光的核心——寂靜。
那海洋空無而荒涼。

　　叟索斯特力士夫人，有名的千里眼，
患了重感冒，仍然公認為
45.　歐洲最賢慧的女人，
占算著一疊邪惡的紙牌。呃，她說
這張是你的牌，溺死的腓尼基水手，
（你看！他的眼眸成了珍珠。）
這張是貝拉多娜，岩間美女，
50.　歷經滄桑的美人。
這張是三支杖的男人，這張是輪盤
這張是獨眼商人，而這一張
空白的紙牌是他拿在背後的東西，
不能給我看到。我找不到那張
55.　絞首的男人哇。怕是被水淹死囉。
我看到了成群的人們，捲成漩渦走著。
謝謝你。要是碰到伊瑰夫人
就告訴她我會親自帶去她的命運星座：
這年頭大家都得非常小心哪。

60.　　虛幻的都市
在冬天黎明時那鳶色的霧中

The Waste Land
1922

A crowd flowed over London Bridge, so many,

I had not thought death had undone so many.[7]

Sighs, short and infrequent, were exhaled,[8]

65. And each man fixed his eyes before his feet.

Flowed up the hill and down King William Street,

To where Saint Mary Woolnoth kept the hours

With a dead sound on the final stroke of nine.[9]

There I saw one I knew, and stopped him, crying: "Stetson!

70. "You who were with me in the ships at Mylae!

"That corpse you planted last year in your garden,

"Has it begun to sprout? Will it bloom this year?

"Or has the sudden frost disturbed its bed?

"Oh keep the Dog far hence, that's friend to men,[10]

75. "Or with his nails he'll dig it up again!

"You! hypocrite lecteur!—mon semblable, —mon frère!"[11]

荒原
1922

人群湧過了倫敦橋上，那麼多，

我沒想到死還沒處置的人有那麼多。

偶爾吐出短促的嘆息，

65. 每個人的眼睛盯住腳前。

湧上了山坡，又湧下威廉王街，

再湧到聖瑪琍·宇諾斯教堂

彌撒的鐘聲在最後第九下敲出死沉沉的餘音。

那裡我遇到一個熟人，「史替生！」就這叫住他。

70. 「美拉耶海戰時你我在同一艦隊呀！

「去年你在花園裡種下的屍體，

「已經長芽了嗎？今年會開花嗎？

「或是突然下了霜把苗床毀壞啦？

「呃，狗雖是人類的朋友，可別讓牠接近，

75. 「不然狗爪準會把它又挖了出來！

「諸位！偽善的讀者喲！——我的同胞，——我的兄弟

喲！」

原註

1. 參照舊約《以西結書》二章一節。

2. 參照舊約《傳道書》十二章五節。

3. 見《瑞斯坦與依素蒂》I，五至八行。

4. 同書III，二十四行。

5. 對於「泰樂牌」的組構我不確知；顯然有所區別地我所使用的是基於自己的方便上。古來這種紙牌中那一張「絞首的男人」有兩方面適合我的目的：（一）這個被吊死的男人在我心中與 Frazer 的「絞死的神」聯想在一起；（二）與第五部弟子們赴阿瑪塢的旅程中包著頭巾的人物聯想在一起。腓尼基水手與商人後來才出現；「人群」也是，而水死在第四部處理。「三支杖的男子」（泰樂牌中可信的人物）我獨斷地與漁夫王聯想在一起。

6. 參照波特萊爾：
   「人群蠕動的都市，充滿了夢的都市。
   「那裡，白天幽靈纏住了路人。」

7. 參照《神曲・地獄篇》三章五五─五七行：
   「死人長長的行列
   要不是我親眼看見，真不相信
   死已經處置了那麼多人。」

8. 參照地獄篇四章二五─二七行：
   「這裡聽不到抱怨和哀號
   「也沒有悲傷的聲音，只有歎息
   「永遠顫動著慘淡的空氣。」

9. 我時常注意到的一個現象。

10. 參照 Webster 的悲劇《白魔》中的輓歌。

11. 見波特萊爾《惡之華》序。

荒原
1922

譯註

「四月最是殘酷的季節……枯乾的球根滋養短暫的生命」：

開始這七行描寫荒地的風景。四月所以「最是殘酷」是因為「孕育著紫丁香於死寂的土原」；但以漁夫王「摻雜著追憶與慾情」的心境當能體驗其「殘酷」的意義。反過來說，「覆蓋著大地以遺忘的雪泥」的冬天所以「使我們溫暖」是因為「枯乾的球根滋養短暫的生命」──荒原上那種冬眠狀態的生，無異是死，但對荒原上的人們來說，具有無限的魅力。〈荒原〉全篇便是從這種隱藏在逆說性表現的背後，以絕望的敏銳的觀察做為出發點，處理有意思的生與無意味的生對立的主題。

「史坦勃爾格・熱湖那邊……夜裡我大半看書……」：

這十一行詩中的主人公以「第一人稱」「意識流」的形式敘述追憶。

「史坦勃爾格・熱湖」，在德國。距巴華利州首府慕尼黑五十公里有個史坦勃爾格鎮，是有名的療養地方。有神經痛療養所、溫泉等。詩中主人公到那裡遊玩時，與那位德國姑娘的談話成為記憶，浮現在主人公的腦裡。

所謂「大公」指巴華利地方的大公。「公園」指大公宅邸裡的公園。

詩中提到的「驟雨」，「柱廊」在荒地上該是不存在的東西，只有在「追憶」中才有。而主人公回憶與瑪琍亞對話的部分，與乾燥不毛的荒地比起來，具有幼年時代所特有的「逍遙自在」的情緒。

「這些蟠纏的根鬚……我要顯示給你的只是一把骨灰的恐怖吧了。」：

這十二行第一次表現出荒原的主題，暗示著死亡，不能再復活的真正的死亡。

「人子」出自舊約以西結書第二章第一節：「他對我說，人子啊！你站起来，我要和你說話。」又三十七章第三節：「他對我說，人子啊，這些骸骨能復活麼？我說，主耶和華啊，你是知道的。」聖經上的「人子」(son of man) 指將以色列人帶回上帝的先知以西結。但詩中的「人子」(Son of man) 當指耶穌，其教堂以第一次大戰後的景象而言，已成廢墟。傳道書十二章中要人在「蚱蜢成為重擔，人所願的也都廢掉」之前，宜念造化之主；但在現世的荒原中，「破碎的形像，曝晒在烈日下，那裡枯木不能成蔭，蟋蟀給不了安慰，而乾燥的岩石沒有水聲」，

豈不是應驗了以西結的預言：「主耶和華對大山，小岡，水溝，山谷如此說：我必使刀劍臨到你們，必也毀滅你們的祭壇。你們的祭壇必然荒涼，你們的偶像必被打碎，我要使你們被殺的人倒在你們的偶像面前……。」（六章三至四節）

「微風清爽地吹著……那海洋空無而荒涼。」：

這十二行突然轉變為愛與死的主題。前四行取自華格納的歌劇《瑞斯坦與依素蒂》：故事敘述瑞斯坦與公主依素蒂的戀愛。依素蒂原已與瑞斯坦的叔叔馬克王訂婚，歌劇開始時瑞斯坦受命引依素蒂登愛爾蘭駛往康俄爾的船。詩中的引句即是水手在船上所唱的歌，途中依素蒂舊戀重萌，到了康俄爾與瑞斯坦會於馬克王的花園——一如詩中的風信子花園——未幾事洩，於決鬥中瑞斯坦受到致命傷，被帶到布列塔尼，等待著依素蒂來到。一個放羊的進來報告說看不到她的船影——「那海洋空無而荒涼。」——與第一句「微風清爽地吹著」預兆幸福的愛情正好形成對比。這個歌劇故事描出愛與死的輪廓。瑞斯坦受了傷，只有依素蒂才能救治他。這也是漁夫王唯一的希望。但愛與希望在痛苦中粉碎了。瑞斯坦的死暗示穀神之死；大寫的「風信子」暗示植物神與愛的犧牲。「風信子姑娘」毫無疑問地，是個聖杯持有者，能追求到聖杯的就可擁有她。但是當她手臂中抱滿了穗狀的，具有性象徵的花時，詩中的主人公，聖杯的追求者，像是漁夫王的他，暴露了追求聖杯失敗的情緒和反應：「說不出話來，兩眼迷茫……」，他在花園裡接受他的創傷，在荒地裡沉思他的廢墟。

「活著麼？死了麼？我什麼也不知道」：

參照但丁《神曲‧地獄篇》三四章二十五行：「我並沒有死，我卻失去了生。」

「只是望著那光的核心——寂靜」：

參照但丁《神曲‧淨界篇》十二章二十八行：「在那光的核心，發出一種聲音。」

「叟索斯特力士夫人……這年頭大家都得非常小心哪。」：

這十七行描寫千里眼的「叟夫人」以紙牌占卜的插曲。那種紙牌叫做「泰樂牌」，原是埃及人用以預言尼羅河底漲落，今吉普賽人仍用以占卜。

「叟索斯特力士夫人」（Madame Sosostris），奇怪地具有男性的名字，

來自埃及國王 Sesostris。艾略特在詩中的用法，典出 Aldous Huxlexy 的 *Crome Yellow*（1921）書中有趣的一幕：書中假慈悲的史克剛在銀行假日一次慈善性的義賣市場裡，打扮成吉普賽女人，自稱是「Sesostris the Sorceress of Ecbatana」能預言吉凶禍福。這個典故具有扮性的主題，在原註「提瑞西斯」中可得到呼應。叟夫人雖不是年輕的，仍象徵「再生」，是風信子姑娘的翻版；她手中的泰樂牌具有性的呪符的意義，無疑地也是聖杯持有者，手中握有許多象徵，相當於風信子花的。

　　這一節仍表現死的主題。「溺死的腓尼基水手」即水死之一例。

「貝拉多娜，岩間美女，歷盡滄桑的美人。」：

　　暗示克麗奧派特拉或黛杜。這些都是 Pater 的「摩娜麗莎」，所謂近代精神之謎的暗示。「貝拉多娜」(Belladonna) 含有毒草茛蓿類植物的意思。不論是「貝拉多娜」也好，「岩間美女」也好，「歷盡滄桑的美人」也好，都是暗示不能生子的，不毛之地一般的女人。「三支杖的男人」原註與漁夫王聯想在一起，或暗示「三肢杖」(the triple phallused) 的男人。

　　「輪盤」可解釋為世上生命的象徵，意味佛教的輪迴。

　　「獨眼商人」與「腓尼基水手」聯結在一起，暗示慾的主題。在第二部所做的「生意」或許就是不能讓叟夫人看到的秘密。

　　「絞首的男人」原註與「絞首的神」聯想在一起，暗示被埋葬的豐作神；另一方面與第五部弟子們赴陌瑪塢的旅程中包著頭巾的人物聯想在一起。這是叟夫人找不到的一張，顯示這位千里眼看不到的事情。

「虛幻的都市……諸位！偽善的讀者喲！……」：

　　這十七行處理頹廢的都市的憂鬱，一如波特萊爾在〈七個老頭兒〉（Les Sept Vieillards）中描寫的巴黎的憂鬱景色。

　　「虛幻的都市」正是原註中波特萊爾的「充滿了夢的都市」，那也是個幽魂的地獄，只是住的是一些「死還沒處置的人」吧了。如此與《神曲‧地獄篇》三、四兩章所描寫的情況聯想在一起。

「聖瑪琍‧宇諾斯教堂」：

　　代表聖杯故事中的城堡。那是追尋者必須跨過水才能到達的地方，正像這些

The Waste Land
1922

人群湧過了倫敦橋上。

「史替生」：

現代人的代表，地獄裡的懦夫（第三章）。他在花園裡種下的屍體（表現埋葬的主題），該是屬於「絞首的神」的。在古代祭祀中，將豐作神 Osiris 的芻像埋葬在地下，以求大地復生。

「美拉耶海戰」：

指羅馬人在西西里島美拉耶地方打敗迦太基的海戰，史替生暗示第一次世界大戰戰友，如此將過去與現在予以聯在一起。「你我在同一艦隊」：暗示彼此命運相關。戰爭的慘酷古今相同；人類的命運不分彼此。因此史替生的遭遇，正是千萬人的遭遇，而讀者即是同胞，即是兄弟，一切的境遇繫於共同的命運。

「狗雖是人類的朋友，可別讓牠接近」：

若埋葬的是神的屍體，則狗爪挖墳顯然褻瀆神物。若埋葬的是聖杯的追尋者，則狗爪揭露他在風信子花園中失敗的羞辱和恐懼。此外，狗在原始文化上與狼都被認為是植物發生的精靈，且在古代有狗吠預告地震的傳說。

總之，這一節反覆著死與豐作神的主題。埋葬屍骸暗示對現實世界中戰爭殺人，棄屍遍野的諷刺。

II.
A Game of Chess

The Chair she sat in, like a burnished throne,[12]
Glowed on the marble, where the glass
Held up by standards wrought with fruited vines
From which a golden Cupidon peeped out
5. (Another hid his eyes behind his wing)
Doubled the flames of sevenbranched candelabra
Reflecting light upon the table as
The glitter of her jewels rose to meet it,
From satin cases poured in rich profusion;
10. In vials of ivory and coloured glass
Unstoppered, lurked her strange synthetic perfumes,
Unguent, powdered, or liquid—troubled, confused
And drowned the sense in odours; stirred by the air
That freshened from the window, these ascended
15. In fattening the prolonged candle-flames,
Flung their smoke into the laquearia,[13]
Stirring the pattern on the coffered ceiling.
Huge sea-wood fed with copper

荒原
1922

II.

棋戲

她的坐椅，像是光澤四射的王座，
在大理石上亮著，支持粧鏡的
柱腳雕飾著葡萄纍纍的藤蔓
從那兒一個金色邱比特探出臉來
5.　（另一個把眼睛矇藏在翼蔭下）
鏡中照耀著七柱燭台的雙重
火焰，將光芒反射在桌上
與她的緞盒子紛紛傾出的
珠光寶氣交輝互映。
10.　象牙與彩色玻璃的化粧瓶
拔開塞子，其中隱藏著她所使用的
奇妙的人造香水，潤油，粉和液劑——
使感官困擾，混亂，淹溺在各種香氣裡；
被窗外清爽地吹進來的風所撩動，
15.　這些香氣上升，使那修長的燭火肥大地燃燒，
縷縷的焰煙吹向方格天花板，
擾亂了鑲板上的模樣。
與銅一起餵進爐裡的粗大海底木

The Waste Land
1922

Burned green and orange, framed by the coloured stone,

20. In which sad light a carvéd dolphin swam.

Above the antique mantel was displayed

As though a window gave upon the sylvan scene [14]

The change of Philomel,[15] by the barbarous king

So rudely forced;[16] yet there the nightingale

25. Filled all the desert with inviolable voice

And still she cried, and still the world pursues,

"Jug Jug" to dirty ears.

And other withered stumps of time

Were told upon the walls; staring forms

30. Leaned out, leaning, hushing the room enclosed.

Footsteps shuffled on the stair.

Under the firelight, under the brush, her hair

Spread out in fiery points

Glowed into words, then would be savagely still.

35.   "My nerves are bad tonight. Yes, bad. Stay with me.

"Speak to me. Why do you never speak. Speak.

   "What are you thinking of? What thinking? What?

"I never know what you are thinking. Think."

   I think we are in rats' alley [17]

荒原
1922

燃燒出綠色和橙紅，周圍框著彩色的石子，

20. 在那悲哀的光中，一隻雕刻的海豚浮泳著。

飾掛在古雅的暖爐棚上的繪畫

有如從窗子俯瞰森林景色一般

那是菲露美的變形，當她被野蠻的國王，

如此殘酷地逼迫成夜鶯；然而夜鶯

25. 那神聖不可侵犯的泣聲響遍荒野，

她不停地悲啼，人類不停地在後面追逐，

「嗟嗟」地醜惡的耳朵都聽到了。

其他的畫描繪現世的枯朽殘株

也掛在牆上；那些炯炯凝視的形象

30. 探出來，倚靠著，將房間四周噓得靜悄悄。

梯階上傳來拖踏的足音。

照著火光，她梳過的頭髮

像火焰的尖芒披散著，

亮光迸出話語，隨後又恢復了可怕的寂靜。

35. 　　「今晚我的心情煩悶，真的很煩悶。陪陪我吧。

「跟我聊聊吧。你怎麼老不開口呢。說話呀。

　　「你在想什麼？想什麼？什麼事啊？

「想什麼總不讓我知道。好好想吧。」

　　我想我們住在鼠巷裡

The Waste Land
1922

40. Where the dead men lost their bones.

"What is that noise?"

The wind under the door.[18]

"What is that noise now? What is the wind doing?"

Nothing again nothing.

45. "Do

"You know nothing? Do you see nothing? Do you remember

"Nothing?"

I remember

Those are pearls that were his eyes.

50. "Are you alive, or not? Is there nothing in your head?" [19]

But

O O O O that Shakespeherian Rag—

It's so elegant

So intelligent

55. "What shall I do now? What shall I do?"

"I shall rush out as I am, and walk the street

"With my hair down, so. What shall we do tomorrow?

"What shall we ever do?"

The hot water at ten.

60. And if it rains, a closed car at four.

荒原
1922

40. 那是死人失去骸骨的地方。

　　　　「那是什麼聲響？」

　　　　　　　　　　　門腳下的風吧。

　　「那又是什麼聲響？風在那兒做什麼呢？」

　　　　　　　　　　沒有啊什麼也沒有啊。

45. 　　　　　　　　　，　　　　「你呀

　　「什麼也不知道？什麼也沒看到？什麼也沒

　　「記著？」

　　　　我記起

　　他的眼眸成了珍珠。

50. 「你活著麼？死了麼？你腦裡什麼都沒有啦？」

　　　　　　　　　　　　　　　只有

　　哦哦哦哦莎士比亞那傢伙的爵士樂——

　　多麼優美啊

　　多麼知性啊

55. 「現在我怎麼辦呢？怎麼辦呢？」

　　「我就這麼衝出去，在街上走

　　「披著散髮。我們明天做什麼呢？

　　「到底我們做什麼好呢？」

　　　　　　　　　十點鐘熱水。

60. 要是下雨，四點鐘一輛轎式汽車。

The Waste Land
1922

And we shall play a game of chess,[20]

Pressing lidless eyes and waiting for a knock upon the door.

  When Lil's husband got demobbed, I said—

I didn't mince my words, I said to her myself,

65. HURRY UP PLEASE ITS TIME

Now Albert's coming back, make yourself a bit smart.

He'll want to know what you done with that money he gave
you

To get yourself some teeth. He did, I was there.

You have them all out, Lil, and get a nice set,

70. He said, I swear, I can't bear to look at you.

And no more can't I, I said, and think of poor Albert,

He's been in the army four years, he wants a good time,

And if you don't give it him, there's others will, I said.

Oh is there, she said. Something o' that, I said.

75. Then I'll know who to thank, she said, and give me a straight
look.

HURRY UP PLEASE ITS TIME

If you don't like it you can get on with it, I said.

Others can pick and choose if you can't.

But if Albert makes off, it won't be for lack of telling.

80. You ought to be ashamed, I said, to look so antique.

荒原
1922

然後我們來玩一盤棋戲，

勉強睜著眼瞼，等待著門上的叩響。

　　當麗兒的丈夫復員回來，我說——

我毫不吞吐，我親自跟她說，

65. **時間到了趕快吧**

現在阿博就要回來了，打扮漂亮一點啊。

他要知道給妳裝假牙的錢

妳怎麼用了。在我面前，他不是這麼說過嗎？

麗兒，妳把牙齒整個拔掉，另外裝上好看的假牙吧，

70. 他說，真的，妳那面孔難看死了。

說的是呢，我說，想想可憐的阿博吧

他當了四年兵啦，需要一些安慰，

要是妳不能給他，別的女人會給的，我說。

哦，有那樣的女人嗎？她說。好像有呢，我說。

75. 不知那是誰，我得向她說謝，麗兒這麼說著，睨視著我。

時間到了趕快吧

假如不願意那樣，妳就好好對待他吧，我說。

假如你不能，別的女人可會看中他把他搶去喲。

假如阿博逃掉了，那可不是沒有跟你說的。

80. 妳看來那樣面老，實在不像樣，我說。

(And her only thirty-one.)

I can't help it, she said, pulling a long face,

It's them pills I took, to bring it off, she said.

(She's had five already, and nearly died of young George.)

85. The chemist said it would be all right, but I've never been the
same.

You are a proper fool, I said.

Well, if Albert won't leave you alone, there it is, I said,

What you get married for if you don't want children?

HURRY UP PLEASE ITS TIME

90. Well, that Sunday Albert was home, they had a hot gammon,

And they asked me in to dinner, to get the beauty of it hot—

HURRY UP PLEASE ITS TIME

HURRY UP PLEASE ITS TIME

Goonight Bill. Goonight Lou. Goonight May. Goonight.

95. Ta ta. Goonight. Goonight.

Good night, ladies, good night, sweet ladies, good night, good
night.

（麗兒不過三十一歲吧了。）

我有什麼辦法呢，她拉長著臉，

都是為了避孕吃藥的啊，這麼說。

（她已經生了五胎，幾乎因最小的喬治難產死去。）

85. 藥劑師說那不會有問題的，可是身體一直就不像從前了。

妳真是個傻瓜，我說。

還好，阿博沒讓你孤守空房，那只有這樣子了，我說，

若不想要孩子，何必結婚呢？

時間到了趕快吧

90. 對了，阿博休假回來的那個禮拜天，他們做了一道熱火腿，

請我吃飯，飽嘗了一頓熱騰騰的美餐——

時間到了趕快吧

時間到了趕快吧

碧兒再見。露兒再見。美兒再見。再見。

95. 拜拜。再見。再見。

再見，小姐們，再見，親愛的小姐們，再見，再見。

原註

12. 參照莎士比亞《安東尼與克麗奧佩特拉》二幕二景一九〇行。

13. 「方格天花板」(Laquearia)。見魏吉爾《伊尼亞德》一章七二六行：「亮燈從金黃的方格天花板上落下來，閃耀的火把驅逐了夜。」

14. 「森林景色」見密爾頓《失樂園》四卷一四〇行。

15. 見奧維德《變形記》第六 Philomela。

16. 參照第三部二〇四行。

17. 參照第三部一九五行。

18. 參照 Webster「風仍在那個門口吹著麼？」

19. 參照第一部三七行、四八行。

20. 參照 Middleton《女人謹防女人》中的西洋棋戲。

荒原
1922

譯註

　　第二部「棋戲」表現的是社會上下兩層沒有愛的性生活，尤其是結了婚的性生活。聖杯的追尋者失去風信子姑娘之後，在這裡又找到了一個聖杯持有者，她可能就是貝拉多娜，「歷盡滄桑的美人」。

「她的坐椅……亮光迸出話語……」：

　　這三十四行描寫這個頹廢的，沒有子女的，貴婦人的生活，顯示近代荒原的一面。

「菲露美的變形」：

　　暗示性的強暴。菲露美，雅典王的女兒，普露尼之姊，曾見虐於普露尼的丈夫特魯（Tereus），切斷她的舌頭。菲露美與普露尼姊妹為了復仇，將特魯的親生子女餐給特魯吃。當特魯追逐時，諸神將菲露美化成燕，普露尼化為夜鶯，而特魯則化作戴勝或鷹。依奧維德之說，化為夜鷹的是菲露美。「枯朽殘株」：象徵菲露美的舌頭，暗示「破碎形象」。

「今晚我的心情煩悶，真的很煩悶……想什麼總不讓我知道……」：

　　這四行表現女人急躁的，神經質的談話，以及男人的沉默，暗示不諧調的一面。

「我想我們住在鼠巷裡……勉強睜著眼瞼……」：

　　這二十四行將有閒的貴婦人的生活與死的主題聯結在一起。

　　她那種神經質的對風聲的抱怨，在他心中引生「鼠巷」，「那是死人失去骸骨的地方」的意象；那正是以西結感靈見枯骨復生的景象：「有聲音，有地震……風從四方而來……氣息就進入骸骨，骸骨便活了，並且站起來。」（三十七章）

The Waste Land
1922

「他的眼眸成了珍珠」：

出自莎士比亞《暴風雨》一幕二景愛麗兒唱的歌。費迪南一聽到這音樂，便憶起溺死的父王。又是水死的主題。

「爵士樂」是當時開始流行的，所以作者諷刺那也是荒原的一個現象。將愛麗兒唱的輓歌說成「爵士樂」頗有諷刺的意味。

「就這麼衝出去，在街上走……」：

受到他的厭惡的譏諷，她那失去理智的動作，正像瘋狂的黛杜，當伊尼亞遺棄她時。這個意象也使人聯想到馬克白（Macbeth）的狂亂。

「棋戲」：

Middleton 的《女人謹防女人》（II. ii）中，被伯爵誘姦的比安嘉的事，便是發生在她的岳母玩著棋戲而失去注意的時侯。這暗示「盲目」的主題。在艾略特所使用的象徵中，我們可以看出：荒原上的人們屬於一種他們不能了解的棋戲，像棋子般被驅使著，不知目的，也沒有選擇。

「勉強睜著眼瞼」：

那是不眠的眼，暗示男女生活中的折磨，等待著死神叩響門聲。

「當麗兒的丈夫復員回來……再見，再見。」

這三十四行與前節處理的上流婦人的生活對照，描寫下層社會，酒場中那些女郎的生活和對話。這與性生活仍有關係，尤其是荒原中特有的現象避孕等表現不育與荒瘠的主題。棋子碧兒、露兒、美兒聚集在酒館裡聽關於麗兒與阿博的不幸：麗兒忍受墮胎與換假牙的痛苦，阿博像史替生一直在戰爭中。

「時間到了趕快吧」：

是打烊的叫聲。在那些女人談話間，可以聽到這句叫聲。似乎是對她們的談話的諷刺或警告，這是「意識流」創作手法的一個特色。

荒原
1922

「碧兒再見……再見」：

出自《哈姆雷特》四幕五景，奧菲里阿瘋狂的告別，使她想起死去的父親。仍是死的主題。

在第三部中象徵聖杯持有者的人物可分為兩類：一是風信子姑娘，如菲露美、比安嘉和奧菲里阿；一是叟夫人、貝拉多娜或麗兒，如克麗奧派特拉與黛杜。像貝拉多娜旳人物都是不育的尤物，帶給的聯想是慾和激情。把貝拉多娜刻畫成脾氣急躁的憤懣的個性，正是強調這一點。貝拉多娜，一個 Circe 或 Siren，將艾略特的追尋者抓在她的掌圈中。

The Waste Land
1922

III.

The Fire Sermon

The river's tent is broken: the last fingers of leaf

Clutch and sink into the wet bank. The wind

Crosses the brown land, unheard. The nymphs are departed.

Sweet Thames, run softly, till I end my song.[21]

5. The river bears no empty bottles, sandwich papers,

Silk handkerchiefs, cardboard boxes, cigarette ends

Or other testimony of summer nights. The nymphs are

departed.

And their friends, the loitering heirs of city directors;

Departed, have left no addresses.

10. By the waters of Leman I sat down and wept . . .

Sweet Thames, run softly till I end my song,

Sweet Thames, run softly, for I speak not loud or long.

But at my back in a cold blast I hear

The rattle of the bones, and chuckle spread from ear to ear.

15. A rat crept softly through the vegetation

Dragging its slimy belly on the bank

While I was fishing in the dull canal

荒原
1922

·

III.

火誡

河流的華蓋塌落了：枯葉最後的手指
緊抓著而陷入濕漉的土堤。風無聲地
吹過鳶色的原野。那些水仙子都已離去。
嫵媚的泰晤士河喲，靜靜地流著，直到我歌已盡。
5.　河上不見空瓶或三明治的紙巾漂浮著，
也沒有手絹、硬紙盒、菸蒂
或其他夏夜的證據品。那些水仙子都已離去。
她們的朋友，那些遊手好閒的都市董事的繼承人
也都離去了，沒有留下地址。
10.　我在麗曼湖濱坐著啜泣……
嫵媚的泰晤士河喲，靜靜地流著，直到我歌已盡，
嫵媚的泰晤士河喲，靜靜地流著，聽我淺唱低吟。
可是在背後一陣冷風中我聽到
骸骨的摩擦聲，以及一再傳到耳邊的竊笑。
15.　一隻老鼠靜靜地從草叢中竄過
在堤上拖著黏黏的腹部，
那時正是冬日黃昏，我在陰沉沉的運河

The Waste Land
1922

On a winter evening round behind the gashouse

Musing upon the king my brother's wreck

20. And on the king my father's death before him.[22]

White bodies naked on the low damp ground

And bones cast in a little low dry garret,

Rattled by the rat's foot only, year to year.

But at my back from time to time I hear [23]

25. The sound of horns and motors, which shall bring

Sweeney to Mrs. Porter in the spring.[24]

O the moon shone bright on Mrs. Porter

And on her daughter

They wash their feet in soda water [25]

30. *Et O ces voix d'enfants, chantant dans la coupole!* [26]

Twit twit twit

Jug jug jug jug jug jug

So rudely forc'd.

Tereu

35. Unreal City

Under the brown fog of a winter noon

Mr. Eugenides, the Smyrna merchant

Unshaven, with a pocket full of currants

荒原
1922

繞著煤氣工廠後面垂釣，
冥想我兄王的舟破死難
20. 以及在他之前我父王的死喪。
白骨裸露橫陳在海底的屍體，以及
丟棄在乾燥窄小頂樓裡的骸骨
年年只是遭受老鼠的踐踏嘎嘎作響。
可是在背後我一再聽到
25. 摩托車和角笛的警聲將史威尼
帶到浴泉的波夫人那裡。
哦，波夫人，沐浴著月光光
月光光，沐浴著波姑娘
母女的浸腳水，蘇達香
30. 哦，少年合唱的歌聲來自圓頂教堂！

啐啐啐
嗟嗟嗟嗟嗟嗟
如此殘忍的逼迫。
特魯

35. 虛幻的都市
在冬日正午鳶色的霧中
優珍尼先生，那位士麥納商人，
沒刮鬍子，衣袋裡塞滿運交葡萄乾

The Waste Land
1922

C.i.f. London: documents at sight,[27]

40. Asked me in demotic French

To luncheon at the Cannon Street Hotel

Followed by a weekend at the Metropole.

At the violet hour, when the eyes and back

Turn upward from the desk, when the human engine waits

45. Like a taxi throbbing waiting,

I Tiresias, though blind, throbbing between two lives,[28]

Old man with wrinkled female breasts, can see

At the violet hour, the evening hour that strives

Homeward, and brings the sailor home from sea,[29]

50. The typist home at teatime, clears her breakfast, lights

Her stove, and lays out food in tins.

Out of the window perilously spread

Her drying combinations touched by the sun's last rays,

On the divan are piled (at night her bed)

55. Stockings, slippers, camisoles, and stays.

I Tiresias, old man with wrinkled dugs

Perceived the scene, and foretold the rest—

I I too awaited the expected guest.

He, the young man carbuncular, arrives,

60. A small house agent's clerk, with one bold stare,

荒原
1922

到倫敦的運費與保險金的即付票據，
40. 以粗俗的法國話請我
到肯濃街飯店午餐，
週末又請我到美脫普旅館。

　　紫羅蘭的時刻，當眼睛和背脊
離開桌子向上挪動，當人體發動機
45. 像計程車發動時的搏動等待著，
我，提瑞西斯雖是盲人，搏動在兩性間
我，年老的提瑞西斯，有著女人萎縮的乳房，能看見
在這紫羅蘭的時刻，趕路回家的時刻，
當黃昏將水手從海上帶回家；
50. 打字員喝茶時間在家，收拾了早餐的杯盤，
點起爐火，打開罐頭裡的食物。
她那晾乾的連褲襯衣，危險地展掛在窗外，
夕陽以最後的光眸觸撫，
長沙發上（晚上，她的床）堆積著
55. 絲襪，拖鞋，短袖襯衣和緊身褡。
我，提瑞西斯，乳房萎縮了的老人
眼見這種情景，能夠預言此後的事情——
我也在等待會到來的客人。
他，那位滿臉面皰的年輕人，來了，
60. 一個矮小的房產介紹所的職員，眼邪膽大的傢伙，

One of the low on whom assurance sits

As a silk hat on a Bradford millionaire.

The time is now propitious, as he guesses,

The meal is ended, she is bored and tired,

65. Endeavours to engage her in caresses

Which still are unreproved, if undesired.

Flushed and decided, he assaults at once;

Exploring hands encounter no defence;

His vanity requires no response,

70. And makes a welcome of indifference.

(And I Tiresias have foresuffered all

Enacted on this same divan or bed;

I who have sat by Thebes below the wall

And walked among the lowest of the dead.)

75. Bestows one final patronising kiss,

And gropes his way, finding the stairs unlit . . .

She turns and looks a moment in the glass,

Hardly aware of her departed lover;

Her brain allows one half-formed thought to pass:

80. "Well now that's done: and I'm glad it's over."

When lovely woman stoops to folly and [30]

Paces about her room again, alone,

荒原
1922

下流人物之一，妄自尊大充滿信心，

有如布拉福德的暴發戶戴著大禮帽。

現在正是個好時機，一如他猜想的，

飯後她一定感到無聊和懶散，

65. 努力向她誘施愛撫的動作

總不致拒絕，即使她不想要。

一陣耳熱他下了決心馬上出擊；

試探的手並沒遭遇到任何抵抗；

他的自負不需要任何反應，

70. 她的冷淡他倒認為是歡迎。

（這張長沙發或是床上所作所為，

我，提瑞西早就經驗過啦；

我曾經坐在西庇斯城牆下，

也曾經在最卑賤的死屍之間走著。）

75. 恩人似的給她一個最後的吻別

他摸索地走下了沒燈光的梯階……

她轉過身來稍微照照鏡子，

似乎沒注意到情人已離去；

她的腦裡浮現出一個片斷的思緒：

80. 「還好，就這麼一回事，過了我倒高興。」

當可愛的女人放蕩一時之後

一個人，在自己的房間踱步，

The Waste Land
1922

She smoothes her hair with automatic hand,

And puts a record on the gramophone.

85.　　"This music crept by me upon the waters" [31]

And along the Strand, up Queen Victoria Street.

O City city, I can sometimes hear

Beside a public bar in Lower Thames Street,

The pleasant whining of a mandolin

90.　And a clatter and a chatter from within

Where fishmen lounge at noon: where the walls

Of Magnus Martyr hold

Inexplicable splendour of Ionian white and gold. [32]

　　　　The river sweats [33]

95.　　　Oil and tar

　　　The barges drift

　　　With the turning tide

　　　Red sails

　　　Wide

100.　　To leeward, swing on the heavy spar.

　　　The barges wash

　　　Drifting logs

　　　Down Greenwich reach

荒原
1922

她以自動的手把亂髮撫平，
將一片唱盤放在留聲機上。

85.　　　「這音樂掠過水面爬近我的身邊」
沿著河濱馬路，流到維多利亞女王街。
都市喲，倫敦喲，我有時聽得到
在泰晤士河下街的酒吧旁邊，
那曼陀鈴幽美的嗚咽，
90.　以及裡邊傳來的嘈嚷和閒聊，
那是漁夫們中午蹓躂歇息的地方：
那裡瑪格納斯殉道教堂牆壁上保存著
難以說明的艾奧尼安式壯麗，純白與金黃。

河面流淌著
95.　　　油脂與瀝青
漂流的遊船
隨潮水漲落
紅色的帆
飽張著
100.　向著下風，在沉重的帆柱上搖動。
遊船沖擊
流木
漂向格林威治河域

Past the Isle of Dogs.

                Weialala leia

                Wallala leialala

                Elizabeth and Leicester [34]

Beating oars

The stern was formed

A gilded shell

Red and gold

The brisk swell

Rippled both shores

Southwest wind

Carried down stream

The peal of bells

White towers

                Weialala leia

                Wallala leialala

"Trams and dusty trees.

Highbury bore me. Richmond and Kew

Undid me.[35] By Richmond I raised my knees

Supine on the floor of a narrow canoe."

荒原
1922

經過狗島區。

105.
　　　　嘿呀啦啦　　咧呀

　　　　嘩啦啦　　咧呀啦啦

　　　伊麗莎白女王與黎西斯特伯爵

以櫓擊波

船尾形成

110.
鍍金的貝殼

紅色與金黃

澎湃的波浪

激起漣漪向兩岸擴溢

西南風

115.
順流而下

運走一串鐘聲

白色的塔影

　　　　嘿呀啦啦　　咧呀

　　　　嘩啦啦　　咧呀啦啦

120.
　「電車與滿是灰塵的樹木。

海波麗生了我。立契蒙和科烏

毀了我。在立契蒙河畔我兩膝豎起

躺臥在狹長的獨木舟底。」

"My feet are at Moorgate, and my heart
125. Under my feet. After the event
He wept. He promised a 'new start.'
I made no comment. What should I resent?"

"On Margate Sands.
I can connect
130. Nothing with nothing.
The broken fingernails of dirty hands.
My people humble people who expect
Nothing."
    la la

135. To Carthage then I came [36]

 Burning burning burning burning [37]
O Lord Thou pluckest me out [38]
O Lord Thou pluckest

burning

荒原
1922

「我的腳在摩爾門，心被

125. 賤踏在自己的腳下。事後

他哭泣了。他答應『痛改前非』。

我無話可說。我還有什麼怨恨呢？」

「在瑪關海灘。

什麼是怎樣

130. 我已聯想不起來。

破裂的指甲，汙穢的手。

我的家人，我卑賤的家人，並不想望

什麼。」

啦啦

135. 然後我來到了迦太基

焚身焚身焚身焚身

主喲，祢拯救我出來

主喲，祢拯救

焚身

The Waste Land
1922

原註

21. 見史本塞〈婚前頌〉。

22. 參照莎士比亞《暴風雨》一幕二景。

23. 參照 Marvell〈給怕羞的她〉。

24. 參照 Day〈群蜂會議〉：
「當側耳傾聽，突然傳來，
「角笛與追獵的聲音，將亞克帖勇
「誘到浴泉的黛安娜那裡，
「我們都看到了裸之狩獵女神……」

25. 這幾行取自一首歌謠，其來源已不得而知；這是澳洲雪梨人告訴我的。

26. 見 Verlaine 詩〈Parsifal〉。

27. 葡萄乾被定有「抵倫敦不含運費和保險金」的價格；而提貨憑單 (B/L) 等以即付票據支付時交給買者。

28. 雖然提瑞西斯事實上不是詩中的主要人物，只是個旁觀者而已，卻是詩中最重要的角色，將其他人物聯結在一起。正像那位賣葡萄乾的獨眼商人融合在腓尼基水手中，而這個水手與那不勒斯王子費迪南是不能完全區別那樣，所有女的當作一個女人來看，而男女兩性在提瑞西斯身上合為一體。事實上，提瑞西斯所觀察的是整首詩中最精要的部分。奧維德的詩中有關這故事的部分，具有研究原始文化上極大的興趣：
「根據故事，天神宙比特有一天喝醉了酒心情痛快，突然向宙諾女神開玩笑說：『關於房事我想妳們女性的快感比男性的快感強得多。』對這個意見女神反對了。於是這件事請賢明的提瑞西斯加以判斷。因他關於房事經驗過了兩方的快感。那是從前當他在綠色的森林裡徘徊時，看到了兩隻大蛇在交尾，他用棒子一打，說也奇怪，瞬間他從男性變成女性。此後七年之間他做了女性。就在第八年他又看到了同樣的大蛇，說：『誰打了你們誰就會變性，你們好像有這種魔力，那麼我再打你們一次看看。』這麼說著，一棒打了下去，瞬間又變回了出生時同樣的男性了。因有過那樣的事情，於是提瑞西斯裁判了諸神開玩笑的爭論，並且支持了天神宙比特的意見。可是宙諾女神不管事情

怎樣，豎起柳眉，一怒之下把提瑞西斯變成目盲。神所做的事其他的神是無法消除的，所以全知全能的天神宙斯特可憐了他，為了補償提瑞西斯的失明，賦予他具有預言能力的榮譽。」

29. 這可能與沙浮（Sappho）的詩句稍有出入，但我記得是「近海的」或「平底輕舟的」漁夫日暮時歸來。

30. 見 Goldsmith《威克斐特牧師》中的歌。

31. 見《暴風雨》，同上。

32. 聖瑪格納斯‧殉道教堂內部，我認為是 Waren 所建造的教堂內部中最美的一個。見《關於十九座都市教堂拆毀的建議書》（P. S. King 社出版）。

33. （三個）泰晤士河女的歌從此開始。她們輪流所說的話包含在二九二行到三〇六行。見《諸神的黃昏》三幕一景。

34. 見 Froude《伊麗莎白女王》第一卷第四章「德‧嘉屈拉致西班牙王菲力普書」：「午後，我們乘著御座船觀看水上競技。（女王）獨自與羅伯公卿和我本人在船尾。這時大家開始雜談，扯到最後羅伯公卿說，因我也在場要是女王願意，他們不結婚是沒有理由的。」

35. 參照《神曲‧地獄篇》五章一三三行：
「請你記起我，我是比亞；
「西納生了我，馬累毀了我。」

36. 見聖奧古斯丁《懺悔錄》：「然後我來到了迦太基，那裡不淨的色慾的大鍋在我耳際喧嚷地沸騰著。」

37. 這些取自佛陀的「火誡」（其重要性相當於基督的登山訓眾），全文見 H. G. 華倫的《佛教翻譯》(哈佛東洋叢書)。華倫氏在西洋人中是研究佛教的偉大先驅者之一。

38. 取自聖奧古斯丁《懺悔錄》。將這兩個代表東方與西方禁慾主義的人物相提並論，正像本詩表現這部分的終極目的一樣，絕非偶然。

譯註

　　這一部仍然描寫荒原世界中有關慾與死的主題，不僅僅是「棋戲」的伸展，而且暴露了道德上的意義。所處理的是婚姻以外的性生活，慾火焚身的性關係。

「河流的華蓋塌落了……嫵媚的泰晤士河喲……」：

　　這十二行描寫泰晤士河畔的秋景。

「嫵媚的泰晤士河喲，靜靜地流著，直到我歌已盡」：

　　這是史本塞〈婚前頌〉中有名的疊句。史本塞的歌是對那些嫵媚的水仙唱的，而艾略特的歌是變調，是對打字員頹廢的性生活與現代人的性沒落而唱出的序曲。艾略特這種「戲仿」（Parody）的筆法，聯結遙遠的事物，以造成近代詩Grotesque的特徵。

「我在麗曼湖濱坐著啜泣……」：

　　這一行使聯想到詩篇一三七：「我們在巴比倫河邊坐著，因追想錫安而啜泣。」「麗曼」（Leman）的含義是「情婦」，暗示荒原中的河水是「慾河」。

「可是在背後一陣冷風中我聽到……特魯」：

　　這二十二行描寫詩中的主人公在河岸上沉思的事情。

「一陣冷風」：

　　風無聲地吹過原野，使人想起以西結見枯骸復生的景象。可是這裡的風沒有生命的氣息，只是象徵死亡的一陣冷風。

「骸骨的摩擦聲」：

　　令人引起《尤利西斯》中的「地獄」的感覺。那裡老鼠竄過墳墓，送葬的行

荒原
1922

列停在都柏林煤氣廠附近，與詩中所描述的很相似。

「我在陰沉沉的運河……垂釣」：

　　魚在原始宗教上的象徵一如聖杯。

「冥想我兄王的舟破死難，以及在他之前我父王的死喪。」：

　　《暴風雨》一幕二景中拿不勒斯王子費迪南聽了愛麗兒唱的歌時說：「我坐在岸上，正哭著我父王的舟破死難。」艾略特將費迪南的話稍加改變使用著。至於「兄王的舟破死難」大概取自 Wolfram 的《Parzival》有關聖杯傳中隱者的話。這個隱者的兄王便是漁夫王。這裡，漁夫王、費迪南、腓尼基水手三人正如原註中所說的「是不能完全區別的」。

「可是在背後我一再聽到，摩托車和角笛的警聲」：

　　Marvell 原來的詩句是：「可是在背後我時時聽到，時間的安翼馬車匆匆而來」。「角笛」見原註 24。

　　將亞克帖勇誘到黛安娜那裡也好，將史威尼誘到波夫人那裡也好，意味特魯與菲露美那種物慾的追逐。史威尼是庸俗的，肉慾的象徵；波夫人，貝拉多娜的化身。

「哦，波夫人……蘇達香」：

　　原註取自澳洲雪梨地方的歌謠。浴泉的黛安娜或波夫人使人聯想到華格納的歌劇《帕西法爾》中洗足的儀式。

　　當騎士帕西法爾制服了慾的誘惑，治癒了國王的創傷敬拜聖杯然後聽到「那少年合唱的歌聲來自圓頂教堂！」（見 Paul Verlaine 詩：〈Parsifal〉）

「啐啐啐……特魯」：

　　這是夜鶯的啼聲，荒原裡到處可以聲到的音樂。史威尼的慾望征服了帕西法爾的禁慾精神，暗示菲露美被誘姦那種事情之發生。「特魯」（Tereu）一方面諧夜鶯的泣聲，一方面指切斷夜鶯的舌頭的暴君，「那野蠻的國王」。取自李里

（Lyly）的劇本《亞歷山大與康芭斯》。

「虛幻的都市……週末又請我到美脫普旅館」：

這八行從憂鬱的音樂又回到荒原中的倫敦。

這位士麥拿商人優珍尼得斯（Eugenides）底名字不管是否具有「優生」（Eugenics）的意義，現在是個墮落的角色。這個男人與第一部出現的「獨眼商人」一致。「獨眼的男人」在聖杯傳說中，是一個知道古代宗教的神秘儀式與魔術，且以此吹噓的人物。但艾略特據為象徵，與腓尼基水手聯想在一起，是慾的象徵，性墮落的代表。他是個男色之徒，將詩中的主人公誘到倫敦城外低賤的旅館，暗示第一部中所謂「他負在背上，不能給我看到的」事情。

「紫羅蘭的時刻……將一片唱盤放在留聲機上」：

前節寫的是男色，這一節處理女色：兩者的題旨都是性的沒落。

那是打字員失去貞操的事情。為了預想，觀察與批判這件事，使用了「我，提瑞西斯」這個神話裡的盲人。原註中說：「事實上，提瑞西斯所觀察的是整首詩中最精要的部分。」依據奧維德的故事，他曾經變了兩次性，因此男女間的事情，他早就經驗過了，且能綜合兩方面的經驗。

「黃昏將水手從海上帶回，人們在家路上競走」：

取目希臘女詩人沙浮（Sappho）的詩句。這位女詩人一向被認為是女性同性愛的代表。英語中 Lesbian Love 意謂女性間的同性愛；而 Lesbos 島即沙浮的誕生地。「將一片唱盤放在留聲機上」：在這一節中有些機械的暗示。心臟底悸動說是「人體發動機」；「留聲機」是機械的；無意識的「自動的手」也是機械的。一旦陷於機械的反應，性失去了原有的意義；而性觀念的改變，由改作 Goldsmith 的歌句中投射出來：「當可愛的女人放蕩一時之後」在《威克斐特牧師》中唯一的路途是死。現在這位打字員放蕩一時之後，反而感到何等的空虛和無聊！

「這音樂掠過水面……焚身」：

這一段再描寫泰晤士河畔的倫敦風情，且敘述三個河女遭受汙辱的經過：仍然是慾的主題。

荒原
1922

「這音樂掠過水面爬近我的身邊」：

這是費迪南聽了愛麗兒所唱的歌，想到父王的舟破死難時說的話。詩中的「音樂」該承上一段留聲機上唱出來的音樂。

在「泰晤士河下街」主人公聽著泰晤士河女的歌唱。詩句形式的改變表示轉折。泰晤士河再也不是靜靜地流著了。

泰晤士河女合唱的歌分成兩部，每部結束以萊茵少女的歌聲「嘿呀啦啦，咧呀，嘩啦啦，咧呀啦啦」。見華格納歌劇《諸神的黃昏》。然後一個輪一個敘述她們被騙失身的往事。

「伊麗莎白女王與黎西斯特伯爵」：

這一幕使人聯想到克麗奧派特拉在西得拿斯河上最初晤見安東尼的情景。伊麗莎白女王，另一個克麗奧派特拉，事實上與波夫人是分不清的，可說都是淫佚的象徵。

三個泰晤士河女，正像《諸神的黃昏》中的三個萊茵河女，每個人都有不堪回首的往事。

第一個，雖然海波麗所生，卻毀於伊麗莎白女王的親信立契蒙和科烏。在泰晤士河上流幽美的立契蒙河畔失身。（立契蒙和科烏也是泰晤士河上流，青春戀人散步和舟遊的地方，有皇宮和公園。）

第二個，她的腳或許就是波夫人或是她女兒的腳，在倫敦城的裡門叫摩爾門的地方失身。

第三個，有著指甲破裂的汙穢的手，在泰晤士河出海口叫瑪關的地方被騙，無疑又是打字員那種事。

泰晤士河女，就這麼失去了萊茵河女的「金指環」。

「然後我來到了迦太基」：

這是禁慾的聖奧古斯丁在《懺悔錄》中的話。「焚身」的是慾火。佛陀與聖奧古斯丁為東西方最大的禁慾主義者。第三部一連串慾火焚身的事件之後，到此以東西禁慾主義者的話結束，寓意顯然。如此，為第五部「雷聲」埋下伏筆。

IV.

Death by Water

Phlebas the Phoenician, a fortnight dead,

Forgot the cry of gulls, and the deep sea swell

And the profit and loss.

A current under sea

5. Picked his bones in whispers. As he rose and fell

He passed the stages of his age and youth

Entering the whirlpool.

Gentile or Jew

O you who turn the wheel and look to windward,

10. Consider Phlebas, who was once handsome and tall as you.

IV.
水死

腓烈巴斯，腓尼基人，死了兩週，
遺忘了海鷗的叫聲，深海的波濤，
以及一切損益得失。
　　　　　　海底下的暗流
5. 竊竊地啃著他的骨頭。載浮載沉地
他經歷過青春到年老的階段，
捲入了漩渦。
　　　　　　基督教徒也好猶太教徒也好
你呀，望著風向轉舵的人，
10. 想想腓烈巴斯的事情吧，他曾是美男子且與你一樣高大。

The Waste Land
1922

譯註

　　「水死」帶來了腓尼基水手以及慾的主題最後的結果。前三行像是腓烈巴斯的墓誌銘。費迪南預知的命運在這裡實現了。「遺忘了一切損益得失」：暗示士麥拿商人不可避免的結局。

　　據維斯頓女士的說法，水死在古代祭祀中使用著。每年在尼羅河口亞歷山大港將神的芻像投入海中，七天後再撈起來，以象徵復活。但是腓烈巴斯已經死了兩週，他的眼眸也沒有變成珍珠，骸骨反而捲入漩渦。「漩渦」要是暗示《奧德賽》中的大漩渦 Charybdis，那顯然是痛苦的命運，無異墮入地獄。那是死前曾是「美男子」的腓烈巴斯縱慾之後應得的報應吧。

The Waste Land
1922

V.

What the Thunder Said

After the torchlight red on sweaty faces
After the frosty silence in the gardens
After the agony in stony places
The shouting and the crying
5. Prison and palace and reverberation
Of thunder of spring over distant mountains
He who was living is now dead
We who were living are now dying
With a little patience

10. Here is no water but only rock
Rock and no water and the sandy road
The road winding above among the mountains
Which are mountains of rock without water
If there were water we should stop and drink
15. Amongst the rock one cannot stop or think
Sweat is dry and feet are in the sand
If there were only water amongst the rock

荒原
1922

V.
雷語

　　在火炬照紅汗淋淋的臉之後
　　在霜蓋滿園的靜默之後
　　在岩石之地的苦惱之後
　　叫聲與哭泣
5.　牢獄與宮殿，以及春雷
　　越過遠山的迴響
　　曾經活著的人現在死了
　　曾經活著的我們氣息奄奄
　　忍受最後的殘喘

10.　　　這裡沒有水只有岩石
　　沒有水只是岩石和砂路
　　沿山蜿蜒而上的砂路
　　岩石的山沒有水
　　假如有水我們會歇腳飲水
15.　在岩石間我們無處歇腳飲水
　　汗已乾而兩腳陷入砂中
　　但願岩石間會有水

The Waste Land
1922

Dead mountain mouth of carious teeth that cannot spit

Here one can neither stand nor lie nor sit

20. There is not even silence in the mountains

But dry sterile thunder without rain

There is not even solitude in the mountains

But red sullen faces sneer and snarl

From doors of mudcracked houses

25.   If there were water

And no rock

If there were rock

And also water

And water

30. A spring

A pool among the rock

If there were the sound of water only

Not the cicada

And dry grass singing

35. But sound of water over a rock

Where the hermit-thrush sings in the pine trees [39]

Drip drop drip drop drop drop drop

But there is no water

Who is the third who walks always beside you? [40]

荒原
1922

蛀齒的死山口中吐不出水

這裡站不得坐不得也躺臥不得

20.　山中甚至沒有寂靜

只是不毛而乾燥無雨的空雷

山中甚至沒有孤獨

只有面紅耳赤愁眉苦臉的冷笑和怒罵，

從泥壁龜裂的房屋門口傳來

25.　　　　　　　　　　假如有水

而沒有岩石

假如有岩石

也有水

有水

30.　　有泉

有岩間的水潭

要是只有水聲

沒有蟬鳴

沒有枯草的吟唱

35.　　只有流過岩石的水聲

伴著隱者畫眉在松間的歌唱

嘀嗒嘀嗒嗒嗒嗒

可是沒有水

經常走在你們身邊那另一個人是誰？

The Waste Land
1922

40. When I count, there are only you and I together

But when I look ahead up the white road

There is always another one walking beside you

Gliding wrapt in a brown mantle, hooded

I do not know whether a man or a woman

45. —But who is that on the other side of you?

What is that sound high in the air

Murmur of maternal lamentation

Who are those hooded hordes swarming

Over endless plains, stumbling in cracked earth

50. Ringed by the flat horizon only

What is the city over the mountains

Cracks and reforms and bursts in the violet air

Falling towers

Jerusalem Athens Alexandria

55. Vienna London

Unreal [41]

A woman drew her long black hair out tight

And fiddled whisper music on those strings

And bats with baby faces in the violet light

60. Whistled, and beat their wings

荒原
1922

40. 我數了數，只有你們和我在一起呀
每當我向著白路的前方遙望
總有另一個人走在你身邊
穿著鳶色披風，包著頭巾滑行
我不知道那是男的或是女的
45. ——到底在你另一邊那個人是誰呀？

　　高空中那是什麼聲音
母性哀悼的咕噥
包著頭巾那群人是誰？他們從無垠的平野蜂擁而過
在平坦的地平線所完全包圍的
50. 裂土上跌跌撞撞，那群人是誰呀
山的那邊是什麼都市
在紫色的夕空中破裂而改造而爆破
倒塌下去的樓塔
耶路撒冷，雅典，亞歷山大城
55. 維也納，倫敦
虛幻的

　　一個婦人拉緊黑長髮
將低聲細語的音樂彈自如弦的髮梢
堇色的夕空中蝙蝠露出嬰兒臉
60. 拍動翅膀，發出噓噓的呼嘯

And crawled head downward down a blackened wall

And upside down in air were towers

Tolling reminiscent bells, that kept the hours

And voices singing out of empty cisterns and exhausted wells.

65.   In this decayed hole among the mountains

In the faint moonlight, the grass is singing

Over the tumbled graves, about the chapel

There is the empty chapel, only the wind's home.

It has no windows, and the door swings,

70. Dry bones can harm no one.

Only a cock stood on the rooftree

Co co rico co co rico

In a flash of lightning. Then a damp gust

Bringing rain

75.   Ganga was sunken, and the limp leaves

Waited for rain, while the black clouds

Gathered far distant, over Himavant.

The jungle crouched, humped in silence.

Then spoke the thunder

80. DA

Datta :[42] what have we given?

荒原
1922

倒懸地趴在黝黑的牆壁上
倒立在空中的還有那些樓塔
敲響了追懷的鐘聲，鳴告彌撒
而歌聲來自乾涸的水塘和枯井。

65.　　在山中這衰敗的谷間
在朧朦的月光下，雜草
颯颯吹過亂墳，在教堂附近，
那不見人影的教堂只是風的老家。
沒有窗子，而門破落動搖，
70.　枯骸傷害不了人哪。
只有風信雞站在屋頂的脊樑上
咯咯哩咯　咯咯哩咯
在雷電的閃光下。然後一陣潮濕的風
帶來了雨

75.　　恆河瘦得見底了，低垂的樹葉
等待著雨，當黑雲越過遙遠的
喜馬拉雅山聚集而來。
密林蹲踞著，鬱悶而沉默。
這時雷語宣說
80.　**鼟**
　達陀（獻出吧）：我們獻出什麼呢？

The Waste Land
1922

My friend, blood shaking my heart

The awful daring of a moment's surrender

Which an age of prudence can never retract

85. By this, and this only, we have existed

Which is not to be found in our obituaries

Or in memories draped by the beneficent spider [43]

Or under seals broken by the lean solicitor

In our empty rooms

90. DA

Dayadhvam: I have heard the key

Turn in the door once and turn once only [44]

We think of the key, each in his prison

Thinking of the key, each confirms a prison

95. Only at nightfall, aethereal rumours

Revive for a moment a broken Coriolanus

DA

Damyata: The boat responded

Gaily, to the hand expert with sail and oar

100. The sea was calm, your heart would have responded

Gaily, when invited, beating obedient

To controlling hands

I sat upon the shore

荒原
1922

朋友喲，獻出動搖心意的血液吧

獻出一時屈服於情慾那種可怕的冒險吧

那種不惑之年的人也無法謹慎克制的情慾喲

85. 這樣，也只有這樣我們才能生存到現在

這，在訃聞上是找不到的

或在仁慈的蛛蜘吐網罩住的墓誌銘上

在空無一物的房間由削瘦律師打開的密封中

也是找不到的啊

90. 罷

達業慈梵（同情吧）：我聽到了鑰匙

在門裡轉動而且只轉動一次

我們想到鑰匙，每個人都在自己的牢獄裡

想到鑰匙，每個人都確認在牢獄裡

95. 只是在日暮時，天上的呢喃

使一個沒落英雄柯理歐勒納斯一時甦醒

罷

達莫它（克制吧）：船輕快地反應

順著對帆和槳熟練的老手

100. 海上風平浪靜，你的心若被要求

一定也會輕快地反應，順從地配合

控制的操手

我坐在岸上

Fishing, with the arid plain behind me [45]

105. Shall I at least set my lands in order?

London Bridge is falling down falling down falling down

Poi s'ascose nel foco che gli affina [46]

Quando fiam uti chelidon [47]—O swallow swallow

Le Prince d'Aquitaine à la tour abolie [48]

110. These fragments I have shored against my ruins

Why then Ile fit you. Hieronymo's mad againe. [49]

Datta. Dayadhvam. Damyata.

Shantih   shantih   shantih [50]

荒原
1922

垂釣，乾燥的平原延伸在背後
105. 至少我該把自己的國土收拾了吧？
倫敦橋倒塌了倒塌了倒塌了
然後他投身在淨火中消失了
我何時才能變成燕子呢——呵燕子燕子喲
阿基泰尼王子在廢墟的塔裡
110. 以這些片斷我支撐了自己的廢墟
那麼就照你的意思吧。西羅尼摩又發瘋了。
達陀。達業慈梵。達莫它。

禪寂　禪寂　禪寂

原註

第五部前段所處理的主題有三：赴阨瑪塢的旅途，接近「危險的禮拜堂」（見維斯頓女士的著作）以及東歐當今的頹廢。

39. 這種鳥學名叫 Turbus aonalaschkae pallasii，鶇類，我曾在加拿大東部魁北克地方聽過這種鳥的鳴聲。Chapman 在《北美東部鳥類手冊》這本書中說：「這種鳥在人煙稀少的森林地或叢藪密集的靜僻處築巢……其鳴聲小而單調，然而聲音清純甘美，轉調悠揚，天下無雙。」所謂「水滴般的歌聲」這種美詞，洵非過言。

40. 以下幾行受到了某個南極探險家記事的啟示（哪個探險家已忘記，大概是屬於 Shackleton 的）：其中敘述有關探險隊在極度疲勞之際不斷地有一種幻覺，總比實際人數多算出一個人來。

41. 從三六七到三七七行參照 Hermann Hesse 的「混亂的一瞥」：「歐羅巴的一半已陷於混亂狀態，至少東歐的一半是那樣的。人們浸在瘋狂的昏醉中，在毀滅的邊緣且走且歌，像 Dmitri Karamasoff 那樣醉醺醺地高唱讚美歌。聖者或預言者聞歌而落淚，一般人民卻感到侮辱而苦笑。」

42. 「Datta dayadhvam damyata」（獻出吧，同情吧，克制吧）。雷神的寓意可在 Brihadaranyaka-Upanishad 5, 1 中找到。翻譯見 Deussen 的《吠陀的優波尼沙土六十篇》四八九頁。

43. 參照 Webster 的〈白魔〉V. vi：
「……他們將再結婚
在蛆蟲喰破你的屍衣之前，在蜘蛛
為你的墓碑銘掛上薄幕之前。」

44. 參照地獄三十三章四十六行：
「那時在那恐怖的塔下
我聽到釘門的聲音。」
又 F. H. Bradley《現象與現實》三四六頁：
「對外界的感覺，與思想和感情一樣，對每個人來說都是個人的。不管怎樣，個人的經驗陷入屬於自己的圈子裡，一個對外部而言是封閉的圈子；而以一

切相同的要素，每個圈子與其周圍的圈子間是互不透明的……要而言之，以
表現在心靈中的存在而言，整個世界在每一個人的心靈中都是特殊的，個人的
的。」

45. 見維斯頓女士著《從祭祀到傳奇》一書，論「漁夫王」那章。

46. 見《煉獄篇》二十六章一四八行：
「『現在，我請求你，讓美德
引導你到階梯的頂端。
請你時常記起我的痛苦。』
說完他便投身在淨火中消失了。」

47. 見《Pervigilium Veneries》。參照第二部與第三部菲露美。

48. 見 Gerard de Nerval，十四行詩〈El Desdichado〉。

49. 見吉德的《西班牙人的悲劇》。

50. 禪寂（Shantih）。附在一篇〈優波尼沙土〉末尾的套語，像這裡所重複的那
樣。這個字的意思是「超越理解的和平」。

譯註

這是〈荒原〉最後的一章，介紹東方的禁慾主義文學。艾略特懂得梵文，這章便是以印度吠陀聖典中的「優波尼沙土」（Upanishad）為中心，表現荒原最後的狀態。

「在火炬照紅汗淋淋的臉之後……忍受最後的殘喘。」：

這九行表現耶穌，忍受苦難之後復活，是荒原上氣息奄奄的人們得救的唯一希望。暗示荒原成為基督教社會的希望。

「這裡沒有水只有岩石……可是沒有水」：

這二十九行描寫不毛之地的景象。精神上因水的渴求而受到磨折。主題的意象從第一部「紅色的岩石」經過「岩間美女」到「沒有水只有岩石」。

「經常走在你們身邊……另一邊那個人是誰呀？」：

這七行一方面表現荒原中身體上與精神上極度疲勞之後常有的幻覺，另一方面暗示耶穌復活之後門徒眼睛迷糊了不認識耶穌，正像平常看不出生命能從死裡復活。（見路加福音二十四章。）

「高空中那是什麼聲音……虛幻的」：

這十一行敘述歐洲文明的危機，東歐文化的崩潰。

「裂土上跌跌撞撞，那群人是誰呀」：

暗示游牧民族威脅歐洲，破壞都市。

「一個婦人拉緊她的黑長髮……而歌聲來自乾涸的水塘和枯井」：

這八行敘述性的頹廢與城市的破碎。「歷盡滄桑的美人」從髮梢彈出細語；

荒原
1922

嬰兒臉的蝙蝠增加了母性哀悼的挫折；樓塔倒立，池塘枯乾，正是傳道書中描述的「衰敗的日子」的景象。

「在山中這衰敗的谷間……帶來了雨」：

這十行描寫宗教的衰落。這裡所描寫的「教堂」與維斯頓女士所說的「危險的禮拜堂」結合在一起，「危險的禮拜堂」在聖杯故事中是考驗騎士的勇氣的地方，但在這裡失去了恐怖，因此也失去了意義。精神上的歸宿已經失去，教堂只是「風的老家」吧了。那「枯骸傷害不了人」的地方原是「鼠巷」。

「恆河瘦得見底了……順從地配合控制的操手」：

這二十八行導向聖河，敘述「優波尼沙土」的禁慾主義。雷電交加，於是雷神訓誡，授荒原上的人民以三支杖，如此復活才有可能：

第一道命令：獻出「那種不惑之年的人也無法謹慎克制的情慾」。這是生存唯一的憑藉。

第二道命令：以同情打開驕傲所封鎖的自我的牢獄。從基督教的觀點，像但丁或密爾頓所說的，人從神或人道中孤立都是由於自大自滿。柯理歐勒納斯一般的美雄便是那樣沒落的。柯氏原為羅馬武士，因罪被國人放逐，逃匿於服爾西族中，後為服族大將，率軍征討羅馬。為避免戰火蹂躪蒼生，其妻母曾代表國人前往懇求停止爭伐，但為其驕傲和自負所拒絕。此外原註引一段哲學上的根據，強調自我孤絕阻止了獻出的可能性。

第三道命令：克制可以免於對情慾的屈服。以水手與第四部意象，強調心與意志的協調。

「我坐在岸上…… 禪寂」：

這十一行描寫生命在荒原中的意義。

詩中的主人公像漁夫王那樣又在岸上垂釣，面對著荒原思索著。以「意識流」的聯想方式加以處理。

「至少我該把自己的國土收拾了吧？」：

這個漁夫王走盡了聖杯之路卻陷於絕望的情況。像是猶大王希西家得病時，

先知以賽亞對他說的：「你該收拾你的家，因你必死不能活了。」（以賽亞三十八章一節）「倫敦橋倒塌了倒塌了」：童謠中的句子。「倫敦橋」代表現代不完整的意象，荒原上的眞理：「破碎的影像」。然後是一些片斷的句子，表現荒地上的苦境。煉獄中的火淨化了罪惡； 為求淨化自願受苦。淨火焚燒在第三部結束時已經暗示了。「變成燕子」表現再生的主題。像阿基泰尼王子在廢塔裡等待春天，以這一點點希望支撐自己的廢墟。

「那麼就照你的意思吧」：

出自吉德的《西班牙人的悲劇》四幕一景。這是劇中西班牙王西羅尼摩的內政大臣受命在宮中演戲時說的話，就利用這個機會他達到了為他兒子復仇的目的後，自殺而死。詩中的主人公面對著荒原，所謂「你的意思」該是指雷神以梵文訴說的意思，也就是「獻出吧」「同情吧」「克制吧」。西羅尼摩所答應上演的戲中，神經質的人物說些別人所不知道的外國話。也許因此詩中故意用梵文重複雷神的三律，像是西羅尼摩的瘋話。

「禪寂」（Shantih）：

原註「超越理解的和平」。

The Hollow Men

空洞的人

·1925·

The Hollow Men

Mistah Kurtz — he dead.

—— *A penny for the Old Guy*

I

We are the hollow men
We are the stuffed men
5.   Leaning together
Headpiece filled with straw. Alas!
Our dried voices, when
We whisper together
Are quiet and meaningless
10.   As wind in dry grass
Or rats' feet over broken glass
In our dry cellar

Shape without form shade without colour,
Paralyzed force, gesture without motion;

空洞的人
1925

空洞的人

.

密司打‧客茲──他死了。

──《獻錢給老蓋吧》

I

　我們是空洞的人
　我們被填塞的人
5.　依靠在一起
　腦袋兒塞滿稻草。唉！
　我們乾澀的聲音，當
　我們在一起喃喃私語
　是靜寂而無意義
10.　像枯草間的風
　或碎杯上的鼠步
　在我們乾燥的地窖裡

　　有狀無形，有影無色，
　無勁之力，無勢之姿；

The Hollow Men
1925

15. Those who have crossed
With direct eyes to death's other Kingdom
Remember us — if at all — not as lost
Violent souls, but only
As the hollow men
20. The stuffed men.

II

Eyes I dare not meet in dreams
In death's dream kingdom
These do not appear:
There the eyes are
25. Sunlight on a broken column
There is a tree swinging
And voices are
In the wind's singing
More distant and more solemn
30. Than a fading star.

Let me be no nearer
In death's dream kingdom

空洞的人
1925

15.　　　那些人，以直視的眼睛越過

走向死的另一王國

記得我們——要是記得——不是永墮地獄的

暴戾靈魂，而只是

空洞的人

20.　被填塞的人。

II

我在夢中不敢相遇的眼睛

在死之夢幻的王國裡

這些不會出現：

那兒，那些眼睛是

25.　斷柱上的陽光

那兒，有樹在搖擺

有聲音

在風的歌唱中

更遙遠而且更嚴肅

30.　甚於逐漸消逝的星子。

　　　不要讓我更靠近

在死之夢幻的王國裡

The Hollow Men
1925

Let me also wear

Such deliberate disguises

35. Rat's coat, crowskin, crossed staves

In a field

Behaving as the wind behaves

No nearer —

Not that final meeting

40. In the twilight kingdom.

III

This is the dead land

this is cactus land

Here the stone images

Are raised, here they receive

45. The supplication of a dead man's hand

Under the twinkle of a fading star.

Is it like this

In death's other kingdom

Waking alone

50. At the hour when we are

空洞的人
1925

讓我也穿上
如此精心設計的偽裝
35. 老鼠的外衣，烏鴉皮，十字形手杖
在原野裡
舉動一如風動
不要更靠近──

不是向那最後的相遇
40. 在暮色的王國裡。

III

這是死的國度
這是仙人掌的國度
這兒，石頭的偶像
被豎起，這兒他們接受
45. 死人舉手的祈求
在逐漸消逝的星光閃亮下。

可就是這樣嗎
在死之另一王國
獨自清醒著
50. 當我們正因

The Hollow Men
1925

Trembling with tenderness
Lips that would kiss
Form prayers to broken stone

IV

The eyes are not here
55.　There are no eye here
In this valley of dying stars
In this hollow valley
This broken jaw of our lost kingdoms.

In this last of meeting places
60.　We grope together
And avoid speech
Gathered on this beach of the tumid river.

Sightless, unless
The eyes reappear
65.　As the perpetual star
Multifoliate rose
Of death's twilight kingdom
The hope only

空洞的人
1925

柔弱而顫慄
想要接吻的嘴唇
卻向斷石述說禱詞

IV

那些眼睛不在這兒
55. 沒有眼睛在這兒
在這眾星臨死的谷間
在這空洞的谷間
我們失去的王國的這個破碎顎骨。

在這最後相遇的地方
60. 我們一起摸索
而且避免交談
聚集在這洶湧的河岸上。

盲目看不見,除非
那些眼睛再出現
65. 像那永恆的星子
多瓣的玫瑰
在死之暮色的王國
空虛的人

The Hollow Men
1925

Of empty men.

V

70. *Here we go round the prickly pear*
Prickly pear prickly pear
Here we go round the prickly pear
At five o'clock in the morning.

    Between the idea
75. And the reality
Between the motion
And the act
Falls the Shadow

                        For Thine is the Kingdom

80.   Between the conception
And the creation
Between the emotion
And the response
Falls the Shadow

85.   *Life is very long*

空洞的人
1925

唯一的希望。

V

70.　嘿，我們圍繞著刺梨仙人掌
　　　仙人掌啊仙人掌
　　　嘿，我們圍繞著刺梨仙人掌
　　　在清早五點鐘。

　　　　　在思想
75.　與現實之間
　　　在動念
　　　與行動之間
　　　「陰影」降落了

因那「天國」屬於祢

80.　　　在受胎
　　　與創造之間
　　　在情感
　　　與反應之間
　　　「陰影」降落了

85.
生命是很長久的

The Hollow Men
1925

    Between the desire

And the spasm

Between the potency

And the existence

90.   Between the essence

And the descent

Falls the Shadow

For Thine is the Kingdom

    For Thine is

95.   Life is

For thine is the

    This is the way the way the world ends

This is the way the way the world ends

This is the way the way the world ends

100.   *Not with a bang but a whimper.*

空洞的人
1925

在欲望
與抽搐之間
在潛能
與存在之間
90. 在本質
與血統之間
「陰影」降落了

           因那「天國」屬於祢

因屬於祢的是
95. 生命是
因屬於祢的是

    就這麼這麼世界終結了
就這麼這麼世界終結了
就這麼這麼世界終結了
100. *沒有砰響只是啜泣。*

Journey of the Magi

東方博士的行旅

·1927·

Journey of the Magi

'A cold coming we had of it,
Just the worst time of the year
For a journey, and such a long journey:
The ways deep and the weather sharp,
5. The very dead of winter.'
And the camels galled, sorefooted, refractory,
Lying down in the melting snow.
There were times we regretted
The summer palaces on slopes, the terraces,
10. And the silken girls bringing sherbet
Then the camel men cursing and grumbling
and running away, and wanting their liquor and women,
And the night-fires going out, and the lack of shelters,
And the cities hostile and the towns unfriendly
15. And the villages dirty and charging high prices:
A hard time we had of it.
At the end we preferred to travel all night,
Sleeping in snatches,

東方博士的行旅
1927

東方博士的行旅 [1]

「我們此行碰到了嚴寒，
正是一年中旅行最困難的
時候，而旅途如此遙遠：
長路漫漫，天氣凜冽，
5.　冬天最是寒冷的時節。」
駱駝皮膚擦傷，腳趾腫痛，鬧起脾氣，
躺臥在融化的雪中，
有時候我們很懷念
山坡上的避暑別墅，陽台，
10.　穿著綢衣的少女們端來果子露，
然後駱駝夫，口出惡言，發牢騷
跑掉了，去尋找他們的烈酒和女人，
而夜火漸熄，沒有庇護的地方，
而城市帶有敵意，鄉鎮很不友善，
15.　而村莊骯髒，大敲竹槓：
我們歷盡了千辛萬苦。
最後我們寧可徹夜趕路，
半睡半醒，斷斷續續，

Journey Of The Magi
1927

With the voices singing in our ears, saying

20. That this was all folly.

    Then at dawn we came down to a temperate valley,

Wet, below the snow line, smelling of vegetation;

With a running stream and a water-mill beating the darkness,

And three trees on the low sky,

25. And an old white horse galloped away in the meadow.

Then we came to a tavern with vine-leaves over the lintel,

Six hands at an open door dicing for pieces of silver,

And feet kicking the empty wine-skins.

But there was no information, and so we continued

30. And arriving at evening, not a moment too soon

Finding the place; it was (you might say) satisfactory.

    All this was a long time ago, I remember,

And I would do it again, but set down

This set down

35. This: were we led all that way for

Birth or Death? There was a Birth, certainly

We had evidence and no doubt. I had seen birth and death,

But had thought they were different; this Birth was

Hard and bitter agony for us, like Death, our death.

東方博士的行旅
1927

耳邊聽到的聲音，在說
20. 這些都是蠢事一樁。

　　於是天亮時我們來到溫暖的山谷，
濕潤，在雪線下，花草芳香；
水流溪澗而水磨拍打著黑暗，
以及低空中的三棵樹
25. 一隻老邁的白馬在牧場上奔馳而去。
然後我們來到一家酒館，葡萄葉掛在窗楣上，
六隻手在打開的門口擲骰子賭銀錢，
而腳踢著倒空了的葡萄酒囊。
可是沒有什麼信息，因此我們繼續前行
30. 在傍晚時到達，就在最後一刻
找到了那個地方；（你可以說）那是如願以償的。

　　這些都是很久以前的事了，我記得，
我可能再走一趟，但是會記下
這點，記下
35. 這點：我們一路被引導，是為了
「生」或「死」？確實有過一次「生」，
我們有證據而且從不懷疑。我曾經見過生和死，
可是以為兩者不同；但是這個「生」
卻給了我們極大的苦痛，就如「死」，我們的死。

Journey Of The Magi
1927

40. We returned to our places, these Kingdoms,
But no longer at ease here, in the old dispensation,
With an alien people clutching their gods.
I should be glad of another death.

東方博士的行旅
1927

40. 我們回到了自己的地方，這些「王國」，
但在這裡不再感到心安，在舊有的宗法下，
當異族的眾生緊緊抓住他們的神。
我該會欣然再死一次。

1　譯註：根據《新約聖經・馬太福音》第 2 章第 1-12 節記載，耶穌降生時，幾
個「博士」在東方看見伯利恆方向的天空上有一顆大星，於是便跟著它來到
了耶穌基督的出生地，朝拜耶穌。

Ash Wednesday

聖灰日

·1930·

Ash Wednesday

I

Because I do not hope to turn again

Because I do not hope

Because I do not hope to turn

Desiring this man's gift and that man's scope

5. I no longer strive to strive towards such things

(Why should the agèd eagle stretch its wings?)

Why should I mourn

The vanished power of the usual reign?

Because I do not hope to know

10. The infirm glory of the positive hour

Because I do not think

Because I know I shall not know

The one veritable transitory power

Because I cannot drink

15. There, where trees flower, and springs flow, for there is

聖灰日
1930

聖灰日 [1]

I

因我不期望能夠再回轉

因我不期望

因我不期望能夠回轉

羨慕這人的天賦那人的能力

5. 我不再盡力去盡力爭取這些東西

（為什麼老鷹該要伸展羽翼？）

為什麼我該要歎惜

消失了的通常的支配力？

　　因我不希望知道

10. 現世脆弱的榮光

因我不想

因我知道我不會知道

名副其實無常的唯一力量

因我不能在那裡暢飲

15. 在那樹花泉湧的地方，因又會是一無所有

Ash Wednesday
1930

nothing again

   Because I know that time is always time
And place is always and only place
And what is actual is actual only for one time
And only for one place
20. I rejoice that things are as they are and
I renounce the blessèd face
And renounce the voice
Because I cannot hope to turn again
Consequently I rejoice, having to construct something
25. Upon which to rejoice

   And pray to God to have mercy upon us
And pray that I may forget
These matters that with myself I too much discuss
Too much explain
30. Because I do not hope to turn again
Let these words answer
For what is done, not to be done again
May the judgement not be too heavy upon us

   Because these wings are no longer wings to fly

聖灰日
1930

　　因我知道時間永遠是時間
地點永遠是而且只是地點
而現實之為現實只是一時
而且只限於一地
20. 我欣見萬物各得其所
我棄絕被祝福的臉
我棄絕那聲音
因我不能期望能夠再回轉
因此我歡欣，必須建構某種
25. 藉以歡欣的基礎

　　向神祈求賜我慈悲
向神祈求讓我遺忘
那些與我自己討論太多
說明太多的事情
30. 因我不期望能夠再回轉
讓這些話回答
那些已經做了，絕不再做的事情
但願最後審判對我們不會太嚴厲

　　因這些羽翼不再是飛翔的羽翼
35. 而只是拍打空氣的簸揚器

Ash Wednesday
1930

35. But merely vans to beat the air

The air which is now thoroughly small and dry

Smaller and dryer than the will

Teach us to care and not to care Teach us to sit still

Pray for us sinners now and at the hour of our death

40. Pray for us now and at the hour of our death.

II

Lady, three white leopards sat under a juniper-tree

In the cool of the day, having fed to satiety

On my legs my heart my liver and that which had been contained

In the hollow round of my skull. And God said

45. Shall these bones live? shall these

Bones live? And that which had been contained

In the bones (which were already dry) said chirping:

Because of the goodness of this Lady

And because of her loveliness, and because

50. She honours the Virgin in meditation,

We shine with brightness. And I who am here dissembled

Proffer my deeds to oblivion, and my love

聖灰日
1930

當前的氣氛全然萎縮而乾枯
比我們的意志更萎縮更乾枯
教我們關心和不關心吧　教我們靜坐吧。

　　現在為我們這些罪人祈禱吧，在我們臨死的時刻
40. 現在為我們祈禱吧，在我們臨死的時刻。

II

「聖女」喲，三隻白豹蹲在檜柏樹下
在日涼的地方，飽腹而坐
在我的腿上我的心上我的肝上，
以及我那空洞的圓頭殼所容納的東西
45. 這些骸骨會復活麼？這些骸骨
會復活麼？而容納在骸骨裡的東西
（雖然已枯乾）卻鳴囀地說：
因這位「聖女」的善良
因她的慈愛，且因她
50. 在冥想中尊崇那位「處女」
使我們光輝照耀。而在此虛情假意的我
將我的行狀獻給遺忘，將我的愛獻給
荒野的後裔以及葫蘆的果實。
如此，使那些豹吐出來的

Ash Wednesday
1930

To the posterity of the desert and the fruit of the gourd.

It is this which recovers

55. My guts the strings of my eyes and the indigestible portions

Which the leopards reject. The Lady is withdrawn

In a white gown, to contemplation, in a white gown

Let the whiteness of bones atone to forgetfulness

There is no life in them. As I am forgotten

60. And would be forgotten, so I would forget

Thus devoted, concentrated in purpose. And God said

Prophesy to the wind, to the wind only for only

The wind will listen. And the bones sang chirping

With the burden of the grasshopper, saying

65.   Lady of silences

Calm and distressed

Torn and most whole

Rose of memory

Rose of forgetfulness

70. Exhausted and life-giving

Worried reposeful

The single Rose

Is now the Garden

Where all loves end

聖灰日
1930

55.　我的腸子我的眼筋肉以及那些不消化的部分
　　　恢復了生氣。「聖女」退去了
　　　穿著白衣，去沉思，穿著白衣。
　　　讓骸骨的白色賠償遺忘吧。
　　　骸骨中沒有生命。正像我被遺忘
60.　而且會被遺忘那樣，我願遺忘
　　　如此虔誠地聚精會神。而且神
　　　對風預言，只對風預言，因為
　　　只有風願意聽從。而骸骨嗚囀地唱著，
　　　以蚱蜢的負重叫聲，說

65.　　　　靜默的「聖女」
　　　安詳地隱忍痛苦
　　　被撕裂可是幾乎完整
　　　追憶的玫瑰
　　　遺忘的玫瑰
70.　力竭而充滿生氣
　　　煩惱而心平氣和
　　　那唯一的「玫瑰」
　　　此時成為「花園」
　　　那裡，所有愛結束
75.　終結不滿足的
　　　愛的苦惱

Ash Wednesday
1930

75. Terminate torment
Of love unsatisfied
The greater torment
Of love satisfied
End of the endless
80. Journey to no end
Conclusion of all that
Is inconclusible
Speech without word and
Word of no speech
85. Grace to the Mother
For the Garden
Where all love ends.

   Under a juniper-tree the bones sang, scattered and shining
We are glad to be scattered, we did little good to each other,
90. Under a tree in the cool of day, with the blessing of sand,
Forgetting themselves and each other, united
In the quiet of the desert. This is the land which ye
Shall divide by lot. And neither division nor unity
Matters. This is the land. We have our inheritance.

聖灰日
1930

滿足了的愛的
更大的苦惱
無止境旅程的
80. 無止境的終點
沒有終結的
一切的終結
沒有字句的話
不成話的字句
85. 感謝「聖女」慈悲
因為在那「花園」裡
所有的愛結束。

　　檜柏樹下的骸骨在歌唱，散亂而輝耀
我們為分散而高興，我們對彼此沒什麼好過，
90. 在日涼的樹蔭下，接受沙土的祝福
他們遺忘自己也互相遺忘，
在荒野的靜寂裡團結在一起。這就是
你們要抽籤劃分的土地。而且分離或團結
都無關緊要。這就是那土地。我們繼承的遺產。

III

95. 在第二階梯第一個拐角

Ash Wednesday
1930

III

95. At the first turning of the second stair
I turned and saw below
The same shape twisted on the banister
Under the vapour in the fetid air
Struggling with the devil of the stairs who wears
100. The deceitul face of hope and of despair.

At the second turning of the second stair
I left them twisting, turning below;
There were no more faces and the stair was dark,
Damp, jaggèd, like an old man's mouth drivelling, beyond
repair,
105. Or the toothed gullet of an agèd shark.

At the first turning of the third stair
Was a slotted window bellied like the figs's fruit
And beyond the hawthorn blossom and a pasture scene
The broadbacked figure drest in blue and green
110. Enchanted the maytime with an antique flute.
Blown hair is sweet, brown hair over the mouth blown,
Lilac and brown hair;

聖灰日
1930

我回轉看見下面
同樣的姿態盤繞著迴欄
在腐臭空氣中的霧底下
與階梯的惡魔掙扎著
100. 當他裝出騙人的希望與絕望的臉。

　　在第二階梯第二個拐角
我離開他們，任其糾纏，回轉下望；
已看不到那些臉而階梯幽暗，
潮濕，鋸齒狀，像老人垂涎無法矯正的嘴巴
105. 或像張牙掀動的老鯊魚的下巴頦。

　　在第三階梯第一個拐角
是一面嵌入的窗子，腹部凸出有如無花果樹的果實
而在山楂花與牧場的景色那邊
寬闊的背影穿著藍色與綠色衣服，
110. 吹著古笛迷醉了五月的季節。
吹拂的髮絲很甜，金髮吹拂在嘴上，
紫丁香與金髮；
解悶，笛音，心思的駐足和腳步
走過第三階梯，
115. 逐漸遠去，遠去；希望與絕望之外的力量
爬著第三階梯。

Distraction, music of the flute, stops and steps of the mind
over the third stair,
115. Fading, fading; strength beyond hope and despair
Climbing the third stair.

Lord, I am not worthy
Lord, I am not worthy

but speak the word only.

IV

120. Who walked between the violet and the violet
Who walked between
The various ranks of varied green
Going in white and blue, in Mary's colour,
Talking of trivial things
125. In ignorance and knowledge of eternal dolour
Who moved among the others as they walked,
Who then made strong the fountains and made fresh the
springs

Made cool the dry rock and made firm the sand

聖灰日
1930

　　　主喲，我是不值得的。
　　主喲，我是不值得的。

　　　　但請只說那個字吧。

IV

120. 　在紫羅蘭與紫羅蘭間行走的人
　　在各種不同的綠色之間
　　行走的人，
　　穿著白色與青色，穿著瑪麗亞的顏色，
　　交談著瑣碎的事情
125. 　帶著對無知與知識的永恆悲哀，
　　這些人，在行走的他人之間走動
　　然後增強噴泉，使泉水清爽

　　　使乾岩冷涼，使細砂黏固
　　以燕草的藍色，瑪麗亞色彩的藍色
130. 　請勿我忘

　　　　這兒是行走於中間的歲月
　　搶走了提琴與橫笛，甦醒了

Ash Wednesday
1930

In blue of larkspur, blue of Mary's colour,
130. Sovegna vos

Here are the years that walk between, bearing
Away the fiddles and the flutes, restoring
One who moves in the time between sleep and waking, wearing

White light folded, sheathing about her, folded.
135. The new years walk, restoring
Through a bright cloud of tears, the years, restoring
With a new verse the ancient rhyme. Redeem
The time. Redeem
The unread vision in the higher dream
140. While jewelled unicorns draw by the gilded hearse.

The silent sister veiled in white and blue
Between the yews, behind the garden god,
Whose flute is breathless, bent her head and signed but spoke no word

But the fountain sprang up and the bird sang down
145. Redeem the time, redeem the dream

聖灰日
1930

在睡眠與清醒的時間中走動的人，穿著

　　折疊的白光，像刀鞘在她身上折疊護罩著。
135. 新的歲月行走著，透過晶瑩迷濛的眼淚
恢復往昔歲月，以新的詩體
恢復古代的韻律。贖回
時間吧。贖回
在更高的夢中未讀的夢境吧
140. 當鑲鑽的獨角獸拖著鍍金的柩車時。

　　靜默的修道女罩著白色與青色面紗
在紫杉樹間，在笛聲停息的
園神後面，低頭畫十字，但一句話也沒說

　　但噴泉湧起，小鳥低鳴
145. 贖回時間吧，贖回夢吧
贖回未聞未說出的字句的標記吧

　　直到風從紫杉樹上搖落上千的細語

　　且在我們這個放逐之後

Ash Wednesday
1930

The token of the word unheard, unspoken

Till the wind shake a thousand whispers from the yew

And after this our exile

V

If the lost word is lost, if the spent word is spent
150. If the unheard, unspoken
Word is unspoken, unheard;
Still is the unspoken word, the Word unheard,
The Word without a word, the Word within
The world and for the world;
155. And the light shone in darkness and
Against the Word the unstilled world still whirled
About the centre of the silent Word.

O my people, what have I done unto thee.

Where shall the word be found, where will the word
160. Resound? Not here, there is not enough silence
Not on the sea or on the islands, not

聖灰日
1930

V

假如失去的話失去了，假如說過的話說過了
150. 假如未聞、未說出的
話沒說出，沒被聽到；
仍然是未說出的話，未聞的道
無言的道，存在這世界中
而且是為了這世界；
155. 而光，照在黑闇中，而且
背叛了道，這個不寧的世界仍在迴旋
圍繞著靜默的道的中心。

　　　　呵！我的人們喲，我向你做了什麼呢。

　　　這話會在哪兒聽到，這話會在哪兒
160. 反響？不在這兒，這兒不夠靜默
不在海上或在島上，不在
大陸，不在荒野或雨地，
因為對在黑暗中行走的人
不論是在白天或在夜晚，
165. 這裡不是適當的時刻，也不是適當的地方
對於那些避開那臉的人沒有恩寵的地方
對於那些在嘈雜中行走而拒絕那聲音的人沒有歡忻的時刻

Ash Wednesday
1930

On the mainland, in the desert or the rain land,

For those who walk in darkness

Both in the day time and in the night time

165. The right time and the right place are not here

No place of grace for those who avoid the face

No time to rejoice for those who walk among noise and deny
the voice

Will the veiled sister pray for

Those who walk in darkness, who chose thee and oppose thee,

170. Those who are torn on the horn between season and season,
time and time, between

Hour and hour, word and word, power and power, those who
wait

In darkness? Will the veiled sister pray

For children at the gate

Who will not go away and cannot pray:

175. Pray for those who chose and oppose

O my people, what have I done unto thee.

Will the veiled sister between the slender

Yew trees pray for those who offend her

聖灰日
1930

　　罩著面紗的修道女，肯為
那些在黑暗中行走，選擇你和反對你的人祈禱嗎
170. 為那些在季節與季節，時間與時間，時刻與時刻，
話與話，力與力之間在角上被扯裂的人們，
為那些在黑暗中等待的人們祈禱嗎？罩著面紗的修道女，
肯為那些在門口
不肯走開也不能祈禱的小孩祈禱嗎？
175. 為那些選擇與反對的人們祈禱吧

　　呵！我的人們喲，我為你做了什麼呢。

　　在纖弱的紫杉樹間，罩著面紗的修道女
肯為冒犯她而恐懼
卻不讓步的那些人祈禱嗎
180. 那些在世人面前承認，在岩石間否認
在最後的青岩前那最後的荒野裡
在花園中的荒野，在乾旱的荒野中的花園裡
口中吐出乾皺的蘋果種籽的人們祈禱嗎

　　呵！我的人們喲

Ash Wednesday
1930

And are terrified and cannot surrender
180. And affirm before the world and deny between the rocks
In the last desert before the last blue rocks
The desert in the garden the garden in the desert
Of drouth, spitting from the mouth the withered apple-seed

O my people.

VI

185. Although I do not hope to turn again
Although I do not hope
Although I do not hope to turn

Wavering between the profit and the loss
In this brief transit where the dreams cross
190. The dreamcrossed twilight between birth and dying
(Bless me father) though I do not wish to wish these things
From the wide window towards the granite shore
The white sails still fly seaward, seaward flying
Unbroken wings

195. And the lost heart stiffens and rejoices

聖灰日
1930

VI

185. 雖然我不期望能夠再回轉
雖然我不期望
雖然我不期望能夠回轉

　　猶豫在利害與得失之間
在這些夢穿過的短暫的過境途中
190. 在生死之間夢穿過的薄暮中
（父喲祝福我吧）雖然我不想望去想望這些事情
從寬敞的窗前向花崗岩的岸邊
白帆仍向海上飛渡，向海上飛渡
沒折斷的羽翼

195. 　　而失去的心堅強起來，歡忻
在失去的紫丁香與失去的海聲中
而虛弱的心奮起，反抗低垂的
秋麒麟草與失去的海的氣味
奮起，促使恢復鵪鶉的叫聲
200. 與鷸鳥的飛旋
而盲目的眼睛創造
空幻的形樣在象牙的大門之間
嗅覺將砂土的鹽味翻新

Ash Wednesday
1930

In the lost lilac and the lost sea voices
And the weak spirit quickens to rebel
For the bent golden-rod and the lost sea smell
Quickens to recover
200. The cry of quail and the whirling plover
And the blind eye creates
The empty forms between the ivory gates
And smell renews the salt savour of the sandy earth

This is the time of tension between dying and birth
205. The place of solitude where three dreams cross
Between blue rocks
But when the voices shaken from the yew-tree drift away
Let the other yew be shaken and reply.

Blessèd sister, holy mother, spirit of the fountain, spirit of
the garden,
210. Suffer us not to mock ourselves with falsehood
Teach us to care and not to care
Teach us to sit still
Even among these rocks,
Our peace in His will
215. And even among these rocks

聖灰日
1930

這是瀕死與誕生之間緊張的一刻
205. 寂寥之地，三個夢穿過
青岩之間的地方
但當紫杉樹上搖落的那些聲音流逝
讓別的紫杉樹被搖落而給予答覆吧。

受祝福的修道女，聖潔之母，噴泉的精靈，花園的精
靈喲，
210. 不要讓我們因欺騙嘲辱自己而痛苦
教我們關心和不關心吧
教我們靜坐吧
即使在這些岩石間，
賜給我們在主心中的平安
215. 即使在這些岩石間
修道女喲，母親喲
以及河的精靈喲，海的精靈喲
不要讓我因分離而痛苦

讓我的叫喊傳給主。

1　譯註：大齋首日，又名聖灰禮儀日、聖灰星期三、聖灰日，是基督教教會年曆的大齋期（四旬期）之起始日。當天教會舉行塗灰禮，牧師或神父會用去年聖枝主日用過的棕櫚枝燒成灰，在信眾的額上畫上十字記號，作為悔改的象徵。

Ash Wednesday
1930

Sister, mother

And spirit of the river, spirit of the sea,

Suffer me not to be separated

And let my cry come unto Thee.

Minor Poems

小詩

·1924-1934·

Eyes that
Last I Saw in Tears

Eyes that last I saw in tears
Through division
Here in death's dream kingdom
The golden vision reappears
5. I see the eyes but not the tears
This is my affliction

  This is my affliction
Eyes I shall not see again
Eyes of decision
10. Eyes I shall not see unless
At the door of death's other kingdom
Where, as in this,
The eyes outlast a little while
A little while outlast the tears
15. And hold us in derision.

小詩
1924-1934

我最後看到的
含淚眼睛

我最後看到的含淚眼睛
在離別時
在這死之夢幻的王國裡
再度出現金黃的幻影
5. 我看到眼睛而不是淚水
這是我的悲傷

　　這是我的悲傷
我再也看不到的眼睛
決斷的眼睛
10. 我看不到的眼睛，除非
在死之另一王國的門口
在那裡，正像在這裡
那些眼睛比暫時持久
暫時比淚水持久
15. 而且嘲弄我們。

The Wind Sprang Up
at Four O'Clock

The wind sprang up at four o'clock

The wind sprang up and broke the bells

Swinging between life and death

Here, in death's dream kingdom

5. The waking echo of confusing strife

Is it a dream or something else

When the surface of the blackened river

Is a face that sweats with tears?

I saw across the blackened river

10. The camp fire shake with alien spears.

Here, across death's other river

The Tartar horsemen shake their spears.

小詩
1924-1934

風在四點鐘吹起

風在四點鐘吹起
風吹起也吹壞了鐘
在生與死之間搖擺
這裡，在死之夢幻的王國
混亂的爭辯甦醒的回聲
那是夢或是什麼
當黑河的表面
成為淚水盈盈的臉？
越過黑河，我看到了
營火顫動著異族的長矛。
這裡，越過另一條死河
韃靼的騎兵揮動著長矛。

Five-Finger
Exercises

I. Lines to a Persian Cat

The songsters of the air repair

To the green fields of Russell Square.

Beneath the trees there is no ease

For the dull brain, the sharp desires

5. And the quick eyes of Woolly Bear.

There is no relief but in grief.

O when will the creaking heart cease?

When will the broken chair give ease?

Why will the summer day delay?

10. When will Time flow away?

II. Lines to a Yorkshire Terrier

In a brown field stood a tree

And the tree was crookt and dry.

In a black sky, from a green cloud

小詩
1924-1934

五指練習曲

I. 給波斯貓

青空的歌手成群來到
羅素廣場的綠地。
樹蔭下感覺不到悠閒：
對絨毛熊的笨腦，尖銳的慾望
5. 以及敏捷的眼睛。
沒有寬慰只有悲傷。
唉，吱吱作響的心何時停止？
搗壞的椅子何時讓人舒適？
為什麼夏日姍姍來遲
10. 當時間如水流逝？

II. 給約克猂

褐色的原野立著一棵樹
那棵樹彎曲而且乾枯。
陰空中，從黛綠的雲間

Natural forces shriek'd aloud,
15. Screamed, rattled, muttered endlessly.
Little dog was safe and warm
Under a cretonne eiderdown,
Yet the field was cracked and brown
And the tree was cramped and dry.
20. Pollicle dogs and cats all must
Jellicle cats and dogs all must
Like undertakers, come to dust.
Here a little dog I pause
Heaving up my prior paws,
25. Pause, and sleep endlessly.

III. Lines to a Duck in the Park

The long light shakes across the lake,
The forces of the morning quake,
The dawn is slant across the lawn,
Here is no eft or mortal snake
30. But only sluggish duck and drake.
I have seen the morning shine,
I have had the Bread and Wine,
Let the feathered mortals take

小詩
1924-1934

自然的力量大聲叫喊，

15. 驚呼，嘎嘎作響，不停地嘟喃。

小狗感到安適和溫暖

在大花毳絨的被毯下，

然而原野焦褐而迸裂

那棵樹受到束縛而枯乾。

20. 波麗可狗或貓也好

傑麗可貓或狗也好

一切都像喪葬業者，必歸於塵土。

這裡，一隻小狗，我躊躇

舉起我的前爪，

25. 躊躇，然後沉沉入睡。

III. 給公園的鴨子

越過湖面長長的燈光顫動著，

早晨震動的力量，

黎明斜斜橫過草坪，

這裡沒有蜥蜴或畜生的蛇

30. 只有呆笨的公鴨和母鴨。

我看到了晨曦照耀，

我吃過了聖酒和麵包，

讓長著羽毛的畜生拿去

That which is their mortal due,
35. Pinching bread and finger too,

Easier had than squirming worm;

For I know, and so should you

That soon the enquiring worm shall try

Our well-preserved complacency.

IV. Lines to Ralph Hodgson Esqre

40. How delightful to meet Mr. Hodgson!

                (Everyone wants to know Him) —

With his musical sound

And his Baskerville Hound

Which, just at a word from his master

45. Will follow you faster and faster

And tear you limb from limb.

How delightful to meet Mr. Hodgson!

Who is worshipped by all waitresses

(They regard him as something apart)

50. While on his palate fine he presses

The juice of the gooseberry tart.

How delightful to meet Mr. Hodgson!

                (Everyone wants to know Him).

畜生所應得的東西，
35. 挾取麵包以及手指餅乾
比蠕動的爬蟲更為容易；
因我知道，你也該知道
不久那些好奇的蠕蟲
將學會我們保存良好的自滿。

IV. 給拉華・郝格遜先生

40. 遇到郝格遜先生真高興！
　　　　（誰不想認識他）——
帶著音樂般的聲音
以及那隻巴斯克威獵犬
只要主人哼叫一聲
45. 就會猛追著你再猛追
把你的肢體撕裂再撕裂。
遇到郝格遜先生真高興！
他被所有女招待崇拜
　　（她們對他另眼看待）
50. 卻向他那高貴的口顎
擠出酸辣的鵝莓汁。
遇到郝格遜先生真高興！
　　　　（誰不想認識他）。

He has canaries

55.   And round his head finches and fairies

In jubilant rapture skim.

How delightful to meet Mr. Hodgson!

                    (Everyone wants to meet Him).

            V. Lines for Cuscuscaraway and Mirza Murad Ali Beg

How unpleasant to meet Mr. Eliot!

60.   With his features of clerical cut,

And his brow so grim

And his mouth so prim

And his conversation, so nicely

Restricted to What Precisely

65.   And If and Perhaps and But.

How unpleasant to meet Mr. Eliot!

With a bobtail cur

In a coat of fur

And a porpentine cat

70.   And a wopsical hat:

How unpleasant to meet Mr. Eliot!

                    (Whether his mouth be open or shut).

他有九百九十九隻金絲雀
55. 在他頭頂四周雀鳥和小仙子
狂喜萬分地踊舞紛飛。
遇到郝格遜先生真高興！
　　　（誰不想認識他）。

V. 給卡斯卡斯凱拉威和莫扎·姆拉德·阿里·貝格

遇到艾略特先生真倒楣！
60. 有牧師一般的面貌，
望之儼然的眉額
不苟言笑的口唇
說起話來意趣橫生
一定附帶「正確地說」
65. 「假如」「或許」和「但是」。
遇到艾略特先生真倒楣！
跟著截尾的雜種狗
穿著毛皮的外衣
帶著豪豬模樣的貓
70. 戴著大黃蜂似的帽子：
遇到艾略特先生真倒楣！
　　　（不論他開口或閉嘴）。

Landscapes

I. New Hampshire

Children's voices in the orchard
Between the blossom- and the fruit-time:
Golden head, crimson head,
Between the green tip and the root.
5. Black wing, brown wing, hover over;
Twenty years and the spring is over;
To-day grieves and to-morrow grieves,
Cover me over, light-in-leaves;
Golden head, black wing,
10. Cling, swing,
Spring,sing,
Swing up into the apple-tree.

II. Virginia

Red river, red river,

小詩
1924-1934

風景組曲

I. 新漢普郡

孩童們的聲音在果園

在花季與果季之間：

金亮的頭，潤紅的頭，

在綠枝與樹根之間。

5. 黑翅膀，褐翅膀，在盤旋；

二十歲與青春飛掠過去；

今日悲歡，明日悲歡，

樹葉間的陽光喲，把我遮藏；

金亮的頭，黑色的翅膀，

10. 握著，盪著，

跳著，唱著，

盪到蘋果樹上。

II. 維及尼亞

紅河，紅河

Slow flow heat is silence

15. No will is still as a river

Still. Will heat move

Only through the mocking-bird

Heard once? Still hills

Wait. Gates wait. Purple trees,

20. White trees, wait, wait,

Delay, decay. Living, living,

Never moving. Ever moving

Iron thoughts came with me

And go with me:

25. Red river river river.

III. Usk

Do not suddenly break the branch, or

Hope to find

The white hart over the white well.

Glance aside, not for lance, do not spell

30. Old enchantments. Let them sleep.

'Gently dip, but not too deep',

Lift your eyes

Where the roads dip and where the roads rise

小詩
1924-1934

靜靜的熱氣慢慢地流
15. 沒有意志平靜如河
平靜。熱氣的流動
是否只通過曾經聽過一次的
知更鳥？平靜的山丘
等待著。門等待著。紫色的樹，
20. 白色的樹，等待著，等待著，
耽擱，敗壞。活著，活著，
未曾移動。一直移動
鐵的思想與我俱來
而且與我同去：
25. 紅的河流河流河流。

III. 約斯克

不要突然折斷樹枝
或希望發現
白色的牡鹿就在白色的井後。
向邊看，目標不是長矛，不要唸
30. 古老的咒符。讓這些安睡吧。
「輕輕地浸，不要太深，」
張開眼睛吧
就在路子低窪的地方，路子隆起的地方

Seek only there

35. Where the grey light meets the green air

The Hermit's chapel, the pilgrim's prayer.

IV. Rannoch, by Glencoe

Here the crow starves, here the patient stag

Breeds for the rifle. Between the soft moor

and the soft sky, scarcely room

40. To leap or to soar. Substance crumbles, in the thin air

Moon cold or moon hot. The road winds in

Littlessness of ancient war,

Langour of broken steel,

Clamour of confused wrong, apt

45. In silence. Memory is strong

Beyond the bone. Pride snapped,

Shadow of pride is long, in the long pass

No concurrence of bone.

V. Cape Ann

O quick quick quick, quick hear the song sparrow,

50. Swamp sparrow, fox-sparrow, vesper sparrow

小詩
1924-1934

只在那裡尋找
35. 灰色的光與綠色大氣交會的地方
隱者的教堂，香客的祈禱。

IV. 格倫科峽谷附近的蘭諾赫

這裡烏鴉挨餓，這裡生性耐性的雄鹿
長大成為獵槍的犧牲。柔靜的湖泊
與柔靜的天空間，幾乎沒有跳躍
40. 或翱翔的地方。物質破碎，在稀薄的空氣中
月冷或月熱。道路彎曲
在古代戰爭的渺小中，
在斷劍的倦怠中，
在混亂的錯誤喧譁中，適切
45. 在靜默中。記憶遠比
骸骨強韌。驕傲折斷
驕傲的影子伸長，在伸長的小路上
沒有骸骨的贊同。

V. 安岬

快呀快來快來快來聽那野雀，
50. 沼雀，狐雀，晚雀的叫聲

At dawn and dusk. Follow the dance

Of goldenfinch at noon. Leave to chance

The Blackburnian wabler, the shy one. Hail

With shrill whistle the note of the quail, the bob-white

55. Dodging the bay-bush. Follow the feet

Of the walker, the water-thrush. Follow the flight

Of the dancing arrow, the purple martin. Greet

In silence the bullbat. All are delectable. Sweet sweet sweet

But resign this land at the end, resign it

60. To its true owner, the tough one, the sea gull.

The palaver is finished.

小詩
1924-1934

在黎明和黃昏。中午時跟隨

金翅雀的舞蹈吧。將那羞怯的

橙胸林鶯委歸偶然吧。以尖銳笛音

向歌唱的鵪鶉喝彩吧，向那閃躲在

55. 月桂樹叢裡的北美鶇。跟隨在步行鳥

水鵪的腳後吧。跟隨

舞蹈之箭，那紫色岩燕的飛行吧。在沉默中

迎接那蚊母鳥吧。一切都是使人愉快的。可愛的可愛的可

愛的

但是最終請放棄這塊土地，把它讓給

60. 它真正的主人，那個堅韌不拔的海鷗吧。

閑聊到此為止。

Lines for
an Old Man

The tiger in the tiger-pit
Is not more irritable than I.
The whipping tail is not more still
Than when I smell the enemy
5. Writhing in the essential blood
Or dangling from the friendly tree.
When I lay bare the tooth of wit
The hissing over the arched tongue
Is more affectionate than hate,
10. More bitter than the love of youth,
And inaccessible by the young.
Reflected from my golden eye
The dullard knows that he is mad.
Tell me if I am not glad!

小詩
1924-1934

給一個老人

陷阱裡的老虎
並不比我更暴躁。
鞭打的尾巴並不更平靜
比起當我聞到敵人
5. 在生來的血泊中折騰
或是吊在友善的樹上。
當我拔掉智慧的牙齒
捲起舌頭發出嘶嘶聲
那是比憎恨更深情,
10. 比青春的愛更惱苦,
而且不是年輕人所能達到的。
我的金色眼睛反映出
傻子知道自己的瘋狂。
你說呀我怎麼不高興!

Choruses from "The Rock"

「磐石」的合唱

·1934·

Choruses From "The Rock"
1934

Choruses
from "The Rock"

I

The Eagle soars in the summit of Heaven,
The Hunter with his dogs pursues his circuit.
O perpetual revolution of configured stars,
O perpetual recurrence of determined seasons,
5. O world of spring and autumn, birth and dying!
The endless cycle of idea and action,
Endless invention, endless experiment,
Brings knowledge of motion, but not of stillness;
Knowledge of speech, but not of silence;
10. Knowledge of words, and ignorance of the Word.
All our knowledge brings us nearer to our ignorance,
All our ignorance brings us nearer to death,
But nearness to death no nearer to God .
Where is the Life we have lost in living?
15. Where is the wisdom we have lost in knowledge?
Where is the knowledge we have lost in information?

「磐石」的合唱 [1]

I

蒼鷹翱翔在天的穹頂，
獵人帶著狗追蹤巡迴。
呵，行星永遠不斷地繞著一定方位，
呵，四季永遠不變地交替循環，
5. 呵，春與秋，生和死的世界！
觀念與行動無止境的輪轉，
無止境的發明，無止境的實驗，
帶來的是動的知識而不是靜止；
是言論的知識而不是沉默；
10. 知道人的話卻不知道**神的**話。
我們的一切知識使我們更接近無知，
我們的一切無知使我們更接近死亡，
接近死亡使我們不能更接近**神**。
我們在**生活**中失去的生命在哪裡？
15. 我們在知識中失去的智慧在哪裡？
我們在資訊中失去的知識在哪裡？

Choruses From "The Rock"
1934

The cycles of Heaven in twenty centuries
Bring us farther from God and nearer to the Dust.

    I journeyed to London, to the timekept City,
20. Where the River flows, with foreign flotations.
There I was told: we have too many churches,
And too few chop-houses. There I was told:
Let the vicars retire. Men do not need the Church
In the place where they work, but where they spend their
Sundays.
25. In the City, we need no bells:
Let them waken the suburbs.
I journeyed to the suburbs, and there I was told:
We toil for six days, on the seventh we must motor
To Hindhead, or Maidenhead.
30. If the weather is foul we stay at home and read the papers.
In industrial districts, there I was told
Of economic laws.
In the pleasant countryside, there it seemed
That the country now is only fit for picnics.
35. And the Church does not seem to be wanted
In country or in suburb; and in the town
Only for important weddings.

「磐石」的合唱
1934

二十世紀**天界**的循環
使我們離**神**更遠而更接近**塵土**。

　　我旅行到倫敦，計時的**都市**，
20.　那裡泰晤士河流著，載浮著外國船隻。
　　那裡我聽到人們說：我們的教堂太多，
　　小飯館太少。在那裡我聽說：
　　讓牧師們退職吧。人們不需要**教堂**
　　在他們工作的地方，只要有地方過禮拜日。
25.　在**都市**裡，我們不需要教堂的鐘：
　　讓教堂的鐘聲敲醒郊外的人們吧。
　　我旅行到郊外，在那裡我聽說：
　　六天裡我們拚命工作，第七天非開摩托車
　　到茵德高地或美敦河岸不可。
30.　要是天氣不好就留在家裡看報。
　　在工業區，那裡我聽說
　　經濟的法則。
　　在令人愉快的鄉下，似乎
　　鄉村如今只適合於野餐。
35.　在鄉村或郊外，**教堂**
　　好像都沒有必要；在都市
　　只用來舉行重大的結婚儀式。

Choruses From "The Rock"
1934

CHORUS LEADER :Silence! and preserve respectful distance.

40. For I perceive approaching

The Rock. Who will perhaps answer our doubtings.

The Rock. The Watcher. The Stranger.

He who has seen what has happened

And who sees what is to happen.

45. The Witness. The Critic. The Stranger.

The God-shaken, in whom is the truth inborn.

Enter the ROCK *, led by a* BOY *:*

THE ROCK: The lot of man is ceaseless labour,

Or ceaseless idleness, which is still harder,

50. Or irregular labour, which is not pleasant.

I have trodden the winepress alone, and I know

That it is hard to be really useful, resigning

The things that men count for happiness, seeking

The good deeds that lead to obscurity, accepting

55. With equal face those that bring ignominy,

The applause of all or the love of none.

All men are ready to invest their money

But most expect dividends.

I say to you: *Make perfect your will.*

「磐石」的合唱
1934

合唱長：肅靜！請保持適當旳距離。

40. 因我看到了接近而來的
磐石。或許他會回答我們的疑問。
磐石。看護人。不可思議的人。
他曾經見過發生了什麼事情。
他能預見將會發生什麼事情。
45. 見證人。批判者。不可思議的人。
受神感動的人，天賦以真理。

少年引導磐石登場：

磐石：人類的命運是不停的勞動，
或不斷的怠惰，那卻更辛苦，
50. 或不定的勞動，那並不快樂。
我曾經單獨踩榨釀酒的葡萄，我知道
成為真正有用並不容易，捨棄
人們認為幸福的事情，尋求
世人不知道的善行，以招來
55. 恥辱的同一張臉，接受
讚美滿天下愛我無一人的境遇。
人們樂意將金錢用來投資
大多都是為了分紅。
我對你們說：*成全你的意志。*

Choruses From "The Rock"
1934

60. I say: take no thought of the harvest,
But only of proper sowing.

The world turns and the world changes,
But one thing does not change.
In all of my years, one thing does not change.
65. However you disguise it, this thing does not change:
The perpetual struggle of Good and Evil.
Forgetful, you neglect your shrines and churches;
The men you are in these times deride
What has been done of good, you find explanations
70. To satisfy the rational and enlightened mind.
Second, you neglect and belittle the desert.
The desert is not remote in southern tropics,
The desert is not only around the corner,
The desert is squeezed in the tube-train next to you,
75. The desert is in the heart of your brother.
The good man is the builder, if he build what is good.
I will show you the things that are now being done,
And some of the things that were long ago done,
That you may take heart. Make perfect your will.
80. Let me show you the work of the humble. Listen.

「磐石」的合唱
1934

60. 我說：莫問收穫
　　但問耕耘。

　　　世界旋轉不停，世界變遷不居，
　　但有一件事永遠不變。
　　在我所有的歲月裡有一件事不變。
65. 不論你怎麼偽裝，仍然不變：
　　善與惡永遠不斷的交戰。
　　健忘的你們，忽視聖堂與教會；
　　生在這時代的你們，嘲弄
　　曾經做過的善行，你們尋求解釋
70. 以滿足理性和受啟發的心靈。
　　其次，你們忽略而且藐視曠野。
　　曠野不是在遙遠的南部熱帶地方，
　　曠野不是在世界的涯角，
　　曠野就在地下列車裡擠在你的身旁，
75. 曠野就在你們弟兄的心中。
　　善人是建樹者，假如他樹立善行。
　　我要將現在正在做的，以及
　　有些老早就做的事情指示給你們，
　　使你們提起勇氣。成全你們的意志。
80. 讓我將謙虛者的工作指示給你們。請聽。

Choruses From "The Rock"
1934

The lights fade; in the semi-darkness the voices of WORKMEN
are heard chanting .

In the vacant places
We will build with new bricks
There are hands and machines
85. *And clay for new brick*
And lime for new mortar
Where the bricks are fallen
We will build with new stone
Where the beams are rotten
90. *We will build with new timbers*
Where the word is unspoken
We will build with new speech
There is work together
A Church for all
95. *And a job for each*
Every man to his work.

Now a group of WORKMEN *is silhouetted against the dim*
sky. From farther away, they are answered by voices of the
UNEMPLOYED.

「磐石」的合唱
1934

*燈光漸弱；在幽暗中傳來**勞動者**的歌聲。*

> 在空曠的地方
> 我們用新的磚子建築
> 有人手，有機械
85. 有燒磚的粘土
> 和做灰泥的石灰
> 磚塊崩塌的地方
> 我們用新的石子建築
> 屋樑腐朽的地方
90. 我們用新的木材建築
> 字句沒說到的地方
> 我們創建新的語言
> 有工作大家在一起
> 教會是大家的
95. 事情各做各的
> 各盡本分工作。

*接著一群**勞動者**以朦朧的天空做背景襯出剪影。從遠方傳來**失業者**回應的聲音。*

Choruses From "The Rock"
1934

No man has hired us
With pocketed hands
100. And lowered faces
We stand about in open places
And shiver in unlit rooms.
Only the wind moves
Over empty fields, untilled
105. Where the plough rests, at an angle
To the furrow. In this land
There shall be one cigarette to two men,
To two women one half pint of bitter
Ale. In this land
110. No man has hired us.
Our life is unwelcome, our death
Unmentioned in " The Times".

Chant of WORKMEN again.

The river flows, the seasons turn
115. The sparrow and starling have no time to waste.
If men do not build
How shall they live?
When the field is tilled

「磐石」的合唱
1934

沒人雇我們

雙手插在衣袋裡

100. 到處垂頭喪氣

我們在曠地閑蕩徘徊

或在無燈的房間打擺。

只有風吹過

未耕作的荒田，那裡

105. 犁鋤被丟置在一角

在田溝邊。在這塊地上

兩個男人只分到一支香菸

兩個女人只給苦啤酒一合半。

在這塊地上

110. 沒人雇用我們

我們的生惹人厭，我們的死

不會登在《時代雜誌》。

再一次**勞動者**的歌。

河水悠悠，四季輪流，

115. 燕八歌和麻雀不把時間浪費。

人要是不建造

怎能活得了？

田野經過耕耘

Choruses From "The Rock"
1934

And the wheat is bread

120. *They shall not die in a shortened bed*

And a narrow sheet. In this street

There is no beginning, no movement, no peace and no end

But noise without speech, food without taste.

Without delay, without haste

125. *We would build the beginning and the end of this street.*

We build the meaning:

A Church for all

And a job for each

Each man to his work.

「磐石」的合唱
1934

小麥變成麵包

120. 他們不會死在太短的臥床上
或在太窄的被單裡。在這街道
沒有開始沒有動靜，沒有寧靜也無終止
只有不成話語的噪音和無味的食物。
不遲誤，不急忙

125. 我們建造這街道的開始和終止
我們建造意義：
教會是大家的
事情各做各的
各盡本分工作。

Choruses From "The Rock"
1934

II

^{130.} Thus your fathers were made

Fellow citizens of the saints, of the household of GOD , being built upon the foundation

Of apostles and prophets, Christ Jesus Himself the chief cornerstone.

But you, have you built well, that you now sit helpless in a ruined house?

Where many are born to idleness, to frittered lives and squalid deaths, embittered scorn in honeyless hives,

^{135.} And those who would build and restore turn out the palms of their hands, or look in vain towards foreign lands for alms to be more or the urn to be filled.

Your building not fitly framed together, you sit ashamed and wonder whether and how you may be builded together for a habitation of GOD in the Spirit, the Spirit which moved on the face of the waters like a lantern set on the back of a tortoise.

And some say: " How can we love our neighbour? For love must be made real in act, as desire unites with desired; we have only our labour to give and our labour is not required.

「磐石」的合唱
1934

II

130. 如此，你們的祖先被造成

聖者的同市民，屬於**神**的家庭，被建立在

使徒與先知的基礎上，**耶穌基督自己**是主要的柱石。

但是你們，是否好好建造了自己，現在絕望地坐在荒廢的

家中的你們？

那裡許多人一出生就被投向怠惰，破碎的人生，汙穢的

死，以及在無蜜的蜂窩裡令人難忍的侮辱，

135. 那些想建造和重建的人們翻出自己的手掌，或徒然妄想在

異地乞求更多施物或使土甕裝滿。

你們的建物架構並不牢固，你們感到羞恥地跪坐著，懷疑

是否以及如何建造自己成為**聖靈**中的**神**的住所，而**聖靈**在

水面上移動有如龜背上的燈籠。

有人說：「我們怎麼愛鄰居呢？因為愛在行為中要真實，

有如欲望與所欲望的東西繫結在一起；我們只能付出勞

力，而我們的勞力卻不是必要的。」

Choruses From "The Rock"
1934

We wait on corners, with nothing to bring but the songs we can sing which nobody wants to hear sung;
Waiting to be flung in the end, on a heap less useful than dung".

140. You, have you built well, have you forgotten the cornerstone?
Talking of right relations of men, but not of relations of men to GOD .
" Our citizenship is in Heaven"; yes, but that is the model and type for your citizenship upon earth.

When your fathers fixed the place of GOD ,
And settled all the inconvenient saints,
145. Apostles, martyrs, in a kind of Whipsnade,
Then they could set about imperial expansion
Accompanied by industrial development.
Exporting iron, coal and cotton goods
And intellectual enlightenment
150. And everything, including capital
And several versions of the Word of GOD :
The British race assured of a mission
Performed it, but left much at home unsure.

「磐石」的合唱
1934

我們在街隅等待著，除了我們能唱沒人想聽的歌以外，什
麼也沒帶；
等待著，等到最後被摔在比糞都不如的堆積上。」

140.　　你們，把自己好好建造了麼，你們忘記了那塊柱石嗎？
你們談論人與人之間的正當關係吧，不要談論人與神之間
的關係。
「我們的市民權在天國」；是的，但那是你們在人間的市
民權的模範和典型。

當你們的祖先固定了神的住所，
將難以對待的聖者，使徒，殉道者，
145.　安頓在威普斯納德公園那種地方，
然後英國人開始帝國的擴張
帶著產業的發展。
輸出了鐵，煤炭和綿製品
以及知識的啟蒙思潮
150.　以及一切，包含資本
和聖經的一些翻譯：
英國人假託為使命
完成了這些，但在本國貽下了許多不安。

Choruses From "The Rock"
1934

Of all that was done in the past, you eat the fruit, either rotten
or ripe.

155 And the Church must be forever building, and always
decaying, and always being restored.

For every ill deed in the past we suffer the consequence:

For sloth, for avarice, gluttony, neglect of the Word of GOD ,

For pride, for lechery, treachery, for every act of sin.

And of all that was done that was good, you have the
inheritance.

160 For good and ill deeds belong to a man alone, when he stands
alone on the other side of death,

But here upon earth you have the reward of the good and ill
that was done by those who have gone before you.

And all that is ill you may repair if you walk together in
humble repentance, expiating the sins of your fathers;

And all that was good you must fight to keep with hearts as
devoted as those of your fathers who fought to gain it.

The Church must be forever building, for it is forever decaying
within and attacked from without;

165 For this is the law of life; and you must remember that while
there is time of prosperity

The people will neglect the Temple, and in time of adversity
they will decry it.

「磐石」的合唱
1934

過去所做的一切，你都把果實吃下去，不論成熟或腐爛。
155. **教會**必須不斷地建立，屢經敗壞，不斷地重建。
過去的一切惡行結果使我們受苦：
由於怠惰，食婪，饕餮，漠視**神的話**，
由於驕傲，肉慾，叛逆，以及每一罪行。
過去的一切善行我們都繼承受福。
160. 當人獨自與死亡對立時，善行與惡行只屬於他個人，
而在這個世上，你們得到在你之前死去的人們所為善惡的
報償。
一切的惡行都可獲得補償，假如你們一起走在虛心懺悔的
道上，為祖先贖罪；
一切的善行你們必須爭取保存，以祖先奮鬥獲得善行的那
種虔誠的心。
教會必須不斷地建立，因不斷地在內部敗壞，且受外來的
襲擊；
165. 因為這是生命的法則；你們必須牢記在心：在得意的時候
人們會漠視聖堂，而在逆境中且加以汙衊。

Choruses From "The Rock"
1934

What life have you if you have not life together?

There is no life that is not in community,

And no community not lived in praise of GOD .

170. Even the anchorite who meditates alone,

For whom the days and nights repeat the praise of GOD ,

Prays for the Church, the Body of Christ incarnate.

And now you live dispersed on ribbon roads,

And no man knows or cares who is his neighbor

175. Unless his neighbour makes too much disturbance,

But all dash to and fro in motor cars,

Familiar with the roads and settled nowhere.

Nor does the family even move about together,

But every son would have his motor cycle,

180. And daughters ride away on casual pillions.

Much to cast down, much to build, much to restore;

Let the work not delay, time and the arm not waste;

Let the clay be dug from the pit, let the saw cut the stone,

Let the fire not be quenched in the forge.

「磐石」的合唱
1934

　　沒有共同的生命，你們的生命怎樣？
沒有不在社會中存在的生命，
沒有不讚美**神**而存在的社會。
170.　即使是獨自冥想的隱士，
晝夜因他而一再讚美**神**，
仍然為**教會**，**基督聖體**的化身而祈禱。
如今你們零落地住在如帶的道路上，
誰也不知道，不關心鄰居是誰
175.　除非鄰居侵犯了他的安寧，
只是騎著摩托車在熟悉的道路上，
僕僕不停地來往奔波。
即使是家人，也不一起出去走動，
每個男孩都想要有自己的機車，
180.　女孩坐在隨便的後座上招搖而去。

　　要拆毀，要建立，要重建的有太多；
工作不要拖，時間和人手不要浪費；
讓粘土從坑裡挖出，讓鋸機切碎石頭，
讓鍛爐裡的火熊熊不熄。

Choruses From "The Rock"
1934

III

185. The Word of the LORD came unto me, saying:

O miserable cities of designing men,

O wretched generation of enlightened men,

Betrayed in the mazes of your ingenuities,

Sold by the proceeds of your proper inventions:

190. I have given you hands which you turn from worship,

I have given you speech, for endless palaver,

I have given you my Law, and you set up commissions,

I have given you lips, to express friendly sentiments,

I have given you hearts, for reciprocal distrust.

195. I have given you power of choice, and you only alternate

Between futile speculation and unconsidered action.

Many are engaged in writing books and printing them,

Many desire to see their names in print,

Many read nothing but the race reports.

200. Much is your reading, but not the Word of GOD ,

Much is your building, but not the House of GOD .

Will you build me a house of plaster, with corrugated roofing,

To be filled with a litter of Sunday newspapers?

1st MALE VOICE : A Cry from the East:

「磐石」的合唱
1934

III

185. **主的話對我這麼說：**
人心叵測的悲慘都市喲，
文明人的可憐的世代喲，
你們在原創力的困惑中被矇騙了，
被自己的發明品的收益出賣了：
190. 我給了你們雙手，你們卻不做禮拜，
我給了你們語言，你們卻廢話連篇，
我給了你們戒律，你們卻自立規章，
我給了你們嘴唇，卻說些友情的感傷，
我給了你們心，彼此卻不能互相信任。
195. 我給了你們選擇的能力，你們只在
無益的思索與無判斷的行動間舉棋不定。
許多人忙著著書立說，然後出版，
許多人渴望自己的名字變成印刷，
許多人除了賽馬的報導不讀不看。
200. 你們所讀的不為不多，卻沒有**神的話**，
你們所建立的也不少，卻不是**神的家**。
你們肯為我建造一個家，塗抹灰泥，屋頂有瓦楞的，
以便塞滿廢棄的星期天報紙？

第一個男聲：呼聲來自東方：

Choruses From "The Rock"
1934

205. What shall be done to the shore of smoky ships?
Will you leave my people forgetful and forgotten
To idleness, labour, and delirious stupor?
There shall be left the broken chimney,
The peeled hull, a pile of rusty iron,
210. In a street of scattered brick where the goat climbs,
Where My Word is unspoken.

2ND MALE VOICE : A Cry from the North, from the West and
from the South
Whence thousands travel daily to the timekept City;
Where My Word is unspoken,
215. In the land of lobelias and tennis flannels
The rabbit shall burrow and the thorn revisit,
The nettle shall flourish on the gravel court,
And the wind shall say: " Here were decent godless people:
Their only monument the asphalt road
220. And a thousand lost golf balls."

CHORUS: We build in vain unless the LORD build with us.
Can you keep the City that the LORD keeps not with you?
A thousand policemen directing the traffic
Cannot tell you why you come or where you go.

「磐石」的合唱
1934

205. 對這些冒煙的船所停泊的港岸將怎麼辦？
　　你們肯聽我那健忘的，被遺忘的國民
　　陷入怠惰，勞動，以及麻痺一般的昏狂？
　　搗壞的煙囪，剝落的船身，堆積的鏽鐵，
　　都將被遺留在磚塊四散的街道，
210. 那裡山羊登爬著，
　　那裡**我**的話沒人談。

　　第二個男聲：呼聲來自北方，來自西方，來自南方
　　每天數千的人們趕來這個計時的都市；
　　那裡**我**的話沒人談，
215. 在山梗菜與網球法蘭絨的國土
　　野兔將會掘穴，荊棘將會煥發新枝
　　蕁麻將會在砂礫的庭院叢生，
　　風將會說：「失去神的好人曾住在這裡：
　　他們唯一的留念品是柏油路
220. 和千百個找不到的高爾夫球。」

　　合唱：我們枉費辛勞如果**主**不與我們一起建造，
　　主不給支持的**都市**，你們何能保存嗎？
　　指揮交通的成千警察不能告訴你
　　你為何而來你去向何方。

Choruses From "The Rock"
1934

225. A colony of cavies or a horde of active marmots

Build better than they that build without the LORD .

Shall we lift up our feet among perpetual ruins?

I have loved the beauty of Thy House, the peace of Thy

sanctuary

I have swept the floors and garnished the altars.

230. Where there is no temple there shall be no homes,

Though you have shelters and institutions,

Precarious lodgings while the rent is paid,

Subsiding basements where the rat breeds

Or sanitary dwellings with numbered doors

235. Or a house a little better than your neighbour's;

When the Stranger says: " What is the meaning of this city?

Do you huddle close together because you love each other?"

What will you answer? " We all dwell together

To make money from each other"? or " This is a community"?

240. And the Stranger will depart and return to the desert.

O my soul, be prepared for the coming of the Stranger,

Be prepared for him who knows how to ask questions.

O weariness of men who turn from GOD

To the grandeur of your mind and the glory of your action,

245. To arts and inventions and daring enterprises,

「磐石」的合唱
1934

225. 一群體的天竺鼠或一部落活躍的土撥鼠
能建造比沒有主的人們所建造的更好。
我們要在永久的廢墟間舉起腳走路麼？
我喜愛主的家的華美與主的聖堂的靜穆，
我清掃了地板，洗淨了祭壇。

230. 沒有聖堂的地方就不會有家庭，
儘管你們有避風雨的地方和公共建物，
有付房租但朝不保夕的住處，
有老鼠在底層的地下室繁殖
或釘有門牌的衛生住宅

235. 或比鄰居稍好幾分的屋子；
當不可思議的人說：「這個都市有什麼意義？
你們緊抱在一起因為你們彼此相愛嗎？」
你們怎麼回答？「我們相處在一起
彼此賺錢取利」？或是「這就是社會啊」？

240. 那麼不可思議的人將會離開而回到曠野吧。
我的靈魂喲，準備迎接不可思議的人來臨吧，
準備迎接知道怎樣質問的人吧。

呵，人們的厭煩，當人們背棄神
轉向人類心中的宏偉與行動的輝煌，
245. 轉向技藝和發明，以及大膽的企業，

Choruses From "The Rock"
1934

To schemes of human greatness thoroughly discredited,

Binding the earth and the water to your service,

Exploiting the seas and developing the mountains,

Dividing the stars into common and preferred,

250. Engaged in devising the perfect refrigerator,

Engaged in working out a rational morality,

Engaged in printing as many books as possible,

Plotting of happiness and flinging empty bottles,

Turning from your vacancy to fevered enthusiasm

255. For nation or race or what you call humanity;

Though you forget the way to the Temple,

There is one who remembers the way to your door:

Life you may evade, but Death you shall not.

You shall not deny the Stranger.

「磐石」的合唱
1934

轉向完全不可信任的人類的偉大企圖
而且支配大地和水源據為己用，
利用海洋，開拓山林，
將星辰分類為平凡與偏愛，
250. 進一步著手設計十全十美的冰箱，
忙著策劃合理的道德，
忙著印刷越多越好的書籍，
圖謀幸福且亂扔空瓶，
從自己的空虛轉向對國家
255. 對民族或者所謂人道的極端狂熱；
雖然你們忘記通達聖堂的道路，
總有人記得通達你們的家門：
你們可能逃避生，但逃避不了死。
你們不能拒絕不可思議的人。

IV

There are those who would build the Temple,

And those who prefer that the Temple should not be built.

In the days of Nehemiah the Prophet

There was no exception to the general rule.

265. In Shushan the palace, in the month Nisan,

He served the wine to the King Artaxerxes,

And he grieved for the broken city, Jerusalem;

And the King gave him leave to depart

That he might rebuild the city.

270. So he went, with a few, to Jerusalem,

And there, by the dragon's well, by the dung gate,

By the fountain gate, by the king's pool,

Jerusalem lay waste, consumed with fire;

No place for a beast to pass.

275. There were enemies without to destroy him,

And spies and self-seekers within,

When he and his men laid their hands to rebuilding the wall

So they built as men must build

With the sword in one hand and the trowel in the other.

「磐石」的合唱
1934

IV

有想建造聖堂的人，
也有認為建造聖堂大可不必的人。
在先知尼希米的時代
一般的法則沒有例外。
265. 在書珊城的宮中，在尼散月裡，
他拿起酒來奉給亞達薛西王，
為耶路撒冷遭毀而面帶愁容；
王賜給詔書差遣他
去重新建造那個城。
270. 於是他帶了幾個人來到耶路撒冷，
到了野狗井，到了糞廠門，
到了泉門和王池，
那裡城牆拆毀，城門被火焚燒；
走獸經過的地方都沒有。
275. 外有仇敵要殺害他，
內有間諜和利己主義者，
當他和弟兄們著手重建城牆時，
因此，他們不得不竭盡所能建造，
一手握著刀劍一手拿著泥鏝。

Choruses From "The Rock"
1934

V

280. O Lord, deliver me from the man of excellent intention and
impure heart: for the heart is deceitful above all things, and
desperately wicked.

Sanballat the Horonite and Tobiah the Ammonite and Geshem
the Arabian: were doubtless men of public spirit and zeal.

Preserve me from the enemy who has something to gain: and
from the friend who has something to lose.

Remembering the words of Nehemiah the Prophet: " The
trowel in hand, and the gun rather loose in the holster."

Those who sit in a house of which the use is forgotten: are like
snakes that lie on mouldering stairs, content in the sun light.

285. And the others run about like dogs, full of enterprise, sniffing
and barking: they say, " This house is a nest of serpents, let us
destroy it,

And have done with these abominations, the turpitudes of the
Christians." And these are not justified, nor the others.

And they write innumerable books; being too vain and
distracted for silence: seeking every one after his own
elevation, and dodging his emptiness.

If humility and purity be not in the heart, they are not in the
home: and if they are not in the home, they are not in the City.

「磐石」的合唱
1934

V

280. 主喲，從意圖堂皇而衷心不潔的人那裡把我救出：那顆心
比什麼都虛偽而且極端邪惡。

和倫人參巴拉與亞捫人多比雅以及亞拉伯人基善：無疑是
具有公德心與熱忱的人。

從有所獲得的敵人和有所損失的朋友中保佑我吧。

牢記**先知**尼希米的話：「鏝子在手上，槍鬆綁在皮套裡。」

坐在忘記用處的屋子裡那些人：像在腐朽的梯階上呼呼曬
著陽光的蛇一樣。

285. 其他人像狗不懷好意地跑來跑去地嗅著、吠著：他們說
「這間屋子是蛇窩，讓我們把它搗毀吧，

讓這些可憎的悖德的**基督徒**也搗毀吧。」這些人，正像從
前的那些都不是正當旳。

他們寫了無數的書；因虛榮心切以及不耐寂寞：每個人尋
求自己的發跡，閃避內心的空虛。

假如心中沒有謙虛和純潔，他們就是不在家：假如他們不
在家，他們就不會在那**都**城裡。

Choruses From "The Rock"
1934

The man who has builded during the day would return to his
hearth at nightfall: to be blessed with the gift of silence, and
doze before he sleeps.

290. But we are encompassed with snakes and dogs: therefore some
must labour, and others must hold the spears.

「磐石」的合唱
1934

白天為建造做工的人，天黑時回到家裡的爐邊：接受寧靜
的賜福和祝福，在入睡之前打盹。

290. 但是我們受到蛇和狗的包圍：因此有些人必須勞動，其他
的人必須手持槍矛。

Choruses From "The Rock"
1934

VI

It is hard for those who have never known persecution,

And who have never known a Christian,

To believe these tales of Christian persecution.

It is hard for those who live near a Bank

295. To doubt the security of their money.

It is hard for those who live near a Police Station

To believe in the triumph of violence.

Do you think that the Faith has conquered the World

And that lions no longer need keepers?

300. Do you need to be told that whatever has been, can still be?

Do you need to be told that even such modest attainments

As you can boast in the way of polite society

Will hardly survive the Faith to which they owe their significance?

Men! polish your teeth on rising and retiring;

305. Women! polish your fingernails:

You polish the tooth of the dog and the talon of the cat.

Why should men love the Church? Why should they love her laws?

She tells them of Life and Death, and of all that they would forget.

「磐石」的合唱
1934

VI

從來不知道迫害，

從來不認識**基督徒**的人，

很難相信**基督徒**受迫害的故事。

住在**銀行**附近的人，

295. 對自己金錢的安全很難懷疑。

住在**警察局**附近的人

對暴力的勝利是難以相信的。

你認為**信仰**已經征服了**世界**

而那些獅子不再需要有人看守了嗎？

300. 已發生的事仍會再發生，這還得說嗎？

即使是像在文明社會那樣能夠誇耀的

一般學識，其存在幾乎不可能超過信仰，

雖然它的意義來自信仰，這還得說嗎？

男人喲！在起床和就寢時把牙齒刷乾淨吧；

305. 女人喲！把手指甲擦亮吧：

你們所刷所擦的是狗牙和貓爪。

人為什麼一定要愛**教會**？為什麼非愛**教會**的律法不可？

教會將**生**與**死**，以及人們會忘記的一切告訴他們。

Choruses From "The Rock"
1934

She is tender where they would be hard, and hard where they
like to be soft.

310. She tells them of Evil and Sin, and other unpleasant facts.

They constantly try to escape

From the darkness outside and within

By dreaming of systems so perfect that no one will need to be
good.

But the man that is will shadow

315. The man that pretends to be.

And the Son of Man was not crucified once for all,

The blood of the martyrs not shed once for all,

The lives of the Saints not given once for all:

But the Son of Man is crucified always

320. And there shall be Martyrs and Saints.

And if blood of Martyrs is to flow on the steps

We must first build the steps;

And if the Temple is to be cast down

We must first build the Temple.

「磐石」的合唱
1934

教會在人們困厄時是仁慈的，在人們需要溫柔時是嚴厲的。

310. 教會告訴他們惡與罪，以及其他不愉快的事實。

人們時常想要逃出

來自外部與內部的黑黯，

夢想一些組織，如此完美認為人不需要善良。

但是真實的人會使

315. 虛偽的人原形畢露。

人子被釘在十字架上非只一次，

殉道者流血非只一次，

聖者奉獻生命非只一次；

十字架上人子釘之於前

320. 殉道者與聖者繼之於後。

要是殉道者的血流在石階上

我們一定先建造石階；

要是聖堂被拆毀

我們一定先建造聖堂。

Choruses From "The Rock"
1934

VII

325. In the beginning GOD created the world. Waste and void.
Waste and void. And darkness was upon the face of the deep.
And when there were men, in their various ways, they struggled in torment towards GOD
Blindly and vainly, for man is a vain thing, and man without GOD is a seed upon the wind: driven this way and that, and finding no place of lodgement and germination.
They followed the light and the shadow, and the light led them forward to light and the shadow led them to darkness,
Worshipping snakes or trees, worshipping devils rather than nothing: crying for life beyond life, for ecstasy not of the flesh.
330. Waste and void. Waste and void. And darkness on the face of the deep.

And the Spirit moved upon the face of the water.
And men who turned towards the light and were known of the light
Invented the Higher Religions; and the Higher Religions were good
And led men from light to light, to knowledge of Good and Evil.

「磐石」的合唱
1934

VII

325. 起初**神**創造天地。混沌空虛。混沌空虛。淵面黑暗。

當有了人類，他們以種種方法，在受苦中掙扎歸向**神**

盲然而且徒然，因人原是虛空，沒有**神**不過是風中的種籽：

到處隨風飄蕩，找不到落跡萌芽的地方。

人類追尋光和影；光將他們導向明亮，影將他們導向黑暗。

他們崇拜蛇和樹；與其無所崇拜，不如崇拜魔鬼：乞求超

越生命的生命，乞求不是肉體的狂喜。

330. 混沌空虛。混沌空虛。淵面黑暗。

而**聖靈**運行水面。

而趨向光，知道光的人們

創立**更高的宗教**；**更高的宗教是好的**

將他們從光導向明亮，導向善與惡的知識。

Choruses From "The Rock"
1934

335. But their light was ever surrounded and shot with darkness

As the air of temperate seas is pierced by the still dead breath

of the Arctic Current;

And they came to an end, a dead end stirred with a flicker of

life,

And they came to the withered ancient look of a child that has

died of starvation.

Prayer wheels, worship of the dead, denial of this world,

affirmation of rites with forgotten meanings

340. In the restless wind-whipped sand, or the hills where the wind

will not let the snow rest.

Waste and void. Waste and void. And darkness on the face of

the deep.

Then came, at a predetermined moment, a moment in time

and of time,

A moment not out of time, but in time, in what we call

history: transecting, bisecting the world of time, a moment in

time but not like a moment of time,

A moment in time but time was made through that moment:

for without the meaning there is no time, and that moment of

time gave the meaning.

345. Then it seemed as if men must proceed from light to light, in

「磐石」的合唱
1934

335. 可是他們的光永遠受著黑暗的包圍和穿透

正像海上溫暖的大氣被北極寒流僵冷的吹息所穿透；

而他們到了盡頭，到了生命明滅地閃動的絕境，

臉容看來像餓死的孩童那樣古老消瘦。

祈禱輪轉，死者的禮拜，現世的否定，遺忘意義的儀式之確認，

340. 在狂風鞭撻無時停息的砂地，或在風不讓雪花休息的山丘。

混沌空虛。混沌空虛。淵面黑暗。

　　　不久，在預先決定的瞬間，在時間中的時間的瞬間來到了，

這瞬間不在時間外，而在時間中，在所謂的歷史中：將時間的世界橫切、切成兩段，在時間中的瞬間，但又不像時間的瞬間，

在時間中的瞬間，而時間是透過那瞬間產生的：因為沒有意義也就沒有時間，而時間的那一瞬間賦予意義。

345. 然後似乎人們必須從光前進到光，在**神的話**的光照中，

Choruses From "The Rock"
1934

the light of the Word,

Through the Passion and Sacrifice saved in spite of their negative being;

Bestial as always before, carnal, self-seeking as always before, selfish and purblind as ever before,

Yet always struggling, always reaffirming, always resuming their march on the way that was lit by the light;

Often halting, loitering, straying, delaying, returning, yet following no other way.

350. But it seems that something has happened that has never happened before: though we know not just when, or why, or how, or where.

Men have left GOD not for other gods, they say, but for no god; and this has never happened before

That men both deny gods and worship gods, professing first Reason,

And then Money, and Power, and what they call Life, or Race, or Dialectic.

The Church disowned, the tower overthrown, the bells upturned, what have we to do

355. But stand with empty hands and palms turned upwards

In an age which advances progressively backwards?

「磐石」的合唱
1934

透過得救的**受難**與**磔刑**，儘管都是消極的存在；

一如從前永遠是動物性的，肉慾的，一如從前永遠是利己的，一如從前是自私的、半瞎的，

但是在燈光照亮的道路上，不斷地掙扎，不斷地肯定，不斷地繼續前進；

時常受阻，徬徨，迷途，耽誤，重返，但是沒有其他的路可以追隨。

350.　　然而似乎從前未曾發生的事已經發生：雖然我們不知道究竟在何時何地因何如何發生。

人們背棄**神**，不是皈依別的神，他們說，是皈依無神；這種事從前未曾發生過：

人們否認眾神又崇拜眾神，先是自認為信仰**理性**，

然後是**金錢**，以及**權力**，以及所謂的**人生**，或人種，或**辯證法**。

教會被否認，塔被推倒，鐘被傾覆，我們除了

355. 空手反掌站立以外有什麼辦法

在這越來越往後前進的時代裡？

Choruses From "The Rock"
1934

VOICE OF THE UNEMPLOYED [afar off]:

In this land

There shall be one cigarette to two men,

360. *To two women one half pint of bitter Ale. . . .*

CHORU: What does the world say, does the whole world stray
in high-powered cars on a by-pass way?

VOICE OF THE UNEMPLOYED [more faintly]

In this land

No man has hired us. . . .

365. CHORUS: Waste and void. Waste and void. And darkness on
the face of the deep.

Has the Church failed mankind, or has mankind failed the
Church?

When the Church is no longer regarded, not even opposed,
and men have forgotten

All gods except Usury, Lust and Power.

「磐石」的合唱
1934

失業者的聲音〔遠遠地〕：

> 在這塊地上

兩個男人只分到一支香菸，

360. 兩個女人只給苦啤酒一合半……

合唱：這世界怎麼說，難道整個世界就迷失在駕著馬力十

足的汽車奔跑在超車的道路上？

失業者的聲音〔更弱〕

> 在這塊地上

沒人雇用我們……

365. **合唱**：混沌空虛。混沌空虛。淵面黑暗。

教會捨棄人類，還是人類捨棄**教會**？

當**教會**不再受尊重，甚至不再被反對時，人們遺忘了

所有的神，除了**高利貸**，**情慾**和**權力**。

Choruses From "The Rock"
1934

VIII

O Father we welcome your words,
370. And we will take heart for the future,
Remembering the past.

The heathen are come into thine inheritance,
And thy temple have they defiled.

Who is this that cometh from Edom?

375.   He has trodden the wine-press alone.

There came one who spoke of the shame of Jerusalem
And the holy places defiled;
Peter the Hermit, scourging with words.
And among his hearers were a few good men,
380. Many who were evil,
And most who were neither.
Like all men in all places,

Some went from love of glory,
Some went who were restless and curious,

「磐石」的合唱
1934

VIII

天上的父喲，我們高興接受祢的話，
370. 我們會用心策勵將來，
記取過去。

異教徒得到你的繼承，
他們褻瀆了你的聖堂。

這位從以東來的人是誰呢？

375. 他獨自踩踏酒醡。

宣說耶路撒冷遭受恥辱。
聖潔的地方被沾汙；
隱居修道者彼得來了，揮著言語的鞭子。
聽他傳教的人中有少許好人，
380. 許多是惡人，
大多數兩者都不是。
正像所有地方所有的人一樣。

有的因為愛慕名聲而去，
有的心神不定好奇而去，

Choruses From "The Rock"
1934

385. Some were rapacious and lustful.

Many left their bodies to the kites of Syria

Or sea-strewn along the routes;

Many left their souls in Syria,

Living on, sunken in moral corruption;

390. Many came back well broken,

Diseased and beggared, finding

A stranger at the door in possession:

Came home cracked by the sun of the East

And the seven deadly sins in Syria.

395. But our King did well at Acre.

And in spite of all the dishonour,

The broken standards, the broken lives,

The broken faith in one place or another,

There was something left that was more than the tales

400. Of old men on winter evenings.

Only the faith could have done what was good of it;

Whole faith of a few,

Part faith of many.

Not avarice, lechery, treachery,

405. Envy, sloth, gluttony, jealousy, pride:

It was not these that made the Crusades,

「磐石」的合唱
1934

385. 有的是貪婪而且好色。
　　許多人將身體交給敘利亞的帆船，
　　或是沿途撒在海上；
　　許多人將靈魂留在敘利亞
　　沉溺在道德的墮落中活下去；
390. 許多人一貧如洗地回來
　　害了病，淪為乞丐，發現
　　陌生人占據自己的家站在門口：
　　受到**東方**的太陽和在敘利亞的
　　七大罪的傷害回到家來。

395. 　　但是我們的**王**在阿克里一切順利。
　　儘管所有不名譽的事，
　　儘管規範被破壞了，生活破碎了，
　　到處信仰破滅了，
　　仍然有些保存下來，那不是
400. 冬日黃昏老人所能說的故事。
　　只有信仰才能使這些成為美好；
　　少數人完整的信仰，
　　多數人部分的信仰。
　　不是貪婪，肉慾，叛逆，
405. 猜忌，怠惰，饕餮，嫉妒，驕傲：
　　不是這些引起了**十字軍**，

Choruses From "The Rock"
1934

But these that unmade them.

Remember the faith that took men from home
At the call of a wandering preacher.
410. Our age is an age of moderate virtue
And of moderate vice
When men will not lay down the Cross
Because they will never assume it.
Yet nothing is impossible, nothing,
415. To men of faith and conviction.
Let us therefore make perfect our will.
O GOD , help us.

「磐石」的合唱
1934

倒是這些破壞了十字軍。

　　　請記起信仰將人們帶出家裡
　　當他們聽到雲遊傳道者的呼喚。
410.　我們的時代是善德平庸
　　以及惡德平庸的時代
　　當人們不想背負十字架
　　因此不願確認十字架。
　　但是沒有不可能的事，絕對沒有，
415.　對於有信仰有確信的人。
　　因此讓我們成全我們的意志吧。
　　神喲，幫助我們吧。

Choruses From "The Rock"
1934

IX

Son of Man, behold with thine eyes, and hear with thine ears

And set thine heart upon all that I show thee.

420. Who is this that has said: the House of GOD is a House of Sorrow;

We must walk in black and go sadly, with longdrawn faces,

We must go between empty walls, quavering lowly, whispering faintly,

Among a few flickering scattered lights?

They would put upon GOD their own sorrow, the grief they should feel

425. For their sins and faults as they go about their daily occasions.

Yet they walk in the street proudnecked, like thoroughbreds ready for races,

Adorning themselves, and busy in the market, the forum,

And all other secular meetings.

Thinking good of themselves, ready for any festivity,

430. Doing themselves very well.

Let us mourn in a private chamber, learning the way of penitence,

And then let us learn the joyful communion of saints.

「磐石」的合唱
1934

IX

人子喲，請用祢的眼睛看，用祢的耳朵聽，用眼睛，
請用心聽我訴說，向祢表示的一切吧。

420. 是誰這麼說：神的家是悲愁的家；
我們必須穿上黑衣，拉長著臉，哀傷地走著，
我們必須走在空壁之間，以顫抖的聲音微弱地呢喃
在若明若滅，零零星星的一些燈光中？
他們將自己的哀愁推給神，將自己在日常生活中

425. 因犯罪與過錯不得不感到的悲傷。
然而他們像準備競賽的駿馬，驕首昂然地走在街上，
打扮自己，匆匆忙忙在市場，在公會所，
以及其他世俗的集會裡。
不忘吹噓自己，有喜宴就參加，

430. 表現良好，得意揚揚。
讓我們獨自在房間裡服喪吧，學習懺悔的方法吧，
也讓我們學習聖者與神充滿喜悅的靈交吧。

Choruses From "The Rock"
1934

The soul of Man must quicken to creation.

Out of the formless stone, when the artist united himself with stone,

435. Spring always new forms of life, from the soul of man that is joined to the soul of stone;

Out of the meaningless practical shapes of all that is living or lifeless

Joined with the artist's eye, new life, new form, new colour.

Out of the sea of sound the life of music,

Out of the slimy mud of words, out of the sleet and hail of verbal imprecisions,

440. Approximate thoughts and feelings, words that have taken the place of thoughts and feelings,

There spring the perfect order of speech, and the beauty of incantation.

LORD, shall we not bring these gifts to Your service?

Shall we not bring to Your service all our powers

For life, for dignity, grace and order,

445. And intellectual pleasures of the senses?

The LORD who created must wish us to create

And employ our creation again in His service

Which is already His service in creating.

「磐石」的合唱
1934

　　人類的靈魂必須甦醒敏於創造。

當藝術家與石頭結合在一起時，就從那無形的石頭中，

435. 不斷地創出生命的新形式，從與石頭的靈魂結合在一起的
人的靈魂；

當與藝術家的眼睛結合在一起時，從那活生生或死板板的
一切無意義的現實形狀中創出新的生命，新的形式，新的
色彩。

從聲音的海洋創出音樂的生命，

從黏糊糊的文字泥濘中，從曖昧的語言表現的雪片與電粒
中，

440. 從未成熟的思想與感情，甚至取代思想與感情的文字中，
創造出詞句的完美秩序，以及呪語的美。

　　主喲，我們可以不奉獻這些贈物給祢的禮拜麼？

為了生命，為了尊嚴、優雅和秩序，

以及五官的知性快感

445. 我們可以不奉獻一切力量給祢的禮拜麼？

造物主一定願望我們創造

再將我們的創造物奉獻在祂的祭壇上

我們的創造本來只是服侍主的創造而已。

For Man is joined spirit and body,
450. And therefore must serve as spirit and body.
Visible and invisible, two worlds meet in Man;
Visible and invisible must meet in His Temple;
You must not deny the body.

Now you shall see the Temple completed:
455. After much striving, after many obstacles;
For the work of creation is never without travail;
The formed stone, the visible crucifix,
The dressed altar, the lifting light,

Light

460. Light

The visible reminder of Invisible Light.

「磐石」的合唱
1934

因為人是精神和肉體的結合，
450. 必須精神和肉體一起奉獻。
人結合了看得見與看不見的兩個世界；
看得見的與看不見的必須結合在主的聖堂；
你們不得否認肉體。

現在，你們該看到完成了的聖堂吧：
455. 經過了許多努力，克服了無數困難；
因為創造的工作永遠免不了勞苦；
石塊平整，十字架在望，
祭壇經過裝飾，高掛著燈光，

光

460. 光

看得見的光令人想起看不見的光。

Choruses From "The Rock"
1934

X

You have seen the house built, you have seen it adorned

By one who came in the night, it is now dedicated to GOD .

It is now a visible church, one more light set on a hill

465. In a world confused and dark and disturbed by portents of
fear.

And what shall we say of the future? Is one church all we can
build?

Or shall the Visible Church go on to conquer the World?

The great snake lies ever half awake, at the bottom of the pit
of the world, curled

In folds of himself until he awakens in hunger and moving his
head to right and to left prepares for his hour to devour.

470. But the Mystery of Iniquity is a pit too deep for mortal eyes to
plumb. Come

Ye out from among those who prize the serpent's golden eyes,

The worshippers, self-given sacrifice of the snake. Take

Your way and be ye separate.

Be not too curious of Good and Evil;

475. Seek not to count the future waves of Time;

But be ye satisfied that you have light

「磐石」的合唱
1934

X

你已經看到了家，有了裝飾的家
那位在夜晚來到的人所建造的家，現在奉獻給**神**。
那就是現在看得見的教堂，山丘上多一盞的燈光
465. 在混亂與黑暗的世界中，而且被恐懼的預感所困擾。
我們對未來怎麼說呢？我們所能建造的只有一座教堂麼？
或是讓那**看得見的教堂**繼續征服**世界**？

那隻巨蛇永遠半醒著眼，盤捲在世界的穴底中，
肚子餓了就睜開眼，左右搖動著頭，等待著貪吞的時間到來。
470. 但是**罪的秘密**是人類的眼睛所不能探測的深穴。來吧
你，棄絕那些讚美蛇的金眼的人們，
那些將自己奉獻為犧牲的蛇的崇拜者。
選擇你的道路，離開吧。
善與惡不必過分探索；
475. **時間**的未來波浪也不必去尋求計量；
但是你們應該滿足有足夠的光

Choruses From "The Rock"
1934

Enough to take your step and find your foothold.

    O Light Invisible, we praise Thee!

Too bright for mortal vision.

480. O Greater Light, we praise Thee for the less;

The eastern light our spires touch at morning,

The light that slants upon our western doors at evening,

The twilight over stagnant pools at batflight,

Moon light and star light, owl and moth light,

485. Glow-worm glowlight on a grassblade.

O Light Invisible, we worship Thee!

    We thank Thee for the lights that we have kindled,

The light of altar and of sanctuary;

Small lights of those who meditate at midnight

490. And lights directed through the coloured panes of windows

And light reflected from the polished stone,

The gilded carven wood, the coloured fresco.

Our gaze is submarine, our eyes look upward

And see the light that fractures through unquiet water.

495. We see the light but see not whence it comes.

O Light Invisible, we glorify Thee!

「磐石」的合唱
1934

能夠舉起腳步，找到立足的地方。

　　看不見的光喲，我們讚美祢！
因為過分明亮人類的眼睛看不見。
480.　**偉大的光喲，我們因渺小的光而讚美祢；**
因早晨教堂的塔尖所觸及的東方的光，
因黃昏時向西邊窗門傾斜的光，
因蝙蝠飛出時靜水池塘上的微光，
因月光和星光，因貓頭鷹和蛾之光，
485.　因草葉上的螢之光。
　　看不見的光喲，我們以崇拜讚美祢！

　　　我們因自己點燃的光而感謝祢，
因祭壇上與內堂裡的光；
因冥想的人們夜半所點的微光
490.　因透過彩色玻璃照射進來的光
因磨亮的石材，鑲金的木雕
彩色的壁畫所反射出來的光。
我們的凝視潛入海底，我們的眼睛仰望
看見騷動的水中那破碎的光。
495.　我們看到光，我們不知道光從哪裡來。
　　看不見的光喲，我們因榮耀讚美祢！

Choruses From "The Rock"
1934

In our rhythm of earthly life we tire of light. We are glad
when the day ends, when the play ends; and ecstasy is too
much pain.

We are children quickly tired: children who are up in the
night and fall asleep as the rocket is fired; and the day is long
for work or play.

We tire of distraction or concentration, we sleep and are glad
to sleep,

500. Controlled by the rhythm of blood and the day and the night
and the seasons.

And we must extinguish the candle, put out the light and
relight it;

Forever must quench, forever relight the flame.

Therefore we thank Thee for our little light, that is dappled
with shadow.

We thank Thee who hast moved us to building, to finding, to
forming at the ends of our fingers and beams of our eyes.

505. And when we have built an altar to the Invisible Light, we
may set thereon the little lights for which our bodily vision is
made.

And we thank Thee that darkness reminds us of light.

O Light Invisible, we give Thee thanks for Thy great glory!

「磐石」的合唱
1934

　　在這地上生活的律動中，我們對光感到疲倦。當一天
結束，當遊戲結束時我們感到高興；狂喜有太多的痛苦。

我們是容易累的小孩：晚上睡不著，放了煙火就睡覺的小
孩；不論工作或遊戲白天都嫌太長。

我們因心緒散亂或精神集中而疲倦，我們睡覺，而且高興
睡覺，

500. 受著血液、晝夜與季節的律動支配。

我們必須吹熄蠟燭，熄了之後再點燃；

必須永遠熄滅，永遠重燃火焰。

因此我們感謝祢，為我們那影子斑駁的渺小的光。

我們感謝祢，感動我們用自己的手指和眼睛的光芒建造、
尋找和形成。

505. 當我們為**看不見的光**建造祭壇完成時，我們會在那上面點
起我們的身體看得見的渺小的光。

黑暗使我們想起光，因此我們感謝祢。

看不見的光喲，我們因祢那偉大的榮光而感謝祢！

1　譯註：基督教《聖經》中多處提到「磐石」，例如《馬太福音》18 章 16 節：
　　「我還告訴你，你是彼得，我要把我的教會建造在這磐石上；陰間的權柄（權
　　柄：原文是門），不能勝過他 。」

Four Quartets

四重奏

·1936·

Four Quartets
1936

Burnt Norton

No.1 of 'Four Quartets'

τοῦ λόγου δὲ ἐόντος ξυνοῦ ζώουσιν οἱ πολλοί
ὡς ἰδίαν ἔχοντες φρόνησιν.

ὁδὸς ἄνω κάτω μία καὶ ὡυτή.
——Diels: *Die Fragmente der Vorsokratiker (Herakleitos).*

I

Time present and time past
Are both perhaps present in time future,
And time future contained in time past.
If all time is eternally present
All time is unredeemable
What might have been is an abstraction
Remaining a perpetual possibility
Only in a world of speculation.
What might have been and what has been
Point to one end, which is always present.

四重奏
1936

焚毀的諾頓 [1]

〈四重奏〉之一

雖說「道」是萬人共通的原則，大多數人活著似乎都有
自我的理解力。

上行道與下行道同是一條路。

—— Diels 編：《蘇格拉底時代哲學者的片斷》

I

5.　時間現在與時間過去
　　二者或許存在於時間未來，
　　而時間未來包含在時間過去中。
　　假如一切時間永遠存在
　　一切時間都無可贖回。

10.　可能曾經有過的是一種抽象
　　留下永遠的可能性，
　　只存在於思索的世界中。
　　可能曾經有過的，以及曾經有過的
　　指向一個終點，那永遠是現在。

Four Quartets
1936

15. Footfalls echo in the memory

Down the passage which we did not take

Towards the door we never opened

Into the rose-garden. My words echo

Thus, in your mind.

20.   But to what purpose

Disturbing the dust on a bowl of rose-leaves

I do not know.

              Other echoes

Inhabit the garden. Shall we follow?

25. Quick, said the bird, find them, find them,

Round the corner. Through the first gate,

Into our first world, shall we follow

The deception of the thrush? Into our first world.

There they were, dignified, invisible,

30. Moving without pressure, over the dead leaves,

In the autumn heat, through the vibrant air,

And the bird called, in response to

The unheard music hidden in the shrubbery,

And the unseen eyebeam crossed, for the roses

35. Had the look of flowers that are looked at.

There they were as our guests, accepted and accepting.

So we moved, and they, in a formal pattern,

四重奏
1936

15. 足音在記憶中迴響
沿著我們沒走過的通道
向著我們沒開過的門
進入玫瑰花園。我的話
如此，回響在你的心中。

20. 　　　　　　但是為了什麼目的
騷擾一盆玫瑰葉上的塵埃
我不知道。
　　　　其他種種回響
棲息在這花園裡。我們跟著去嗎？

25. 快快，小鳥說，把它們找出來，把它們找出來，
就在那拐角兒。穿過第一道門，
進入我們的最初世界，我們要跟隨
那隻畫眉的欺矇嗎？進入我們的最初世界。
就在那兒，顯得高貴，但看不見，

30. 沒有壓力地移動，越過枯葉
在秋暖中，穿過顫動的空氣，
於是小鳥叫了，應和著
灌木中隱然聽不見的音樂
而看不見的眼神交叉，因為玫瑰

35. 具有引人觀賞的花容。
就在那裡，像我們的客人，招待也被招待。
於是我們行動，他們也一樣，以正式的模樣，

Four Quartets
1936

Along the empty alley, into the box circle,
To look down into the drained pool.
40   Dry the pool, dry concrete, brown edged,
And the pool was filled with water out of sunlight,
And the lotos rose, quietly, quietly,
The surface glittered out of heart of light,
And they were behind us, reflected in the pool.
45.   Then a cloud passed, and the pool was empty.
Go, said the bird, for the leaves were full of children,
Hidden excitedly, containing laughter.
Go, go, go, said the bird: human kind
Cannot bear very much reality.
50.   Time past and time future
What might have been and what has been
Point to one end, which is always present.

II

Garlic and sapphires in the mud
Clot the bedded axle-tree.
55.   The trilling wire in the blood
Sings below inveterate scars
Appeasing long forgotten wars.

四重奏
1936

　　沿著無人的小路，走進黃楊樹的圓圈，
　　向下望著沒有水的池塘。
40. 乾涸的池塘，乾涸的水泥，褐色的邊緣，
　　而池塘充滿陽光照射的水，
　　而水蓮升起，靜靜地，靜靜地，
　　池面在陽光的中心閃耀著，
　　這些都在我們背後，映照在池塘裡。
45. 然後一片雲飄過，而池塘空空。
　　去吧，小鳥說，到那邊，葉蔭下滿是小孩，
　　興奮地隱藏著，忍住笑聲。
　　去吧，去吧，去吧，小鳥說，人類
　　不堪忍受太多的現實。
50. 時間過去與時間未來
　　可能曾經有過的以及曾經有過的
　　指向一個終點，那永遠是現在。

II

　　泥沼中的大蒜與藍寶石
　　凝結在被埋置的輪軸上。
55. 血液中顫動的金絲
　　在痼疾的傷痕底下歌唱
　　平息久被遺忘的爭戰。

Four Quartets
1936

The dance along the artery
The circulation of the lymph
60. Are figured in the drift of stars
Ascend to summer in the tree
We move above the moving tree
In light upon the figured leaf
And hear upon the sodden floor
65. Below, the boarhound and the boar
Pursue their pattern as before
But reconciled among the stars.

At the still point of the turning world. Neither flesh nor
fleshless;
Neither from nor towards; at the still point, there the dance is,
70. But neither arrest nor movement. And do not call it fixity,
Where past and future are gathered. Neither movement from
nor towards,
Neither ascent nor decline. Except for the point, the still point,
There would be no dance, and there is only the dance.
I can only say, there we have been: but I cannot say where.
75. And I cannot say, how long, for that is to place it in time.

The inner freedom from the practical desire,

四重奏
1936

沿著動脈的舞蹈

淋巴腺的循環

60. 在群星的漂移中成形

攀升到樹中的夏天

我們移動在移動的樹上方

在有花紋模樣的葉子上的光中

且在潮濕的地面底下

65. 聽到野豬獵犬和野豬

爭相追逐自己的模型一如從前

但在繁星中獲得了和解。

在流轉的世界中那靜點。不是肉體也不是非肉體；

不是來自也不是歸向；在那靜止點，舞蹈就在那裡，

70. 但不是停止也不是移動。那不叫做固定，

在那裡過去與未來集合在一起。移動不是來自那裡，也不

是歸向那裡，

不是上升也不是下降。除了那個點，那個靜止點之外

不會有舞蹈，因而只有舞蹈在那裡。

我只能說：我們一直在那裡：但我說不出在哪裡。

75. 而且我說不出，已有多久，因那樣也就將它置於時間中。

來自現實欲望的內在自由，

Four Quartets
1936

The release from action and suffering, release from the inner

And the outer compulsion, yet surrounded

By a grace of sense, a white light still and moving,

80. Erhebung without motion, concentration

Without elimination, both a new world

And the old made explicit, understood

In the completion of its partial ecstasy,

The resolution of its partial horror.

85. Yet the enchainment of past and future

Woven in the weakness of the changing body,

Protects mankind from heaven and damnation

Which flesh cannot endure.

                          Time past and time future

90. Allow but a little consciousness.

To be conscious is not to be in time

But only in time can the moment in the rose-garden,

The moment in the arbour where the rain beat,

The moment in the draughty church at smokefall

95. Be remembered; involved with past and future.

Only through time time is conquered.

四重奏
1936

從行動與受苦中獲得的解脫，從內在

與外在強迫中獲得的解脫，然而

由於感官的福報，被靜止而移動的白光所包圍，

80. 沒有動作的高揚，沒有排除的

專注，讓新的和舊的世界

兩者都變明確，可以被理解，

在部分狂喜的完成中，

部分恐怖的解除中。

85. 然而過去與未來的連結

由身體無常的弱點所織成

保護著人類免遭天堂和地獄的詛咒

那是肉體所難以忍受的。

　　　　　　　　　　時間過去與時間未來

90. 只容許些微的意識。

意識的存在不存在時間中

但是只有在時間中，在玫瑰園中的瞬間

在雨打園亭中的瞬間，

在下霧時通風的教堂中的瞬間

95. 才被人想起；涉及到過去與未來。

只有透過時間，時間才被征服。

Four Quartets
1936

III

Here is a place of disaffection

Time before and time after

In a dim light: neither daylight

100. Investing form with lucid stillness

Turning shadow into transient beauty

With slow rotation suggesting permanence

Nor darkness to purify the soul

Emptying the sensual with deprivation

105. Cleansing affection from the temporal.

Neither plenitude nor vacancy. Only a flicker

Over the strained time-ridden faces

Distracted from distraction by distraction

Filled with fancies and empty of meaning

110. Tumid apathy with no concentration

Men and bits of paper, whirled by the cold wind

That blows before and after time,

Wind in and out of unwholesome lungs

Time before and time after.

115. Eructation of unhealthy souls

Into the faded air, the torpid

Driven on the wind that sweeps the gloomy hills of London,

四重奏
1936

III

這裡是一個憤懣的地方

時間以前與時間以後

在朦朧的光中：既不是日光

100. 以明亮的靜止附與形體

以暗示久遠的緩慢旋轉

將暗影轉成無常的美，

也不是藉以淨化靈魂的黑闇，

以剝奪清空官能的世界

105. 清洗感情中現世的一切。

既不是充實也不是空虛。只是一閃

掠過時間驅使下緊繃的臉

因分心而心煩意亂的那些臉

充滿幻想和意義的空虛

110. 無所專注的腫起的冷漠無感

人們與報紙碎片，被冷風吹起

在時間之前和時間之後迴舞，

不健全的肺部所吐納的風

在過去和未來的時間中。

115. 不健康的靈魂的噯氣

吐入稀薄的空氣中，那些麻木不仁的

隨風吹起，掃過倫敦陰鬱的山丘，

Hampstead and Clerkenwell, Campden and Putney,

Highgate, Primrose and Ludgate. Not here

120. Not here the darkness, in this twittering world.

Descend lower, descend only

Into the world of perpetual solitude,

World not world, but that which is not world,

Internal darkness, deprivation

125. And destitution of all property,

Desiccation of the world of sense,

Evacuation of the world of fancy,

Inoperancy of the world of spirit;

This is the one way, and the other

130. Is the same, not in movement

But abstention from movement; while the world moves

In appetency, on its metalled ways

Of time past and time future.

IV

Time and the bell have buried the day,

135. The black cloud carries the sun away.

Will the sunflower turn to us, will the clematis

四重奏
1936

漢普斯鐵和克拉肯威爾，肯普頓和帕特尼，
海格特，普林露色和路德格特。
120. 黑闇不在這裡，不在這嘈嚷不休的世界。

　　再往下走，一路往下
向著永恆的孤獨世界，
非世界的世界，但那不是世界，
向著內部的黑闇，
125. 向著所有財產的剝奪和貧乏，
向著感官世界的枯竭，
向著幻想世界的撤離，
向著精神世界的癱瘓；
這是一個方法，另一個
130. 也是一樣，不在動中
而在動的戒絕中；然而這世界移動著
在欲望的本能中，在自己的
時間過去與時間未來的軌道上。

　　　　　　　IV

時間與晚鐘埋葬了一日，
135. 黑雲帶走了太陽。
向日葵會轉向我們嗎，鐵線蓮

Four Quartets
1936

Stray down, bend to us; tendril and spray

Clutch and cling?

Chill

140. Fingers of yew be curled

Down on us? After the kingfisher's wing

Has answered light to light, and is silent, the light is still

At the still point of the turning world.

V

Words move, music moves

145. Only in time; but that which is only living

Can only die. Words, after speech, reach

Into the silence. Only by the form, the pattern,

Can words or music reach

The stillness, as a Chinese jar still

150. Moves perpetually in its stillness.

Not the stillness of the violin, while the note lasts,

Not that only, but the co-existence,

Or say that the end precedes the beginning,

And the end and the beginning were always there

155. Before the beginning and after the end.

And all is always now. Words strain,

四重奏
1936

會迷途，彎向我們；藤蔓和細枝
會緊抓纏住我們嗎？
冷冷的
140. 紫杉樹的手指會捲曲
垂向我們嗎？在翡翠鳥的羽翼
一一回應了光而沉默之後，光靜止
在這輪轉世界的靜止點上。

V

言語移動，音樂移動
145. 只在時間中；但是只有活的東西
才能死去。言語，在說出之後
到達沉默。只有藉著形式和樣型，
言語與音樂才能
到達靜止，像靜止的中國花瓶
150. 永遠在靜止中移動。
只要餘音還在，就不是梵哦玲的靜止，
不僅如此，而且是共存，
或者說結束存在於開始之前，
而結束和開始恆常在那裡
155. 在開始之前，在結束之後。
而一切恆是現在。言語緊繃，

Four Quartets
1936

Crack and sometimes break, under the burden,

Under the tension, slip, slide, perish,

Decay with imprecision, will not stay in place,

160. Will not stay still. Shrieking voices

Scolding, mocking, or merely chattering,

Always assail them. The Word in the desert

Is most attacked by voices of temptation,

The crying shadow in the funeral dance,

165. The loud lament of the disconsolate chimera.

The detail of the pattern is movement,

As in the figure of the ten stairs.

Desire itself is movement

Not in itself desirable;

170. Love is itself unmoving,

Only the cause and end of movement,

Timeless, and undesiring

Except in the aspect of time

Caught in the form of limitation

175. Between un-being and being.

Sudden in a shaft of sunlight

Even while the dust moves

There rises the hidden laughter

四重奏
1936

有時震裂或折斷，在重荷之下，
張力之下溜動，滑倒，淪喪，
因不精確而腐敗，不會停留在一處，
160. 不會靜止不動。尖叫的聲音
責罵，嘲笑，或只是閑聊，
經常攻擊言語。曠野中主的話
最受誘惑的聲音襲擊，
葬禮的舞蹈中哭泣的影子，
165. 哀傷的怪獸高聲的慟哭。

　　　樣型的細節是動，
有如十級階梯的形態。
欲望本身是動
它本身並不令人欲望；
170. 愛本身是不動的
只是動的原因和目的，
超時間，而且非欲望的，
除非以時間的樣相
以具有侷限性的形態
175. 被夾在非存在與存在之間。
突然在一柱陽光中
甚至當塵埃移動時
隱藏在葉叢中

Of children in the foliage

180. Quick now, here, now, always—

Ridiculous the waste sad time

Stretching before and after.

四重奏
1936

一群小孩的笑聲揚起，

180.　現在趕快，這裡，現在，隨時——

荒謬的是那徒然悲傷的時間

在之前和之後不斷延伸。

1　譯註：焚毀的諾頓指位於英格蘭北諾頓 Gloucestershire 郡的一座英國鄉間住宅，有玫瑰園遺址。

East Coker

No.2 of 'Four Quartets'

I

In my beginning is my end. In succession

Houses rise and fall, crumble, are extended,

Are removed, destroyed, restored, or in their place

Is an open field, or a factory, or a by-pass.

5. Old stone to new building, old timber to new fires,

Old fires to ashes, and ashes to the earth

Which is already flesh, fur and faeces,

Bone of man and beast, cornstalk and leaf.

Houses live and die: there is a time for building

10. And a time for living and for generation

And a time for the wind to break the loosened pan

And to shake the wainscot where the field-mouse trots

And to shake the tattered arras woven with a silent motto.

In my beginning is my end. Now the light falls

15. Across the open field, leaving the deep lane

四重奏
1936

東科克 [1]
〈四重奏〉之二

I

　　我的開始裡有我的結束。連續不斷地
　　房子建起又倒塌，粉碎，被擴建
　　被移走，破壞，重建，或者在原地
　　變成曠野，或工廠，或開路。
5.　從舊石頭到新建築，舊木材到新火焰，
　　舊火焰到灰燼，而灰燼到大地
　　地上早有肉身，皮毛和糞便，
　　人和動物的骸骨，玉米稈和樹葉。
　　房屋活過，死去：有建造的時間
10.　有活存的時間，跨過世代
　　有時間讓風吹破鬆懈的嵌板，
　　震動野鼠奔竄的壁板，
　　震動掛在壁上織有沉默箴言的破毯。

　　　我的開始裡有我的結束。這時陽光落下
15.　橫過曠野，使得在樹枝的遮蔭下的

Four Quartets
1936

Shuttered with branches, dark in the afternoon,

Where you lean against a bank while a van passes,

And the deep lane insists on the direction

Into the village, in the electric heat

20. Hypnotised. In a warm haze the sultry light

Is absorbed, not refracted, by grey stone.

The dahlias sleep in the empty silence.

Wait for the early owl.

                    In that open field

25. If you do not come too close, if you do not come too close,

On a summer midnight, you can hear the music

Of the weak pipe and the little drum

And see them dancing around the bonfire

The association of man and woman

30. In daunsinge, signifying matrimonie—

A dignified and commodiois sacrament.

Two and two, necessarye coniunction,

Holding eche other by the hand or the arm

Whiche betokeneth concorde. Round and round the fire

35. Leaping through the flames, or joined in circles,

Rustically solemn or in rustic laughter

Lifting heavy feet in clumsy shoes,

Earth feet, loam feet, lifted in country mirth

四重奏
1936

深長小路，在午後顯得陰暗，

在那兒你靠向土堤，當一輛卡車經過，

而濃蔭的小路堅持伸向

村落的方向，處於電熱的

20. 催眠狀態。在暖暖的霧靄中

悶熱的陽光被灰岩吸收，而不是折射。

大麗花在空虛的無聲中沉睡。

等待早來的貓頭鷹。

在那原野中

25. 假如你不走得太近，假如你不走得太近，

在一個夏日夜半，你可以聽到

微弱的笛聲和小鼓的音樂，

且看見他們圍著篝火舞蹈

男女互相交往

30. 兩人共舞，意味著結婚——

莊嚴而綽約的聖禮。

兩兩成雙，天作之合，

手牽手　臂交臂

表示琴瑟和諧。圍著繞著篝火

35. 躍過火焰，或加入繞圈，

鄉土氣的莊嚴或在純樸的笑聲中

舉起笨重的腳，穿著笨拙的鞋子

沾泥的腳，沃土的腳，在鄉村的歡樂中舉起

Four Quartets
1936

Mirth of those long since under earth
40. Nourishing the corn. Keeping time,
Keeping the rhythm in their dancing
As in their living in the living seasons—
The time of the seasons and the constellations
The time of milking and the time of harvest
45. The time of the coupling of man and woman
And that of beasts. Feet rising and falling
Eating and drinking. Dung and death.

Dawn points, and another day
Prepares for heat and silence. Out at sea the dawn wind
50. Wrinkles and slides. I am here
Or there, or elsewhere. In my beginning.

II

What is the late November doing
With the disturbance of the spring
And creatures of the summer heat,
55. And snowdrops writhing under feet
And hollyhocks that aim too high
Red into grey and tumble down

四重奏
1936

那是長久以來在地底下

40. 滋養穀物那些人的歡笑。跟著節拍

跟著他們舞蹈的節奏

如他們跟著生活季節的生活

季節和星座的時節

擠奶的時節，收穫的時節

45. 男人和女人交媾的時節

還有動物的時節。腳舉起又落下。

飲食男女。糞便和死亡。

　　　東方既白，又是另一天

為暑熱和無言作準備。在那海上黎明的風

50. 吹起皺紋滑行。我在這兒

或在那兒，或者哪兒也不在。在我的開始中。

II

歲時十一月末，

有何關聯：與春天的騷動

以及盛夏的生物，

55. 以及在腳下折騰的雪花蓮、

以及嚮往過高、由紅轉灰

而墜落的蜀葵，

Late roses filled with early snow?
Thunder rolled by the rolling stars
60. Simulates triumphal cars
Deployed in constellated wars
Scorpion fights against the Sun
Until the Sun and Moon go down
Comets weep and Leonids fly
65. Hunt the heavens and the plains
Whirled in a vortex that shall bring
The world to that destructive fire
Which burns before the ice-cap reigns.

That was a way of putting it—not very satisfactory:
70. A periphrastic study in a worn-out poetical fashion,
Leaving one still with the intolerable wrestle
With words and meanings. The poetry does not matter.
It was not (to start again) what one had expected.
What was to be the value of the long looked forward to,
75. Long hoped for calm, the autumnal serenity
And the wisdom of age? Had they deceived us
Or deceived themselves, the quiet-voiced elders,
Bequeathing us merely a receipt for deceit?
The serenity only a deliberate hebetude,

四重奏
1936

沾滿初雪晚開的玫瑰？

因迴旋的流星而迴響的雷聲

60.　猶如凱旋的戰車

在星際大戰中所展開的

天蠍座與太陽相搏

直到日落，月沉

彗星哭泣而獅子座流星雨橫飛

65.　獵尋天宇和原野

捲入一個漩渦，將這世界

帶向毀滅的火焰

不斷燃燒直到冰河統領一切。

　　　可以這麼說──雖不滿意：

70.　陳腐詩論的迂言法研究，

仍然留給人、與字句和意義

難以忍受的角力。這種詩無關重要。

這不是（再說一遍）人們所曾期待的。

長久期待的東西，

75.　長久希望的平靜，秋天的安祥

以及老年的智慧，會有什麼價值？

說話低聲的長者矇騙了我們，或是矇騙了他們自己，

而遺留給我們的只是受騙的收據？

安祥只是故意的遲鈍，

Four Quartets
1936

80. The wisdom only the knowledge of dead secrets
Useless in the darkness into which they peered
Or from which they turned their eyes. There is, it seems to us,
At best, only a limited value
In the knowledge derived from experience.

85. The knowledge imposes a pattern, and falsifies,
For the pattern is new in every moment
And every moment is a new and shocking
Valuation of all we have been. We are only undeceived
Of that which, deceiving, could no longer harm.

90. In the middle, not only in the middle of the way
But all the way, in a dark wood, in a bramble,
On the edge of a grimpen, where is no secure foothold,
And menaced by monsters, fancy lights,
Risking enchantment. Do not let me hear

95. Of the wisdom of old men, but rather of their folly,
Their fear of fear and frenzy, their fear of possession,
Of belonging to another, or to others, or to God.
The only wisdom we can hope to acquire
Is the wisdom of humility: humility is endless.

100. The houses are all gone under the sea.

四重奏
1936

80. 智慧只是已死秘密的知識
除非是在他們窺探進去的黑暗中
或是從中他們把眼睛轉開。在我們看來
至多，只是有限的價值
如果知識來自經驗。

85. 知識制約樣式，而且偽造事實，
因為樣式時時刻刻在更新
而且每一時刻是一個新而驚人的、
對我們至今一切的評估。我們只是，在受騙中
從不會再有傷害的迷濛中覺醒。

90. 居於中間，不只是在道的中間
而且是一路上，在暗林中，在荊棘中，
在沒有安全立足點的沼澤邊緣，
而且受到怪獸，幻光的恐嚇，
冒著妖術魅惑的危險。不要讓我聽見

95. 老人的智慧，寧可聽他們的愚行，
他們對恐懼和瘋狂的恐懼，他們對占有的恐懼，
占有屬於另一個人，或別人的，或者上帝的。
我們所能希望獲得的唯一智慧
是謙虛的智慧：謙虛無止境。

100. 所有的房子都消失在海底下。

The dancers are all gone under the hill.

III

O dark dark dark. They all go into the dark,
The vacant interstellar spaces, the vacant into the vacant,
The captains, merchant bankers, eminent men of letters,
105. The generous patrons of art, the statesmen and the rulers,
Distinguished civil servants, chairmen of many committees,
Industrial lords and petty contractors, all go into the dark,
And dark the Sun and Moon, and the Almanach de Gotha
And the Stock Exchange Gazette, the Directory of Directors,
110. And cold the sense and lost the motive of action.
And we all go with them, into the silent funeral,
Nobody's funeral, for there is no one to bury.
I said to my soul, be still, and let the dark come upon you
Which shall be the darkness of God. As, in a theatre,
115. The lights are extinguished, for the scene to be changed
With a hollow rumble of wings, with a movement of darkness
on darkness,
And we know that the hills and the trees, the distant
panorama
And the bold imposing facade are all being rolled away—

四重奏
1936

所有的舞者都消失在山丘下。

III

呵　黑暗黑暗黑暗。一切陷入黑暗
空闊的星際空間，從空缺到空缺
船長，商品銀行家，傑出的文人，
105.　藝術的慷慨恩主，政治家和統治者，
傑出的公僕，委員會的主席諸公，
工業的大咖和小承包商，都陷入黑暗
而日月黯然，以及歐洲皇族家譜
以及股票交易公報，董事名錄
110.　而感知冰冷，失去了行動的動機。
而我們跟他們一起走進沉默的葬禮，
不是誰的葬禮，因為沒有人埋葬。
我對我的靈魂說，稍安勿躁，讓黑暗找上你
那將是上帝的幽闇。有如，在劇院，
115.　燈光熄滅，以便換景
以振翅的空洞聲響，以黑暗疊加黑暗的動作，
而我們知道山崗和樹木，遠處的全景
以及膽大壯觀的正面都會一一被捲走——

Or as, when an underground train, in the tube, stops too long
between stations

120. And the conversation rises and slowly fades into silence
And you see behind every face the mental emptiness deepen
Leaving only the growing terror of nothing to think about;
Or when, under ether, the mind is conscious but conscious of
nothing—
I said to my soul, be still, and wait without hope

125. For hope would be hope for the wrong thing; wait without
love,
For love would be love of the wrong thing; there is yet faith
But the faith and the love and the hope are all in the waiting.
Wait without thought, for you are not ready for thought:
So the darkness shall be the light, and the stillness the
dancing.

130.   Whisper of running streams, and winter lightning.
The wild thyme unseen and the wild strawberry,
The laughter in the garden, echoed ecstasy
Not lost, but requiring, pointing to the agony
Of death and birth.

135.   You say I am repeating
Something I have said before. I shall say it again.

四重奏
1936

或者如，當地下鐵路的列車穿行，在車站之間停留太久
120. 而會話揚起又慢慢消失於沉默
而你在每一張臉後看見精神空虛加深
只留下逐漸滋長的、無話可說的恐懼；
或者，恍惚間，精神雖有意識卻什麼也沒意識到——
我對我的靈魂說，稍安勿躁，等待而不帶希望
125. 因為所希望的會是錯誤的希望；等待而沒有愛
因為所愛的會是錯誤的愛；雖然還有信仰
可是信仰、愛和希望都在等待中。
等待而沒有思想，因為你還沒準備好思想；
於是黑暗將成為光，而靜止成為舞姿。

130. 　　　溪流的細語，以及冬日的閃電。
看不見的野百里香和野草莓，
花園裡的笑聲，回響的狂喜
不是迷失，而是要求，指向
死與生的苦惱。
135. 　　　　　　　你說我一再重複
我以前說過的事。我要再說一次。

Shall I say it again? In order to arrive there,

To arrive where you are, to get from where you are not,

    You must go by a way wherein there is no ecstasy.

140. In order to arrive at what you do not know

    You must go by a way which is the way of ignorance.

In order to possess what you do not possess

    You must go by the way of dispossession.

In order to arrive at what you are not

145.   You must go through the way in which you are not.

And what you do not know is the only thing you know

And what you own is what you do not own

And where you are is where you are not.

IV

The wounded surgeon plies the steel

150. That questions the distempered part;

Beneath the bleeding hands we feel

The sharp compassion of the healer's art

Resolving the enigma of the fever chart.

四重奏
1936

我該再說一次？為了到達那兒，

到達你在的地方，從你不在的地方出發，

　　你必須沿著沒有狂喜的一條路。

140.　為了到達你所不知道的

　　　你必須沿著一條路、一條無知的路。

為了擁有你所沒擁有的

　　　你必須沿著放棄擁有的道路。

為了到達你不存在的地方

145.　　你必須經過你不存在的道路。

而你所不知道的卻是你唯一知道的

而你所有的是你所沒有的

而你所在的地方是你不在的地方。

IV

受傷的外科醫生使用鋼刀

150.　追問有毛病的部位；

在流血的手底下，我們感受到

治癒者的醫術，以銳利的慈愛

解決了體溫表的謎語。

Four Quartets
1936

Our only health is the disease

155. If we obey the dying nurse

Whose constant care is not to please

But to remind of our, and Adam's curse,

And that, to be restored, our sickness must grow worse.

The whole earth is our hospital

160. Endowed by the ruined millionaire,

Wherein, if we do well, we shall

Die of the absolute paternal care

That will not leave us, but prevents us everywhere.

The chill ascends from feet to knees,

165. The fever sings in mental wires.

If to be warmed, then I must freeze

And quake in frigid purgatorial fires

Of which the flame is roses, and the smoke is briars.

The dripping blood our only drink,

170. The bloody flesh our only food:

In spite of which we like to think

That we are sound, substantial flesh and blood—

Again, in spite of that, we call this Friday good.

四重奏
1936

我們唯一的健康是疾病
155. 假如我們聽從臨死護士的話
　　她的加護照顧不是為了安慰我們
　　而是提醒我們，亞當的詛咒，
　　甚至為了恢復，我們的病情必須更加惡化。

　　整個地球是我們的醫院
160. 得到破產的百萬富人的捐贈
　　在這醫院裡，假如一切順利，我們將會
　　為照顧不顧一切的父親而死去
　　因他絕不離棄我們，而是到處保護我們。

　　惡寒從腳底上升到膝蓋，
165. 發燒在腦髓的鐵線中歌唱。
　　為了取暖，那麼我必須凍僵
　　在嚴寒的煉獄火中顫抖，
　　那火焰是野玫瑰，煙是荊棘。

　　滴淌的血是我們唯一的飲料，
170. 沾血的肉是我們唯一的食物：
　　儘管如此，我們寧可認為
　　我們是健全而有實質的血肉之軀——
　　而且，儘管如此，我們認為這是耶穌受難的聖週五。

Four Quartets
1936

V

So here I am, in the middle way, having had twenty years—
175. Twenty years largely wasted, the years of l'entre deux guerres
Trying to use words, and every attempt
Is a wholly new start, and a different kind of failure
Because one has only learnt to get the better of words
For the thing one no longer has to say, or the way in which
180. One is no longer disposed to say it. And so each venture
Is a new beginning, a raid on the inarticulate
With shabby equipment always deteriorating
In the general mess of imprecision of feeling,
Undisciplined squads of emotion. And what there is to conquer
185. By strength and submission, has already been discovered
Once or twice, or several times, by men whom one cannot hope
To emulate—but there is no competition—
There is only the fight to recover what has been lost
And found and lost again and again: and now, under conditions
190. That seem unpropitious. But perhaps neither gain nor loss.
For us, there is only the trying. The rest is not our business.

四重奏
1936

V

於是我在這裡，在中間，已有二十年——

175. 大多浪費的二十年，在兩次戰爭之間的歲月

每次企圖使用語言

都是全新的開始，不一樣的失敗

因為人們剛學到較會使用語言時

卻發現要說的已不需要說了，

180. 或者已不是準備要說的。因此每一次冒險

都是新的開始，對不善辭令的攻擊

卻以一再退步的簡陋裝備

陷入感情無法準確表達的一般混亂中

未經訓練的情緒的小部隊。

185. 況且需要以強勢和順從征服的，已被發現，一再地甚至好

幾次，正是

人們不能寄望

對抗——可是沒有競爭——的那些人。

只有奮力恢復一再失去

而又找到的東西：而當今似乎處於

190. 不吉利的情勢。但也許無關得失。

對我們，只有盡力而為。其餘的不關我們的事。

Home is where one starts from. As we grow older

The world becomes stranger, the pattern more complicated

Of dead and living. Not the intense moment

195. Isolated, with no before and after,

But a lifetime burning in every moment

And not the lifetime of one man only

But of old stones that cannot be deciphered.

There is a time for the evening under starlight,

200. A time for the evening under lamplight

(The evening with the photograph album).

Love is most nearly itself

When here and now cease to matter

Old men ought to be explorers

205. Here or there does not matter

We must be still and still moving

Into another intensity

For a further union, a deeper communion

Through the dark cold and the empty desolation,

210. The wave cry, the wind cry, the vast waters

Of the petrel and the porpoise. In my end is my beginning.

四重奏
1936

家是一個人出發的地方。隨著年歲增加
世界越來越疏遠，而生與死的樣式
更加複雜。沒有緊張的時刻
195. 孤零零的，沒有過去也沒有未來
而是一生時時刻刻都在燃燒
而且不只是一個人的一生
而是難以解讀的古代石碑的一生。
既有星光下夜晚的時刻
200. 也有燈光下夜晚的時刻
（照相簿的夜晚）。
愛最接近它本身
一旦此時此地不再是問題。
老人應該是探險者
205. 這裡或那裡不是問題
我們必須靜止而靜止移動
進入另一緊張
為了進一步的融合，更深的靈契
透過黑暗寒冷和空虛的孤寂，
210. 浪在喊叫，風在喊叫，海燕和海豚的
無涯海原。我的結束就是我的開始。

1　譯註：東科克（East Coker）是位於英國英格蘭西南部的薩默塞特郡
　　（Somerset）的一個鄉村，北臨布里斯托灣。

Four Quartets
1936

The Dry Salvages [1]

No.3 of 'Four Quartets'

I

I do not know much about gods; but I think that the river

Is a strong brown god—sullen, untamed and intractable,

Patient to some degree, at first recognised as a frontier;

Useful, untrustworthy, as a conveyor of commerce;

5. Then only a problem confronting the builder of bridges.

The problem once solved, the brown god is almost forgotten

By the dwellers in cities—ever, however, implacable.

Keeping his seasons and rages, destroyer, reminder

Of what men choose to forget. Unhonoured, unpropitiated

10. By worshippers of the machine, but waiting, watching and

waiting.

His rhythm was present in the nursery bedroom,

In the rank ailanthus of the April dooryard,

In the smell of grapes on the autumn table,

And the evening circle in the winter gaslight.

四重奏
1936

岣岸礁岩

〈四重奏〉之三

I

我對異神所知不多；但我認為河流

是一個強大的褐色的神——繃著臉，倔強不馴，難以對付的，

有幾分的耐性，最初被認為是一個開疆者；

有用的，不值得信任的，像商業的運送者；

5. 後來只是造橋者所面臨的一個問題。

問題一旦解決，褐色的神就幾乎

讓城市的居民給遺忘了——可是永遠記恨在心。

忘不了自己的季節和憤怒，一個破壞者，

提醒人們寧願忘卻的事情。未受機器崇拜者的尊崇，

10. 得不到慰藉，只是等待，眼睜睜地等待。

河流的節奏存在於幼兒的臥室

於四月前庭繁茂的椿樹，

於秋日餐桌上葡萄的氣味，

以及冬季瓦斯燈下的晚會。

15. The river is within us, the sea is all about us;

The sea is the land's edge also, the granite

Into which it reaches, the beaches where it tosses

Its hints of earlier and other creation:

The starfish, the horseshoe crab, the whale's backbone;

20. The pools where it offers to our curiosity

The more delicate algae and the sea anemone.

It tosses up our losses, the torn seine,

The shattered lobsterpot, the broken oar

And the gear of foreign dead men. The sea has many voices,

25. Many gods and many voices.

                           The salt is on the briar rose,

The fog is in the fir trees.

                               The sea howl

And the sea yelp, are different voices

30. Often together heard: the whine in the rigging,

The menace and caress of wave that breaks on water,

The distant rote in the granite teeth,

And the wailing warning from the approaching headland

Are all sea voices, and the heaving groaner

35. Rounded homewards, and the seagull:

And under the oppression of the silent fog

四重奏
1936

15. 　　河流在我們體內，海包圍著我們；
海也是陸地的邊沿，
海所滲透的花崗岩，它在海灘拋擲
令人聯想到創世及其他創造物：
海星，馬蹄蟹，鯨魚的背骨；
20. 水塘提供給我們的好奇心
更微妙的藻類以及海葵。
海翻起我們失去的東西，扯破的大漁網，
破碎的捕蝦簍，斷折的划槳
以及死了的外地人的衣物。海有許多聲音，
25. 許多神和許多聲音。

　　　　　　鹽在荊棘的玫瑰上，
霧氣在樅樹林間。
　　　　海的嚎哮
以及海的叫喊，是不同的聲音
30. 常常聽起來混在一起：索具的哀鳴
破浪在海上激起的威嚇和愛撫
在遠方一再拍打花崗岩牙齒的浪濤，
以及接近陸岬發出警告的哀號
這些都是海的聲音，而起伏的吹鳴浮標
35. 轉向家鄉，以及海鷗：
以及在靜默的霧氣壓迫下

The tolling bell

Measures time not our time, rung by the unhurried

Ground swell, a time

40. Older than the time of chronometers, older

Than time counted by anxious worried women

Lying awake, calculating the future,

Trying to unweave, unwind, unravel

And piece together the past and the future,

45. Between midnight and dawn, when the past is all deception,

The future futureless, before the morning watch

When time stops and time is never ending;

And the ground swell, that is and was from the beginning,

Clangs

50. The bell.

II

Where is there an end of it, the soundless wailing,

The silent withering of autumn flowers

Dropping their petals and remaining motionless;

Where is there an end to the drifting wreckage,

55. The prayer of the bone on the beach, the unprayable

Prayer at the calamitous annunciation?

四重奏
1936

悠揚的鐘聲

計量時間，那不是我們的時間；

海底捲起的巨浪緩緩移動，它所敲響的時間，

40. 比計時器的時間更古老

比憂心如焚的女人所思量的時間更古老

當她清醒地躺在床上，計算未來，

盡力想要拆織，捲回，解開

而將過去和未來串在一起，

45. 在午夜和黎明之間，當過去盡是欺騙，

而未來沒有未來，在凌晨守望之前

當時間停止而時間永無了時；

而滔天巨浪，從一開始而且曾經，

鏗然敲響

50. 鐘聲。

II

不幸何時才是終了，無聲的悲嘆，

秋天的花默默凋萎

落下花瓣而且靜止不動；

船難的殘骸最後漂流何處，

55. 沙灘上白骨的禱告，無以禱告的

禱告，面對著不幸災厄的聞報？

Four Quartets
1936

There is no end, but addition: the trailing
Consequence of further days and hours,
While emotion takes to itself the emotionless
60. Years of living among the breakage
Of what was believed in as the most reliable—
And therefore the fittest for renunciation.

There is the final addition, the failing
Pride or resentment at failing powers,
65. The unattached devotion which might pass for devotionless,
In a drifting boat with a slow leakage,
The silent listening to the undeniable
Clamour of the bell of the last annunciation.

Where is the end of them, the fishermen sailing
70. Into the wind's tail, where the fog cowers?
We cannot think of a time that is oceanless
Or of an ocean not littered with wastage
Or of a future that is not liable
Like the past, to have no destination.

75. We have to think of them as forever bailing,

四重奏
1936

沒有終了，反而追加：拖著
隨後日月和時間的尾巴，
當感動自身成為毫無感動
60. 而生活在歲月的殘片中
那些曾被相信是最為可靠的歲月──
因此宣布放棄是最適當的。

最後追加一句，逐漸失去的
自豪或是對權力逐漸失去的憤慨，
65. 沒有熱忱的信仰可能被當作沒有信仰，
在慢慢漏水的漂流小船上，
默默靜聽無可否認的
宣告：最後聞報的鐘聲。

這些何時終了，漁夫把船
70. 駛入霧氣畏縮的風尾？
我們無法想像沒有海洋的時候
或是垃圾凌亂的海洋
或是不可靠的未來
一如沒有目的地的過去。

75. 我們必須想到漁夫們經常在排水

Four Quartets
1936

Setting and hauling, while the North East lowers

Over shallow banks unchanging and erosionless

Or drawing their money, drying sails at dockage;

Not as making a trip that will be unpayable

80. For a haul that will not bear examination.

There is no end of it, the voiceless wailing,

No end to the withering of withered flowers,

To the movement of pain that is painless and motionless,

To the drift of the sea and the drifting wreckage,

85. The bone's prayer to Death its God. Only the hardly, barely prayable

Prayer of the one Annunciation.

It seems, as one becomes older,

That the past has another pattern, and ceases to be a mere sequence—

Or even development: the latter a partial fallacy

90. Encouraged by superficial notions of evolution,

Which becomes, in the popular mind, a means of disowning the past.

The moments of happiness—not the sense of well-being,

Fruition, fulfilment, security or affection,

Or even a very good dinner, but the sudden illumination—

95. We had the experience but missed the meaning,

四重奏
1936

張帆，拖網，當東北季風低吹過
保持不變而且不受侵蝕的淺灘
或者去提款，在碼頭晾乾船帆；
不至於出海一趟，而結果因漁獲
80. 沒通過檢查而得不到付款。

　　沒有終了的時候，而無聲的哀嘆，
凋謝的花朵，凋謝無時終了，
無痛感而一動不動的痛苦的動作無時終了，
海的漂流以及漂流的殘骸無時終了，
85. 白骨向死亡的主宰的禱告。只有幾幾乎無法禱告的
唯一「聞報」的禱告。

　　隨著年紀的增長，似乎
過去有了另一模式，不再僅僅是連續──
甚至也不是進展：後者是一種偏頗的謬論
90. 受到進化論膚淺觀念的鼓勵，
而在一般人的心中，成為否認過去的手段。
幸福的時刻──不是指樂活，
成果，實現，安心或摯愛的感覺，
或甚至是一頓很好的晚餐，而是指突然的啟示亦即頓悟──
95. 我們有這經驗但不了解意義，

Four Quartets
1936

And approach to the meaning restores the experience

In a different form, beyond any meaning

We can assign to happiness. I have said before

That the past experience revived in the meaning

100. Is not the experience of one life only

But of many generations—not forgetting

Something that is probably quite ineffable:

The backward look behind the assurance

Of recorded history, the backward half-look

105. Over the shoulder, towards the primitive terror.

Now, we come to discover that the moments of agony

(Whether, or not, due to misunderstanding,

Having hoped for the wrong things or dreaded the wrong things,

Is not in question) are likewise permanent

110. With such permanence as time has. We appreciate this better

In the agony of others, nearly experienced,

Involving ourselves, than in our own.

For our own past is covered by the currents of action,

But the torment of others remains an experience

115. Unqualified, unworn by subsequent attrition.

People change, and smile: but the agony abides.

Time the destroyer is time the preserver,

Like the river with its cargo of dead negroes, cows and chicken coops,

四重奏
1936

　　而接近意義意味著回復過去的經驗
　　以不同的形式，超過我們所能
　　給予幸福的任何意義。我以前說過
　　過去的經驗在意義中復活
100.　這不只是一個人一生的經驗
　　而是許多世代的經驗——遺忘不了
　　可能很難表達的某種東西：
　　以回顧的眼光，看看歷史記載的保證背後，
　　從肩膀上，側目回顧
105.　看看那原始的恐怖。
　　這時，我們開始發現，苦惱的瞬間
　　（不論是否由於誤解，問題不在於
　　對錯誤事情抱持希望或害怕錯誤的事情），
　　也是永恆的，與時間那種永恆是一樣的。
110.　我們更能體會這點
　　當我們處在別人的苦惱中，幾乎體驗到
　　感同身受，甚於對我們自身的苦惱。
　　因為我們本身的過去受到行動潮流的曚蔽，
　　而對別人的折騰依然只是一種
115.　無條件的經驗，不因後來的悔罪而有所磨損。
　　人們改變，微笑著：可是苦惱持續不變。
　　時間是破壞者，時間也是保存者，
　　就像河上的貨船，運載死去的黑人，母牛和鷄籠，

Four Quartets
1936

The bitter apple, and the bite in the apple.

120. And the ragged rock in the restless waters,

Waves wash over it, fogs conceal it;

On a halcyon day it is merely a monument,

In navigable weather it is always a seamark

To lay a course by: but in the sombre season

125. Or the sudden fury, is what it always was.

III

I sometimes wonder if that is what Krishna meant—

Among other things—or one way of putting the same thing:

That the future is a faded song, a Royal Rose or a lavender spray

Of wistful regret for those who are not yet here to regret,

130. Pressed between yellow leaves of a book that has never been opened.

And the way up is the way down, the way forward is the way back.

You cannot face it steadily, but this thing is sure,

That time is no healer: the patient is no longer here.

When the train starts, and the passengers are settled

135. To fruit, periodicals and business letters

四重奏
1936

苦蘋果，以及蘋果的咬痕，
120. 不寧的海上凹凸不平的岩石，
受波浪沖洗，霧氣籠罩；
風平浪靜的時日它只是一個紀念碑，
天氣可以出航時，它經常是
引導航線的標識：可是在晦暗季節
125. 或是突起的狂濤中，岩石仍像往昔一樣。

III

我有時候在想，那是否克利西納的本意——
其中，或許是藉以表達同樣意思的一種說法：
未來是一首消逝了的歌，一朵皇室玫瑰或者一根薰衣草花枝
帶著憂傷的後悔，對那些還沒出生來表示後悔的人，
130. 被壓在從來沒打開的一本書發黃的書頁間。
而且上行道就是下行道，前頭路就是回頭路。
你無法堅定地面對它，但這事是真的，
時間不是治癒者：病人已經不在人間。
當列車開動，而旅客安頓下來
135. 吃水果，看報刊，處理商務信件，

(And those who saw them off have left the platform)

Their faces relax from grief into relief,

To the sleepy rhythm of a hundred hours.

Fare forward, travellers! not escaping from the past

140. Into different lives, or into any future;

You are not the same people who left that station

Or who will arrive at any terminus,

While the narrowing rails slide together behind you;

And on the deck of the drumming liner

145. Watching the furrow that widens behind you,

You shall not think 'the past is finished'

Or 'the future is before us'.

At nightfall, in the rigging and the aerial,

Is a voice descanting (though not to the ear,

150. The murmuring shell of time, and not in any language)

'Fare forward, you who think that you are voyaging;

You are not those who saw the harbor

Receding, or those who will disembark.

Here between the hither and the farther shore

155. While time is withdrawn, consider the future

And the past with an equal mind.

At the moment which is not of action or inaction

You can receive this: "on whatever sphere of being

四重奏
1936

（這些送行的人都已離開月台）
他們的臉，從悲傷變成輕鬆，
應和著一百小時的節奏的催眠。
旅人喲，往前走！不要逃避過去
140.　逃到不同的人生，或者未來；
你與離開那車站
或者將到達任何終點的那些人不同
當你背後越來越窄的軌道滑成一道；
而在鼓聲震響的郵輪甲板上
145.　望著航跡在你背後越來越擴大
你不要認為「過去已經結束」
或是「未來前程在望」。
夜來，在索具和天線中
有一種聲音在歌唱（雖然不是對著耳朵，
150.　喃喃不斷的時間的貝殼，也不是任何語言）
「往前走吧，自認為是遠航的旅人們；
你們不是那些眺望著港口
逐漸遠去的人，也不是那些要下船的人。
如今在此地和此後的岸上之間
155.　當抽出時間的時候，以相等的心情
考慮未來和過去吧。
在既不是作為也不是無作為的瞬間
你可以接受這點：『臨死時一個人的繫心之念

The mind of a man may be intent

At the time of death"—that is the one action

(And the time of death is every moment)

Which shall fructify in the lives of others:

And do not think of the fruit of action.

Fare forward.

           O voyagers, O seamen,

You who came to port, and you whose bodies

Will suffer the trial and judgement of the sea,

Or whatever event, this is your real destination.'

So Krishna, as when he admonished Arjuna

On the field of battle

           Not fare well,

But fare forward, voyagers.

IV

Lady, whose shrine stands on the promontory,

Pray for all those who are in ships, those

Whose business has to do with fish, and

Those concerned with every lawful traffic

And those who conduct them.

四重奏
1936

不論是在於哪種存在領域』——
160. 這種執念是一種作為
（而死的瞬間是時時刻刻的）
導致在別人的生命中結了果：
然則不要考慮這種作為的結果。
往前走吧。

165. 　　　　　　　遠航的旅人喲，航海者喲，
來到港口的你們，身體
將接受海的審判和判決的你們，
不論如何，這是你們真正的目的地。」
因此，一如克利西納在戰場上
170. 對亞吉納的告誡所說的。
　　　　　　　　　不是告別，
還是往前走吧，遠航的旅人。

IV

聖母喲，您的神殿聳立在岬角上，
為所有乘船的人們禱告，那些
175. 從事漁業的人，以及
那些與每一合法貿易有關的人
還有那些指導他們的人。

Repeat a prayer also on behalf of
Women who have seen their sons or husbands
180. Setting forth, and not returning:
Figlia del tuo figlio,
Queen of Heaven.

Also pray for those who were in ships, and
Ended their voyage on the sand, in the sea's lips
185. Or in the dark throat which will not reject them
Or wherever cannot reach them the sound of the sea bell's
Perpetual angelus.

V

To communicate with Mars, converse with spirits,
To report the behaviour of the sea monster,
190. Describe the horoscope, haruspicate or scry,
Observe disease in signatures, evoke
Biography from the wrinkles of the palm
And tragedy from fingers; release omens
By sortilege, or tea leaves, riddle the inevitable
195. With playing cards, fiddle with pentagrams
Or barbituric acids, or dissect

四重奏
1936

　　請一再禱告，也為那些女人
她們看著兒子和丈夫出發
180. 卻不見他們回來：
汝子的女兒，
天上的王后喲。

　　也為在船上的那些人禱告，
而他們的航行終於觸礁，流入海的口唇
185. 或者黑暗的喉嚨不把他們吐出來
或在海的鐘聲，永恆的祈禱鐘
傳不到他們的任何地方。

V

與火星通訊，與神靈對話，
報導海怪的行為，
190. 描述占星術、臟占或水晶占，
署名觀察病狀，從手掌的皺紋
喚起一生的傳記，
從手指看出悲劇；以抽籤
或茶葉斷言吉凶，
195. 以撲克牌解謎注定的命運，以五芒星形
或是巴比妥酸玩弄手法，或者剖析

Four Quartets
1936

The recurrent image into pre-conscious terrors—
To explore the womb, or tomb, or dreams; all these are usual
Pastimes and drugs, and features of the press:
200. And always will be, some of them especially
When there is distress of nations and perplexity
Whether on the shores of Asia, or in the Edgware Road.
Men's curiosity searches past and future
And clings to that dimension. But to apprehend
205. The point of intersection of the timeless
With time, is an occupation for the saint—
No occupation either, but something given
And taken, in a lifetime's death in love,
Ardour and selflessness and self-surrender.
210. For most of us, there is only the unattended
Moment, the moment in and out of time,
The distraction fit, lost in a shaft of sunlight,
The wild thyme unseen, or the winter lightning
Or the waterfall, or music heard so deeply
215. That it is not heard at all, but you are the music
While the music lasts. These are only hints and guesses,
Hints followed by guesses; and the rest
Is prayer, observance, discipline, thought and action.
The hint half guessed, the gift half understood, is Incarnation.

四重奏
1936

重複出現的心象而歸於意識以前的恐怖——
探究子宮、墳墓，或者夢；這些都是
普通的娛樂和麻藥，以及新聞特稿：
200. 這些將永遠如此，其中有些特別是，
當民族災難和困境發生時
不論是在亞洲沿岸，或在倫敦的埃奇威爾路。
人類的好奇心探索過去和未來
而且固執在那一次元。但是領會
205. 無限時間與時間的交叉點，
是聖者的一個職業——
不是職業，而是某種有給有得的交易
一生至死，對愛、
熱誠、無私和無我的奉獻。
210. 對大部分的我們，只有未被關注的
瞬間，在時間之中和之外的瞬間，
迷失在太陽的光芒中，恍神的發作
看不見的野百里香，或者冬日的閃電
或者瀑布，或者音樂，聽得如此沉醉
215. 你完全沒聽到，但是只要音樂繼續
你就變成那音樂。這些都只是暗示和猜想，
暗示跟隨著猜想；而其餘的是
禱告，戒律，苦行，冥想和行動。
一半猜想的暗示，一半領悟的天賦，這是神的權化。

Four Quartets
1936

220. Here the impossible union
Of spheres of existence is actual,
Here the past and future
Are conquered, and reconciled,
Where action were otherwise movement
225. Of that which is only moved
And has in it no source of movement—
Driven by daemonic, chthonic
Powers. And right action is freedom
From past and future also.
230. For most of us, this is the aim
Never here to be realised;
Who are only undefeated
Because we have gone on trying;
We, content at the last
235. If our temporal reversion nourish
(Not too far from the yew-tree)
The life of significant soil.

四重奏
1936

220. 於此，兩種存在領域的
不可能的結合實現了，
於此，過去和未來
被克服，而且和解，
否則行動只是

225. 被移動的運動
當中沒有運動的原動力——
只是受到惡魔和地獄力的驅使。
正當的行動是自由
不受過去也不受未來的拘束。

230. 對於大部分的我們，這是
在這世上未曾實現的目標；
我們立於不敗之地
只因我們至今一再努力；
我們，最後該會瞑目

235. 假如我們的現世生命返回先祖
（距離紫杉樹不太遠）
能夠滋養意義深遠的土地的生命。

Four Quartets
1936

原註

1.　「The Dry Salvages」該是「les trois sauvages」（三個野蠻人）的訛傳，
　　是指一小群的岩礁，上有信標燈塔，在麻薩諸塞州東北角安妮海岬的岸邊。
　　「Salvages」的發音與「assuages」叶韻。Groaner（呻吟者）：指吹鳴的
　　浮標。

Four Quartets
1936

Little Gidding

No. 4 of 'Four Quartets'

I

Midwinter spring is its own season
Sempiternal though sodden towards sundown,
Suspended in time, between pole and tropic.
When the short day is brightest, with frost and fire,
5. The brief sun flames the ice, on pond and ditches,
In windless cold that is the heart's heat,
Reflecting in a watery mirror
A glare that is blindness in the early afternoon.
And glow more intense than blaze of branch, or brazier,
10. Stirs the dumb spirit: no wind, but pentecostal fire
In the dark time of the year. Between melting and freezing
The soul's sap quivers. There is no earth smell
Or smell of living thing. This is the spring time
But not in time's covenant. Now the hedgerow
15. Is blanched for an hour with transitory blossom
Of snow, a bloom more sudden

四重奏
1936

小吉丁 [1]

〈四重奏〉之四

I

仲冬的春天自成一個季節
是永遠的雖然近日落時濕淋淋，
時間停頓在極地與熱帶之間。
當短短的一日，因霜與火，最為明亮的時候，
5. 短暫的太陽在池塘和溝渠上點燃冰，
在無風的寒冷亦即心的熱火中，
從水鏡中反射出
午後盲目刺眼的亮光。
而且比燃燒的樹枝或火缽更強烈的輝光
10. 騷動暗啞的靈魂：無風，只有聖靈降臨節的火
照亮年中這一黑暗的季節。在溶化和凍結之間
靈魂的樹液在顫動。沒有泥土的氣息
或是生物的氣息。這是春的季節
但不在時間的約定中。此時樹籬
15. 因無常的雪花一時變白，
比夏天的花季更突然的

Four Quartets
1936

Than that of summer, neither budding nor fading,

Not in the scheme of generation.

Where is the summer, the unimaginable

20. Zero summer?

      If you came this way,

Taking the route you would be likely to take

From the place you would be likely to come from,

If you came this way in may time, you would find the hedges

25. White again, in May, with voluptuary sweetness.

It would be the same at the end of the journey,

If you came at night like a broken king,

If you came by day not knowing what you came for,

It would be the same, when you leave the rough road

30. And turn behind the pig-sty to the dull façade

And the tombstone. And what you thought you came for

Is only a shell, a husk of meaning

From which the purpose breaks only when it is fulfilled

If at all. Either you had no purpose

35. Or the purpose is beyond the end you figured

And is altered in fulfilment. There are other places

Which also are the world's end, some at the sea jaws,

Which also are the world's end, some at the sea jaws,

四重奏
1936

盛開，不是萌芽也不是凋謝，
不在生育的結構中。
夏天在哪兒，難以想像的
20.　零夏天？

　　　　　假如你從這條路來
走你可能會走的道路
從你可能會來的地方來，
假如你在山楂子盛開時節從這條路走來，你會發現樹籬
25.　又都變白了，在五月，帶著官能的美。
那會是一樣的，到了旅途的終點，
假如你晚上來像一個落魄的國王，
假如你白天來不知道你為什麼來，
那會是一樣的，當你離開崎嶇不平的路
30.　繞到豬圈後面走向無趣的建築正面
以及墓碑。而且你以為你來的目的
只是為了一個貝殼，一個意義的外莢，
從中，意圖必然落空一旦獲得滿足，
如果真的獲得滿足。你若不是沒有意圖
35.　就是你的意圖是在心中的目的之外，
而在滿足中已經改變。有些其他地方
也是世界的終點，有的在海的顎口，
或在越過陰暗湖面的地方，在沙漠或城市——

But this is the nearest, in place and time,
40. Now and in England.

If you came this way,
Taking any route, starting from anywhere,
At any time or at any season,
It would always be the same: you would have to put off
45. Sense and notion. You are not here to verify,
Instruct yourself, or inform curiosity
Or carry report. You are here to kneel
Where prayer has been valid. And prayer is more
Than an order of words, the conscious occupation
50. Of the praying mind, or the sound of the voice praying.
And what the dead had no speech for, when living,
They can tell you, being dead: the communication
Of the dead is tongued with fire beyond the language of the
living.
Here, the intersection of the timeless moment
55. Is England and nowhere. Never and always.

四重奏
1936

可是在地點和時間上，最接近的是
40. 此時，在英格蘭。

假如你從這條路來，
走任何一條路，從任何地方出發
在任何時候或任何季節，
那會都是一樣的：你會不得不丟棄
45. 感覺和觀念。你來這兒不是為了證明事實，
訓導自己，告知好奇心
或進行報導。你來這兒是為了跪下
這是祈禱一向應驗的地方。而且禱告不限於
字句的次序，自覺的
50. 祈禱心的專注，或者禱告的聲音。
而死者，在世時，無法用語言表達的，
他們能告訴你，就是死：死者的傳達
是以火的舌頭，超越活者的語言。
這裡，永恆瞬間的交叉點，
55. 是英格蘭而不是任何地方。永遠不是而且始終不是。

Four Quartets
1936

II

Ash on an old man's sleeve
Is all the ash the burnt roses leave.
Dust in the air suspended
Marks the place where a story ended.
Dust inbreathed was a house—
The walls, the wainscot and the mouse,
The death of hope and despair,
  This is the death of air.

There are flood and drouth
Over the eyes and in the mouth,
Dead water and dead sand
Contending for the upper hand.
The parched eviscerate soil
Gapes at the vanity of toil,
Laughs without mirth,
  This is the death of earth.

Water and fire succeed
The town, the pasture and the weed.
Water and fire deride

四重奏
1936

II

一個老人袖子上的灰
都是焚燒的玫瑰留下的灰。
浮懸在空中的灰塵
標示一個故事結束的地方。
60. 吸進去的灰塵曾是住屋——
牆壁、壁板和老鼠，
希望和絕望的死，
　　　　這是大氣的死。

有洪水和旱災
65. 在眼上，在口中，
死的水和死的沙
互爭看誰居上風。
剔骨除腸的乾枯土壤
對著徒勞的虛榮目瞪口呆，
70. 沒有歡笑的笑，
　　　　這是土地的死。

　　水和火跟隨著
城鄉、牧場和雜草。
水和火嘲笑

Four Quartets
1936

75. The sacrifice that we denied
Water and fire shall rot
The marred foundations we forgot,
Of sanctuary and choir.
This is the death of water and fire.

80. In the uncertain hour before the morning
Near the ending of interminable night
At the recurrent end of the unending
After the dark dove with the flickering tongue
Had passed below the horizon of his homing
85. While the dead leaves still rattled on like tin
Over the asphalt where no other sound was
Between three districts whence the smoke arose
I met one walking, loitering and hurried
As if blown towards me like the metal leaves
90. Before the urban dawn wind unresisting.
And as I fixed upon the down-turned face
That pointed scrutiny with which we challenge
The first-met stranger in the waning dusk
I caught the sudden look of some dead master
95. Whom I had known, forgotten, half recalled
Both one and many; in the brown baked features

四重奏
1936

75. 我們所否定的犧牲。

水和火將腐蝕

我們所遺忘被汙損的基礎，

聖堂和唱詩班席位。

　　　這是水和火的死。

80.　在天亮之前的未確定時刻

　　　接近無底洞夜晚的盡頭

　　　在無止盡重複出現的盡頭

在暗黑的鴿子閃現出舌頭

　　飛過回家的水平線下之後，

85.　枯葉仍在嘎嘎作響如錫罐

滾過別無聲音的柏油路，

　　在冒起煙的三個地區之間，

　　我遇見一個在遊蕩而腳步匆匆的人，

似乎被吹向我，有如金屬葉片

90.　在無法抵抗的都市黎明的風前。

　　當我凝視著朝下的臉

我們挑戰以尖銳眼光仔細檢視

　　在逐漸褪去的暮色中初次見到的陌生人，

　　我突然看到某位已故的大師

95. 我曾經認識，忘記了，一半想起，

　　同時是一個也是多個；在曬成褐色的面貌中

Four Quartets
1936

The eyes of a familiar compound ghost
Both intimate and unidentifiable.
   So I assumed a double part, and cried
100.   And heard another's voice cry: 'What! are you here?'
Although we were not. I was still the same,
   Knowing myself yet being someone other—
   And he a face still forming; yet the words sufficed
To compel the recognition they preceded.
105.   And so, compliant to the common wind,
   Too strange to each other for misunderstanding,
In concord at this intersection time
   Of meeting nowhere, no before and after,
   We trod the pavement in a dead patrol.
110. I said: 'The wonder that I feel is easy,
   Yet ease is cause of wonder. Therefore speak:
   I may not comprehend, may not remember.'
And he: 'I am not eager to rehearse
   My thoughts and theory which you have forgotten.
115.   These things have served their purpose: let them be.
So with your own, and pray they be forgiven
   By others, as I pray you to forgive
   Both bad and good. Last season's fruit is eaten
And the fullfed beast shall kick the empty pail.

四重奏
1936

一個熟悉的複合幽靈的眼睛
既親近又無法確認。

於是我承擔兩個角色，呼叫

100. 而聽到另一個叫聲：「怎麼！你在這兒？」
雖然我們不是。我還是我，

知道我自己還是另外的一個人——

而他，一個還在成形的臉；然而這些對話足以
勉強當作打招呼，表示彼此認識。

105. 於是，順從共同的風向，

彼此太陌生就不會產生誤解，

協和一致，在這交叉的時刻

不在哪兒見過面，不在過去也不在未來，

我們在鋪道上，走出死的巡邏。

110. 我說：「我對驚奇的感覺是安易，

然而安易是驚奇的原因。因此請說吧：

我可能不了解，也可能記不住。」

他說：「我不太想複誦

我的思想和理論，那些你都已經忘了，

115. 這些事已達到了目的；就算了吧。

因此對你自己的事，就祈求別人把它忘掉吧，

正像我祈求你的寬恕，

不論是好是壞。上一季節的水果已經吃了

而餵飽了的動物將踢開空水桶。

120. For last year's words belong to last year's language

And next year's words await another voice

But, as the passage now presents no hindrance

To the spirit unappeased and peregrine

Between two worlds become much like each other,

125. So I find words I never thought to speak

In streets I never thought I should revisit

When I left my body on a distant shore.

Since our concern was speech, and speech impelled us

To purify the dialect of the tribe

130. And urge the mind to aftersight and foresight,

Let me disclose the gifts reserved for age

To set a crown upon your lifetime's effort.

First, the cold friction of expiring sense

Without enchantment, offering no promise

135. But bitter tastelessness of shadow fruit

As body and soul begin to fall asunder.

Second, the conscious impotence of rage

At human folly, and the laceration

Of laughter at what ceases to amuse.

140. And last, the rending pain of re-enactment

Of all that you have done, and been; the shame

Of motives late revealed, and the awareness

四重奏
1936

120. 因為去年的字句屬於去年的語言
而明年的字句等待另一種聲音。
可是，現在由於在越來越相似的
兩個世界之間游移不寧的
精神通道沒有呈現出阻礙，
125. 因此我發現了我從來沒想過要說的話，
在我從來沒想過再去的街道
當我已把我的身體留在遙遠的岸邊。
既然我們關切的是言語，而言語驅使我們
淨化部族的方言
130. 而促使心靈去反觀和預見，
讓我披露保存給老年的賜物，
為你終生的努力戴上皇冠。
首先，逐漸失去知覺的冷冷摩擦
毫無迷惑，沒有期待
135. 只有幽靈水果苦澀的無味感，
當肉體和靈魂開始分裂的時候。
其次，對人類的愚行感到憤怒的
自覺無力感，以及
對不再有樂趣的事物的苦笑。
140. 最後，一再重演的傷痛，
對過去做過、有過的一切；
對事後才發覺的動機的可恥，以及

Of things ill done and done to others' harm

    Which once you took for exercise of virtue

145.   Then fools' approval stings, and honour stains.

From wrong to wrong the exasperated spirit

    Proceeds, unless restored by that refining fire

    Where you must move in measure, like a dancer.'

The day was breaking. In the disfigured street

150.   He left me, with a kind of valediction,

    And faded on the blowing of the horn.

III

There are three conditions which often look alike

Yet differ completely, flourish in the same hedgerow:

Attachment to self and to things and to persons, detachment

155. From self and from things and from persons; and, growing

between them, Indifference

Which resembles the others as death resembles life,

Being between two lives—unflowering, between

The live and the dead nettle. This is the use of memory:

For liberation—not less of love but expanding

160. Of love beyond desire, and so liberation

From the future as well as the past. Thus, love of a country

四重奏
1936

對做錯了而傷害到別人的一切的自覺
　雖然你曾經認為這些舉動是美德。
145.　　其次是愚人的贊同刺痛，而名譽沾汙。
從過錯到過錯，被激怒的靈魂
　繼續，除非讓那地獄的淨火拯救回來，
　在那兒你的動作必須按照尺度。一如舞蹈者。」
天快亮了。在面目不同的街頭
150.　　他離我而去，以一種告別的方式，
　　而在號角的鳴聲中消失。

III

有三種狀態時常看起來很像
卻完全不同，繁茂在同一個籬牆：
依附自我、事物和人們，脫離
155.　自我、事物和人們；以及，在這兩者之間滋長的冷漠
類似對別人，有如死之對於生，
存在於兩種生命之間——不開花，
在活的和死的蕁麻之間。這是記憶的用處：
為了解放——不是愛的減少而是
160.　超越欲望的愛的擴大，因此
從未來乃至過去中解放出來。如此，對一個國家的愛

Begins as attachment to our own field of action

And comes to find that action of little importance

Though never indifferent. History may be servitude,

165. History may be freedom. See, now they vanish,

The faces and places, with the self which, as it could, loved them,

To become renewed, transfigured, in another pattern.

    Sin is Behovely, but

All shall be well, and

170. All manner of thing shall be well.

If I think, again, of this place,

And of people, not wholly commendable,

Of no immediate kin or kindness,

But of some peculiar genius,

175. All touched by a common genius,

United in the strife which divided them;

If I think of a king at nightfall,

Of three men, and more, on the scaffold

And a few who died forgotten

180. In other places, here and abroad,

And of one who died blind and quiet

Why should we celebrate

四重奏
1936

開始於對我們自己的行動領域的執著
進而發現，行動無關重要
但絕不冷漠。歷史或許是奴役，
165. 歷史或許是自由。看吧，現在這些都消失而去，
那些臉、場所，與盡可能愛它們的自我一起
將獲得更新，變貌，以另一種樣式。

　　　罪是「無可逭」，可是
一切會是美好，而且
170. 凡事一切會是美好。
假如我再次想到這個地方，
以及人們，不完全是值得稱道，
亦無直接的親屬關係或親切感，
可是具有某種特殊的才能，
175. 大家都被一個共通的天才所感動，
在分裂他們的鬥爭中團結在一起；
假如我想到一個國王在夜晚
想到三個人，甚至更多，在斷頭台上
以及有些人死去而被遺忘
180. 在別處，此地和國外，
想到一個眼瞎而默默死去的人，
為什麼我們要為這些

These dead men more than the dying?

It is not to ring the bell backward

185. Nor is it an incantation

To summon the spectre of a Rose.

We cannot revive old factions

We cannot restore old policies

Or follow an antique drum.

190. These men, and those who opposed them

And those whom they opposed

Accept the constitution of silence

And are folded in a single party.

Whatever we inherit from the fortunate

195. We have taken from the defeated

What they had to leave us—a symbol:

A symbol perfected in death.

And all shall be well and

All manner of thing shall be well

200. By the purification of the motive

In the ground of our beseeching.

四重奏
1936

已死去的人而不是瀕死的人祝賀？
召喚玫瑰的幽魂
185. 既不是往後鳴鐘
也不是詛咒。
我們無法復活舊黨派
我們無法恢復舊政策
或者跟從古老的鼓聲。
190. 這些人，以及那些反對他們的人
和他們所反對的那些人，
接受沉默的制度
而被包括在單一的政黨中。
不論我們從幸運者中繼承了什麼
195. 我們從失敗者中得到了
他們不得不留給我們的——一個象徵：
以死達到完美的象徵。
而一切會是美好，而且
凡事一切會是美好
200. 藉著初心的淨化
在我們懇望的地下。

Four Quartets
1936

IV

The dove descending breaks the air

With flame of incandescent terror

Of which the tongues declare

205. The one discharge from sin and error.

The only hope, or else despair

   Lies in the choice of pyre or pyre—

   To be redeemed from fire by fire

   Who then devised the torment? Love.

210. Love is the unfamiliar Name

Behind the hands that wove

The intolerable shirt of flame

Which human power cannot remove.

   We only live, only suspire

215.   Consumed by either fire or fire.

V

What we call the beginning is often the end

And to make an end is to make a beginning.

The end is where we start from. And every phrase

四重奏
1936

IV

鴿子從天而降衝破大氣
帶著白熱恐怖的火焰
以其舌頭宣示
205. 罪與過失的一個解脫。
唯一的希望，或者說絕望
　　就看這堆柴或那堆柴的選擇──
　　為了以火從火中獲得救贖。

　　那麼是誰設計了這種苦行？「愛」。
210. 「愛」是那個不熟悉的「名字」
在雙手背後編織
這難以忍受的火焰的襯衫
那是人的力量無法解脫的。
　　我們只能活下去，只能嘆息
215. 　　被這火或那火焚燒殆盡。

V

我們所謂的開始往往是結束
而著手結束亦即著手開始。
結束是我們開始的地方。每個適當的片語

And sentence that is right (where every word is at home,

220. Taking its place to support the others,

The word neither diffident nor ostentatious,

An easy commerce of the old and the new,

The common word exact without vulgarity,

The formal word precise but not pedantic,

225. The complete consort dancing together)

Every phrase and every sentence is an end and a beginning,

Every poem an epitaph. And any action

Is a step to the block, to the fire, down the sea's throat

Or to an illegible stone: and that is where we start.

230. We die with the dying:

See, they depart, and we go with them.

We are born with the dead:

See, they return, and bring us with them.

The moment of the rose and the moment of the yew-tree

235. Are of equal duration. A people without history

Is not redeemed from time, for history is a pattern

Of timeless moments. So, while the light fails

On a winter's afternoon, in a secluded chapel

History is now and England.

240. With the drawing of this Love and the voice of this Calling

四重奏
1936

和句子（其中每一字句都很舒適地

220. 以自己的位置支援別的字句，

這種字句既不心虛也不誇張，

舊詞和新語從容交易，

日常的字句精準不帶俗氣，

正式的字句準確而不賣弄學問，

225. 完美的伴侶在一起共舞）

每一字句都是一個結束，一個開始，

每一首詩是一篇墓誌銘。而一個動作

一個腳步，走向斷頭台，走向火，走入海的喉嚨

或者走向難以辨認的石碑：而這就是我們開始的地方。

230. 我們與瀕死的人一起死去：

看哪，他們走了，而我們跟隨他們。

我們與死者一起出生：

看哪，他們回來，帶著我們一起。

玫瑰的瞬間和紫杉樹的瞬間

235. 持續的時間相等。一個沒有歷史的民族

無法從時間中贖回，因為歷史是

諸多永恆瞬間的一個樣式。因此，當著陽光轉弱

在一個冬日的下午，一個僻靜的教堂，

歷史就是現在，且是英格蘭。

240. 以這種「愛」的引導和這種「感召」的聲音

Four Quartets
1936

We shall not cease from exploration

And the end of all our exploring

Will be to arrive where we started

And know the place for the first time.

245. Through the unknown, remembered gate

When the last of earth left to discover

Is that which was the beginning;

At the source of the longest river

The voice of the hidden waterfall

250. And the children in the apple-tree

Not known, because not looked for

But heard, half-heard, in the stillness

Between two waves of the sea.

Quick now, here, now, always—

255. A condition of complete simplicity

(Costing not less than everything)

And all shall be well and

All manner of thing shall be well

When the tongues of flame are in-folded

260. Into the crowned knot of fire

And the fire and the rose are one.

四重奏
1936

我們不會停止探索

而我們所有探索的目的

是為了到達我們的出發點

而且初次認識那個地方。

245. 通過未知，記憶的門

當有待最後發現的土地

竟是曾經開始的地方；

在最長河流的源頭

隱蔽瀑布的聲音

250. 以及在蘋果樹中的孩子們

不為人知，因為未曾被尋找

但聽說過，半聽說過，在海上

兩個波浪之間的靜止中。

快，現在，此地，現在，無時無刻——

255. 一個全然純樸的的條件

（至少以所有的一切為代價）

而一切會是美好

凡事一切會是美好

當火焰的舌頭捲起

260. 結成火的王冠

而火和玫瑰合而為一。

---

1 譯註：小吉丁是位於英格蘭東劍橋郡的一個小社區，建於 17 世紀，歷史悠久，
毀於戰火。

附錄

艾略特生平

- **1888 年 9 月 26 日**

Thomas Stearns Eliot 生 於 美 國 Missouri 州 的 St. Louis。 父 Henry Ware Eliot（1843-1919）是實業家，母為 Stearns 家族出身的 Charlotte Champe Eliot（1843-1930）。父母於 1868 年結婚；T. S. Eliot 是家中排行第七的么子。

Eliot 家族出於英國 Devonshire，到了 Andrew Eliot（1627-1704）這一代從英國 Somersetshire 的 East Coker 村，移居至美國 Massachusetts。詩人的祖先數代都是 Boston 商人。Rev. Andrew Eliot, D. D.（1718 -78）曾當 North Church 的牧師，後當選為 Harvard 大學的校長。

詩人艾略特的祖父 Rev. William Greenleaf Eliot, D. D.（1811-87）於 1834 年畢業於 Harvard 大學的 Divinity School 神學院，在 St. Louis 建立了最早的教堂 Unitarian Church。另一方面致力於 Washington 大學的設立，於 1872 年擔任該大學的名譽校長。他有四個兒子，其中兩個當過聖職，而最小的兒子是律師，次子 Henry Ware Eliot，也就是艾略特的父親，1863 年畢業於 Washington 大學，在 St. Louis 經營 Hydraulic Press Brick Co.，並擔任該公司負責人。詩人的母親是 Boston 商人之女，是和 John Winthrop 一同於 1630 年在 Bay Colony 上陸的 Issac Stearns 家族的後代。頗有文學才能且具創作熱心，也擅長撰

寫傳記，1926 年曾出版過詩劇 *Savonarola*。艾略特母親的祖先也曾當過 Harvard 大學的校長。

- **1894 年（6 歲）**

  9 月，入學 Smith Academy （St. Louis）。這是 Washington 大學的附屬學校。

- **1902 年（14 歲）**

  知道著名詩人 Thomas Babington Macaulay 的 Horatius，也讀過詩人 Lord Alfred Tennysonn 的 Revenge，尤其深受 Edward Fitzgerald 翻譯 Omar Khayyám 的 *Rubáiyát*《魯拜集》之感動，且開始接近更多詩人如 Byron、Shelley、Keats、Rossetti 和 Swinburne。

- **1905 年（17 歲）**

  轉學到 Milton Academy （Boston）就讀。

- **1906 年（18 歲）**

  入學 Harvard 大學。同學有 John Reed（美國著名記者），Bronson Cutting（曾任美國參議員），Stuart Chase（美國經濟學家），Walter Lippmann（美國知名作家）等。聽 Irving Babbitt 的法國文學，George Santayana 的哲學，W. D. Briggs 的英國文學，Bertrand Russell 的論理學等課。另一方面埋頭研究 Elizabethan Drama，在 Briggs 教授的指導下攻讀 John Donne。

- **1907 年（19 歲）**

  向 *The Harvard Advocate* 投寄詩稿。發表 "Conversation Galante"。

- **1908 年（20 歲）**

  讀到 Arthur Symons 的 *The Symbolist Movement in Literature*，

深受影響。

- **1909 年（21 歲）**

  修完 Harvard 大學的 Undergraduate Course，取得 B. A.，繼續讀 Graduate Course，攻哲學。擔任 *The Harvard Advocate* 的編輯。當時在該誌投稿的詩人主要有 Conrad Aiken、R. P. Blackmur、Richard Ghormley Eberhart、Archibald MacLeish、F. O. Matthiessen、P. Warren、C. Williams 等。

- **1910 年（22 歲）**

  取得 M. A. 學位。哲學的研究之外兼及詩作："Portrait of a Lady"（1909-10），"The Love Song of J. Alfred Prufrock"（1910-11）等。渡法，在 Sorbonne 攻讀法國文學和哲學。

- **1911 年（23 歲）**

  9 月回到 Harvard，此後三年為哲學博士論文 "Experience and the Objects of Knowledge in the Philosophy of F. H. Bradley" 兼攻形而上學、論理學、心理學、印度哲學、佛教、梵文等。

- **1913 年（25 歲）**

  任 Harvard 大學哲學系助理。7 月赴德國 Marburg 大學留學。

- **1914 年（26 歲）**

  因第一次大戰爆發，渡英，入 Oxford 大學（Merton College），主修以 Aristotle 為中心的希臘哲學，獲得 M. A. 學位。開始定居於 London。9 月 22 日 Eliot 第一次拜訪當時住在倫敦的 Ezra Pound（1885-1972）。當天 Pound 寫信給美國詩誌 *Poetry* 的主編 Harriet Monroe（1860-1936），報告美國新詩人之出現。此為 Eliot 與 Pound 交友的開始。

- **1915 年（27 歲）**

6 月經 Pound 介紹在 *Poetry* 詩誌上發表 "The Love Song of J. Alfred Prufrock"。7 月在 Wyndham Lewis 主編的 *The Blast* 誌上發表詩作 "Preludes" 和 "Rhapsody on a Windy Night" 等，引起英美詩壇的注意。6 月 26 日和倫敦畫家的女兒 Miss Vivianne Haigh Haigh-Wood（1888-1947）結婚。

- **1916 年（28 歲）**

  在 Highgate School 教「法語、拉丁語、初級算數、圖畫、游泳、地理、歷史、棒球」。4 月完成博士論文，雖送往 Harvard 大學審查，但沒出席參加口試。

- **1917 年（29 歲）**

  6 月因 *The Egoist* 誌的編輯 Richard Aldington 參加大戰，由 Eliot 繼任編輯，直到 1919 年停刊為止。在 *The New Statesman*、*Art & Letters* 誌上發表評論。*Ezra Pound : His Metrics and Poetry* 匿名由 Alfred A. Knopf 社出版；6 月詩集 *Prufrock and Other Observations* 出版。秋入 Lloyds Bank 工作。

- **1918 年（30 歲）**

  接到美國海軍召集令，但以健康上的理由免役。

- **1919 年（31 歲）**

  1 月父親 Henry Ware Eliot 去世，享年 78 歲。母親從 S. Louis 移居至 Cambridge（Massachusetts）。開始在 John Middleton Murry 編的雜誌 *The Athenaeum* 以及 *Little Review*、*Art and Letters*、*New Statesman*、*Times Literary Supplement* 等雜誌上執筆，成為定期評論家。10 月在 *The Egoist*（9-10 月號）發表 "Tradition and the Individual Talent"。詩集 *Poems* 由 Ricmond Hogarth 社出版。

- **1920 年（32 歲）**

  Ara Vos Prec 由 London 的 Ovid 社出版。*The Sacred Wood* 則在 Methuen 社出版。

- **1921 年（33 歲）**

  11 月 "The Metaphysical Poets" 在 *The Times Literary Supplement* 發表。秋 *The Waste Land* 的初稿（H. Kenner 所謂的「ur-Waste Land」），在瑞士的 Lausanne 完成。當時 Eliot 經由 Pound 的介紹，在該地靜養。回到倫敦的途中經過巴黎，將原稿（約 800 行）請 Pound 加以推敲。

- **1922 年（34 歲）**

  10 月 Eliot 主筆的雜誌 *The Criterion* 創刊，由 Cobden-Sanderson 社（London）發行。在創刊號上發表經由 Pound 修改刪去了一半的 "The Waste Land"（434 行）。單行本在同年由紐約的 Boni & Liveright 社出版。所謂「ur-Waste Land」的原稿寄贈給美國人 John Quinn 氏，但該氏於 1924 年去世，該原稿至今下落不明。*The Waste Land* 發表後獲得 The Dial Award，獎金 2,000 美元。

- **1923 年（35 歲）**

  The Waste Land 的英國版單行本由 Hogarth Press 以 hand-print 出版。"The Function of Criticism" 發表。

- **1924 年（36 歲）**

  評論集 *Homage to John Dryden* 出版。

- **1925 年（37 歲）**

  詩集 *Poems 1909-1925* 由 Faber & Gwyer 社出版。辭去 Lloyd's Bank 的工作，參加 Faber & Gwyer 出版社的企劃。

- **1926 年（38 歲）**

  秋受聘為 Cambridge 大學 Trinity College 的 Clark Lecturer。*The Criterion* 改由 Faber & Gwyer 社發行。母親的詩劇 *Savonarola : A Dramatic Poem* 由 Cobden-Sanderson 社出版，Eliot 寫序文。

- **1927 年（39 歲）**

  歸化英國籍，成為英國國教會的一員。此後詩作及散文的宗教色彩漸濃。在 Shakespeare Association 講演 "Shakespeare and the Stoicism of Seneca"。*Journey of the Magi* 出版。

- **1928 年（40 歲）**

  評論集 *For Lancelot Andrewes* 出版。Faber & Gwyer 社的名稱變更為 Faber & Faber 社。*A Song for Simeon* 出版。

- **1929 年（41 歲）**

  Dante 評論集出版。在倫敦的 The City Literary Institute 發表 "Experiment in Criticism" 講演。

- **1930 年（42 歲）**

  詩 *Ash-Wednesday* 由 Putnam 社出版 600 部的限定版，數日間普及版於倫敦和紐約同時出版。母親 Charlotte 去世，享年 87 歲。

- **1931 年（43 歲）**

  評論集 *Thoughts after Lambeth* 出版。

- **1932 年（44 歲）**

  評論集 *Selected Essays 1917-1932* 出版，但是實際的年代該是 1919-1932。從 11 月到翌年春天受聘為 Charles Eliot Norton Professor of Poetry，在 Harvard 連續講演。

- **1933 年（45 歲）**

將在 Harvard 講演的講稿改題為 *The Use of Poetry and the Use of Criticism* 出版。春，在 Virginia University 講演 "A Primer of Modern Heresy"。

- **1934 年（46 歲）**

  將在 Virginia University 講演的講稿改題為 *After Strange Gods* 出版。為了募集倫敦主教區四十五教會基金，詩劇 *The Rock* 在 Sadler's Wells Theatre 公演（5 月 28 月—6 月 9 日）。評論集 *Elizabethan Essays* 出版。

- **1935 年（47 歲）**

  6 月在 Canterbury Festival 上演詩劇 *Murder in the Cathedral*，後由 Faber & Faber 社出版。

- **1936 年（48 歲）**

  詩集 *Collected Poems 1909-1935* 由 Faber & Faber 和紐約的 Harcourt Brace 同時出版，其中含有 "Burnt Norton"。*Essays Ancient and Modern* 出版。

- **1939 年（51 歲）**

  詩劇 *The Family Reunion* 在 Westminster Theatre 上演。1 月 *The Criterion* 停刊。3 月在 Cambridge 講演 "The Idea of a Christian Society"，講稿於 10 月由 Faber & Faber 出版。9 月第二次大戰爆發。*Old Possum's Book of Practical Cats* 出版。

- **1940 年（52 歲）**

  East Coker 發表。

- **1941 年（53 歲）**

  Burnt Norton、*The Dry Salvages*、*Points of View* 等出版。

- **1942 年（54 歲）**

在 Glasgow 大學 W. P. Ker 的紀念會上講演 "The Music of Poetry"。當選 The Classical Association 的會長。*Little Gidding* 出版。

- **1943 年（55 歲）**

詩集 *Four Quartets* 在美國 Harcourt Brace, & Co. 出版。詩論 *Reunion by Destruction* 出版。

- **1944 年（56 歲）**

詩集 *Four Quartets* 在倫敦出版。當選 The Virgil Society 的會長。10 月在 The Presidential Lecture 上講演 "What is a Classic ?"。

- **1947 年（59 歲）**

1 月妻 Vivienne 去世。3 月在 The British Academy 講演 "Milton"。

- **1948 年（60 歲）**

10 月諾貝爾獎授予「現代詩第一位開拓者」艾略特。接受喬治六世的有功勳章 The Order of Merit。同年獲 Cambridge, Yale, Princeton, Columbia 等大學授予文學博士學位。*Notes towards the Definition of Culture* 出版。在國會圖書館講演 "From Poe to Valéry"。

- **1949 年（61 歲）**

The Edinburgh Festival 上演 *The Cocktail Party*（1950 年出版）博得好評。在 Poet's Theatre Guild 講演 "The Aims of Poetic Drama"。

- **1950 年（62 歲）**

7 月在 The Italian Institute 講演 "A Talk on Dante"。10 月渡美，11 月在 Harvard 大學舉行 Theodore Spensen 紀念講演 "Poetry

and Drama"。*The Cocktail Party*、*Poems Written in Early Youth*
出版。

- **1951 年（63 歲）**

  Selected Essays 增訂版。*Murder in the Cathedral* 拍成電影。9 月
  英國廣播協會（B.B.C.）播送 *Virgil and the Christian World*。

- **1952 年（64 歲）**

  就任 London Library 館長，發表 "An Address to Members of the
  London Library"。任 Oxford, Cambridge 兩大學的名譽講師。
  接受法國國家榮譽軍團勳章 Légion d'Honneur。

- **1953 年（65 歲）**

  6 月在 Washington 大學一百周年紀念會上講演 "American
  Literature and the American Language"。在 The Edinburgh Festival
  上演 *The Confidential Clerk*。 在 The National Book League 第
  十一屆年會上講演 "The Three Voices of Poetry"。

- **1954 年（66 歲）**

  接受德國文藝獎 The Hanseatic Goethe Prize。"Religious Drama:
  Mediaeval and Modern" 發表。詩 *The Cultivation of Christmas
  Trees* 出版。

- **1955 年（67 歲）**

  5 月在 Hamburg 大學接受 Goethe 獎。*Goethe as the Sage*、*The
  Literature of Politics* 出版。

- **1956 年（68 歲）**

  在 Minnesota 大學舉行的 Seymour 紀念會上講演 "Frontiers of
  Criticism"。

- **1957 年（69 歲）**

1 月和秘書 Valerie Fletcher 結婚。評論集 *On Poetry and Poets* 出版。

- **1958 年（70 歲）**

  詩劇 *The Elder Statesman* 在 The Edinburgh Festival 上演（翌年出版）。

- **1963 年（75 歲）**

  詩集 *Collected Poems, 1909-62* 出版。

- **1964 年（76 歲）**

  將 1916 年完成的博士論文 *Knowledge and Experience in the Philosophy of F. H. Bradley* 出版。

- **1965 年（77 歲）**

  1 月 4 日因肺氣腫疾病過世。未亡人將其評論集 *To Criticize the Critic* 出版。1967 年 1 月 4 日葬於倫敦西敏寺的「詩人之墓」。

艾略特與我

今天能夠在中國參加艾略特百歲誕辰紀念會，我感到非常高興。同時，我想藉這個機會，回顧一下二十多年來艾略特與我的關係，尤其是我對他的翻譯介紹，以及他對我的詩觀與創作的影響，作為紀念這位傑出的詩人和批評家的一點獻禮。

艾略特開始在我心中形成一種不可忽視的存在，是在我進了臺灣大學開始寫詩的時候。六〇年代初期，臺灣文壇開始大量引進西方文藝思潮，其中現代主義和存在主義具有較大的影響。我當時深深感到要從事新詩創作，不能不了解西方的現代詩；要了解西方的現代詩，不能不了解艾略特。當時課堂上用的「英國文學史」，有的已直接將現代標題改為「艾略特時代」，這種定斷使我毫無條件地肯定艾略特是當代最大的詩人，是擺在我立志寫詩這條路前的一座高山，無法迴避，必須攀登和征服。於是，我開始閱讀他的作品。

要深切了解一個詩人的作品，最有效的辦法是透過翻譯。於是，我開始嘗試把艾略特的詩翻成中文。那時，我已經加入臺大外文系白先勇等人創辦的《現代文學》。這個雜誌一開始就是文學創作與翻譯雙管齊下，每期以專輯方式介紹西方現代主義的作品，我當時翻譯〈普魯佛洛克與其他的觀察〉以及〈荒地〉（即〈荒原〉）等艾略特的作品，大多發表在《現代文學》上，也有一些發表在後來（1964 年）創刊的《笠》詩刊上。那時一口氣

將艾略特的詩作品，除了〈四重奏〉，大部分都譯了一遍。在翻譯〈荒原〉時，參考幾種日文譯本，其中西脇順三郎的翻譯，公認是日文最佳的譯本。當時我深深體驗到，翻譯西洋的文學作品時，如能參考日文的譯註，大有事半功倍的效益。這份體驗使我下定決心，到日本留學，以便精通日文。

　　1966 年到了日本，先在京都大學英文學系進修。一年之後，我已能充分利用日文研究資料，此時的興趣開始轉向日本文學，而且覺得與其念英美文學，不如全心鑽研日本文學，更有實質的意義。於是在京都大學研修一年之後，便轉到關西學院大學攻讀日本文學碩士學位，課餘，仍繼續對艾略特及其他英美現代詩人的涉獵。

　　到了日本，令人驚訝的是，日本學者對艾略特的作品和文學評論的介紹，可說已經達近乎過剩程度。當時，中央公論社的《艾略特全集》五卷，已經出版。根據我當時（1968）的記錄，艾略特作品的日譯單行本有三十二種，研究單行本有二十三種，一部分論及艾略特的學術著作至少有八十種，論述艾略特的論文，至少在四百五十篇以上。從這個例子，日本人在譯介西方文學方面的實際成績可見一斑，而當時在臺灣關於艾略特的譯介，除了葉維廉先生和我的〈荒原〉兩種譯本，以及夏濟安和朱乃長先生的〈傳統與個人才具〉論文之外，只是一些零星的作品，相關有系統的評介專書，事實上一本也沒有。我對艾略特的興趣，本來只是在詩方面，可是對艾略特這樣一個在理論和批評均能成一家之言的詩人，如果對他創作理論和批評觀，沒有一定的了解，是不可能真正了解他的創作品的。有了這個想法，我開始翻譯他的文學評論。

　　大約前後兩年，我選譯艾略特最重要的評論文章共十八篇，分成五個單元：（1）傳統論；（2）詩和劇的原理論；（3）批評的機能論；（4）作家論；（5）文學的宗教性。對這些論文，我充分利用日文資料，詳加譯註，同時附加艾略特年譜，以及當時所能搜集到的英文和日文有關艾略特的書誌，並撰寫一篇〈艾略特的文學論〉做為解說。這就是 1969 年 3 月由朋友創辦的田園出版社出版的《艾略特文學評論選集》。

　　這本書具有相當的學術水平，出版時，臺灣的文學界和翻譯界都感到非常驚訝。我當時人還在日本，書出版之後不久，就從日本轉到美國史丹福大學繼續求學。後來有一年，臺灣的名詩人余光中先生到美國與我見面時，他表示，當時曾在電視藝文訪問節目上，鄭重推荐這本書。我相信此書，對後來臺灣的年輕詩人和中文系出身的文學者，具有一定的影響。1970 年到美國之後，我又繼續翻譯了艾略特的《詩的效用與批評的效用》。這本書在 1972 年由臺北純文學出版社出版。此後，在翻譯路上，我從艾略特轉到波特萊爾，而今，能重新整理年輕時譯過的艾略特的詩，出版一本《艾略特詩選》，是我二十多年來一直希望實現的心願。

　　現在回顧起來，在我一生追求詩的生涯中，為了創作詩，找到了艾略特；而由於翻譯艾略特，認識了西脇順三郎。西脇是二〇年代將法國超現實主義等前衛藝術思潮介紹到日本詩壇的一員大將，他本人專攻古代中世紀英語和英文學，是艾略特的研究家，也是一位名詩人。他的英美文學背景和對現代詩的豐富學識，使我決定以他做為碩士學位論文的研究對象。也曾經將他的一本融會東方和西方詩觀的《詩學》翻譯成中文（1969），後來

再根據我的碩士論文的資料，合併出版《西脇順三郎的詩與詩學》（1980）。由於研究西脇，我開始閱讀法國象徵詩人的作品，進而翻譯波特萊爾的《惡之華》；也因波特萊爾，再轉而研究中唐晚詩人李賀。這一系列的追尋，可以說都是以艾略特所啟示的現代詩觀做為底流而貫穿其間的。

　　艾略特說過，一個詩人在二十五歲以後，如果還想繼續寫詩，不能沒有歷史意識。在我二十五歲的時候，讀到艾略特這句話，感受特別深刻。這句話支持著我對東西方詩學理論的持續探索，同時更深覺傳統的重要，加深對中國文學傳統的認識，致使我從日本轉到美國研讀時，決定到史丹福大學師從劉若愚教授，以中國文學理論和古典詩做為博士學位論文的研究方向。

　　艾略特對我的影響，是多方面的。從人生路程的重要決定，到基本詩觀和創作，更是具有直接或間接的重大影響。詩是什麼的追究，感受性的重視，知性的強調，自我的超越，藝術的經營，以及歷史意識和古典傳統的尋求等概念和探索，可以說，都是艾略特啟示的，至於我自己的詩中，隱藏有多少艾略特的影子，那是一個極機密，或許期待有緣人的探索。

　　總之，在我的詩路歷程上影響最大的四位詩人是：艾略特、西脇順三郎、波特萊爾和李賀。我不得不承認，沒有艾略特，或許不會認識或研究其他三個詩人，也許不會成為今天的我。沒有艾略特，作為一名現代詩人，或許不會發現中國的文學傳統對我的創作生命極具重大意義。我必須承認，是艾略特，使我的詩路歷程從西方和東洋，又回到中國文學傳統。今天，在紀念艾略特這個對我個人特別有意義的日子，談論艾略特與我，意味著西洋和東方的兩大文學傳統，在我創作的心靈上產生匯合、交響和共

鳴。作為一個以中文創作的現代詩人，我不得不對艾略特所給予
的啟示和影響，由衷致以最大的感激和最高的敬意。

(原發表於上海社會科學院「艾略特誕辰一百周年紀念會」，1988 年 9 月)

艾略特的文學論

　　一位作家的文學論，不外意謂著作家所特有的創作以及批評理論。將作家所具有的優異感受性、學識和經驗，所產生出來的創作手法加以客觀地敘述，亦即作家的創作理論；將他批評文學作品或批評作家的方法加以理論化與客觀地敘述，亦即他的批評理論。本文擬就艾略特的創作理論和批評理論兩方面加以探討，以便對他的文學論有個根本的了解。因此對於構成他的理論基礎的「感受性」（Sensibility）之性質不能不先加以究明。

　　我們在談論到文學的鑑賞或批評時，常常提到批評者的感受性的問題。對於作品所具有的美或者特殊的妙味加以直覺判斷，便是這種感受性；感受性不發達的人，當然談不上將詩當作詩，將文學當作文學加以品味，遑論鑑賞作品特有的美或者詩的妙處。因此這種感受性是使文學的鑑賞或批評成為一種根本的性能。

　　這種感受性是與生俱來的，但是有時候感受性的發達，止於某一個程度，有時候不斷地受到新刺激，感受性不至於僵化固定。猶如一顆多面體的晶玉，各面反射力的程度互異一致，感受性本是由知性、情感、感覺等種種機能，構成一種有機體，在各種機能相互間，密接微妙的關聯。大體上，感覺的反應喚起情感，而知道反應要達到反省、分析的地步，往往需要相當的時間。外界的刺激使我們的末梢神經發生震動，而這種震動幅度構成一團

印象。分析或批判這種印象的能力，可說是相當高次的感受性。但是當這些知性、情感、感覺的機能發達成為一種有機的統一體時，一接觸到新的刺激，馬上呈現出知情難分的反應狀態。這種狀態，我們稱為直覺。艾略特論查普曼（Chapman）、韋伯斯特（Webster）等伊麗莎白時代劇作家的特性時，認為他們的「知性直接地在於感覺的尖端」（The intellect was immediately at the tips of the senses.），這意味著他們的感受性極為敏銳而發達，且經常從事著有機的活動。

再說感受性，由於舊經驗的反覆，或者同種經驗的累積，而呈現出一種習慣的反應狀態，雖不能說是自覺，但是對於新刺激的性質，卻能加以直覺地識別。因此隨著感受性的發達，能注意到從來未曾注意過的地方，品味纖細的妙趣，識別異同，以及鑑賞特殊的美妙。感受性，是由於經驗的反覆累積，本身不斷地更新生長，伴隨著逐漸形成判斷的標準，養成判斷能力。艾略特認為批評是一種感受性的發達（a development of sensibility），理由在此。

但是感受性不單單是一種反應力，同時包含著咀嚼同化的能力。要是感受性止於舊經驗的反覆，不久也就固定化而成為一種定型，不僅生氣全失，反應力也變遲鈍。因此，要使感受性不斷發達，必須不斷添加新經驗。換言之，由於新經驗而受到刺激時，感受性不僅被喚醒，而且在允許的能力範圍內，不得不呈現出的反應。感受性呈現出新的反應，意味著某種變質，即使是極其微小的變質，因經驗不斷地累積，感受性不斷地生長，複雜性不斷地增加。本來這種變化與具有統一性的成長，並不一定是就感受性一般而論，而是艾略特所謂「優秀的感受性」"superior sensibility" 或者「真正具有鑑賞力的精神」"a really appreciative mind" 中所具有的現象。要言之，這種優秀的感受性恰如一個大熔爐，將一切的經驗融在其中。亦即具有這種感受性的人，對於一個極為相異，甚至是相反的經驗，或者一般人認為毫不相關的經驗，卻能夠捉住內在互相的關聯性，加以理解和把握。十七世紀初的所謂「形而上詩人」（Metaphysical Poets）便是具有這種優秀的感受性。他們能夠將思想感覺加以把握，將思考和感受性融合在一起，「將自己的思想像薔薇的芳香一般直接感覺」"feel their thought as immediately as the odour of a rose"，這便是艾略特所謂「感受性的統一」（unification of sensibility）。但在艾略特看來，密爾頓以後這種思想和感情統一的感受性卻開始崩壞解體，成為分裂的狀態。這種近代特有的弊病，至今未曾改善。十八世紀的近代詩人，在語言上雖有改革，而感受性卻是粗雜，失去了有機的統一，導致近代詩走上衰退之途。

　　暫且不論艾略特這種英詩觀。且說詩人所表現的，在某種意義上說來，不外是詩人的經驗；即使在表現思想的時候，並非直接使用抽象的形式來敘述，而是藉用某種「感情的等價物」（emotional equivalent）加以表現；這一切依據詩人的感受性捕捉而來的東西。如此創作，事實上也是以感受性為基礎的。艾略特以批評和創作，為感受性之兩方面，可說基於這種理由。

　　前面說過，我們所謂的「印象」，是感受性對於外界刺激的反應。然而在艾略特看來，批評根本的職能之一是在於究明對象的本質，而對象是根據給予批評家的印象為基礎，經批評家的探究而顯現出它的性質。就這種意味而言，批評不外是使用語言表現出由許多知覺的統一所構成的印象。如此，印象成為批評家

從事批評活動時的必要條件。印象本來就免不了是主觀的。因此
規定批評家對作品之根本態度的，一如艾略特所認為的，是批評
家的氣質（temperament），而成為批評活動之素材的印象，亦
即支配著批評家對於作品之反應程度的，是他的感受性。因此任
何一種批評可說都免不了主觀的限制。

　　這種說法似乎很容易使讀者誤解，以為艾略特所從事的是
一種「印象批評」。事實上，印象批評是艾略特所極力反對且再
三駁斥的。因此批評的究極，如果只立於主觀的基礎，而不去發
現自己的印象之任何客觀的根據，結果必然陷於主觀漫然獨語
的弊病，現出混亂而無秩序的世界。甚至，在極端的印象批評
中，所謂批評與其對象的作品，在本質上，無疑成為另一種的創
作。如此，批評的對象，畢竟，不過是達到新創作的一塊跳板而
已。王爾德（Oscar Wilde）和西蒙茲（Arthur Symons）所謂「創
造的批評」"Creative Criticism" 或是「審美的批評」"Aesthetic
Criticism" 事實上正是這種東西。總之，讀者的興趣不在於批評
的對象即作品本身，而在於批評家的身上；在這種情形之下當然
允許獨語或是漫談的存在。這種類型的批評家，他們的第一個任
務不在於正視對象，研究作品，而是在作品中「發現一種代替自
己實現藝術作品的存在」。他們在批評中創造出自己的哈姆雷
特，以代替莎士比亞的哈姆雷特。「這種類型的批評家生來具有
屬於創造之類的心靈，但是因為創造力有某些缺點，代之而從事
於批評。」關於哈姆雷特，哥德和柯律治（S. T. Coleridge）都是
屬於這一類型的。如此，他們所表現的，與其說是批評，毋寧說
是創作，然而並沒有達到純粹創作的領域。這就是艾略特所謂的
「蒼白化了的創作」"etiolated creation"。這種類型的批評家最是

危險，貽害讀者最甚。

　　普通所謂的「解釋」（interpretation）或「鑑賞」（appreciation）事實上是屬於主觀的批評，很難說得上是真正的批評。但是使批評家陷於這種錯誤的根本，原因在於本來該是「知性」（intelligence）活動的批評工作中受到情緒的侵入。因此，批評之第一探究（inquiry）要義在途中受到妨礙，結果所產生出來的東西，嚴格說來，稱不上是批評。艾略特認為「解釋」和「鑑賞」都是「怠惰心」"lazy mind"的產物，而這種「批評」，並不是知力活動的結果，只是基於對象在情感上的刺激的自我陶醉而已。

　　事實上在批評的名稱下通過的著作，除了上述那種「蒼白化了的創作」以外，還有一種看來最為理知的所謂「哲學的批評」"philosophic criticism"。這種批評所犯的情緒的毛病，絕不輕於所謂印象批評。Sir Edmund Gosse（1849-1928）認為「詩是知性活動的最高度組織的形式」"Poetry is the most highly organized form of intellectual activity"，便是其中顯著的一例。這種定義使用科學上的用語，一看好像具有明確的意義，但仔細一想，所暗示的意思卻是非常曖昧。艾略特注意到的這種缺陷，他稱為「語言上的疾病」"verbal disease"，完全是近代的產物。十九世紀以來，由於知識領域的擴大，同一個單詞往往被用來表達不同的意思；當我們面對著我們不太了解的事物，我們總是很容易用情緒來代替思想。所謂哲學的批評，抽象的批評，"abstract style in criticism"便是屬於這一類型，事實上是極為 sentimental 的。

　　那麼，艾略特所意味的真正的批評是什麼呢？怎樣才是真正的批評呢？

　　艾略特在〈批評的機能〉中說：「當我談到批評，這裡所意指的當然是使用文字對於藝術作品加以註釋和說明」；接著又說：「在另一方面，批評必須始終抱持某種目的；大體說來，該是在於闡明藝術作品以及匡正趣味」（the elucidation of works of art and the correction of taste）。很明顯地艾略特認為批評的任務不外是（1）藝術作品的闡明；（2）趣味的匡正。因此批評的對象是藝術作品，而不是批評家本身；批評的職責是在究明藝術作品的本質。批評家的態度必須盡力矯正個人的偏見和任性，虛心地接近對象，客觀地追求真實的判斷。換句話說，批評的工作是在給予自己的印象以客觀的妥當性。但是怎樣才能使自己的印象予以客觀的妥當性呢？艾略特在論約翰・卓萊頓（John Dryden）時說：「對於我們所偏愛的一些作品試圖導入某種法則時，所希望的只是弄清楚我們在自己所喜愛的詩中，找到樂趣的理由。」換句話說，就是說明自己從詩中獲得印象的理由。

　　然而，為了說明作品的本質，首先當然必須抓住作品的本質。因此對於作品必須有深刻的理解，批評家必須對於作品具有濃厚的興趣，充分的知識也就成為先要的條件。在艾略特看來，史文朋（A. C. Swinburne）由於知性不純，因此不能成為完全的批評家，他之所以能夠成為傑出的批評家，是因為他對於自己的題材具有十分的興趣和知識。然而批評家真正要完成批評的使命，只對對象具有興趣和知識是不夠的。他在判斷作品的真價，決定作品所占的位置時，必須具有關於這方面更廣泛而深遠的專門的知識。構成廣泛知識的大部分，艾略特認為，是歐洲的文學傳統。要言之，那是過去文學的生命要素，也是作品判斷的標準。

　　關於批評的目的，批評家的先要條件，以及批評的標準

等，已如上述。然而究明作品本質的批評方法呢？從〈威伯理（Charles Whibley）論〉以及〈批評的機能〉中，我們知道艾略特明白地指出，批評主要的兩個手段是比較和分析（comparison and analysis）。

比較和分析，就像艾略特本人所認為的，是互相補足的手段。換句話說，在比較中含有分析，在分析中含有比較，單純地只是一方面的活動是不可能的。但是在理論上加以分開說明的話，分析力的活動是以分析批評之先決條件的印象感覺（Sensation）開始，進而將作品中本質性的東西和附屬性的東西加以分離，將絕對的東西加以區別。而且，由於比較而發現自他印象的相異，因並列對照而產生出反省吟味的動機，以及以傳統作為決定作品價值的標準等，經常都是知性的活動。溫達姆（George Wyndham）、威伯理等不能成為「完全的批評家」雖有種種原因，事實上主要是由於他們缺乏這種分析解剖的能力。然而艾略特並不認為這種分析解剖的能力是萬能的；他說：「即使是最老練的批評家，究極而言，只能指出他認為是真品的詩而已。」

前面說過，艾略特所意味的「傳統」也就是批評的標準。那是由既存的紀念物所構成的一種理想的秩序。由於參與每一件新作品的評價，傳統的存在和性質益趨明顯；每一作家所持有的價值是由於他被放在傳統——雖是過去所產生至今仍然保存生命的一聯作品之間，而顯現出來的。如此，我們對於傳統的意義和價值不能不進一步加以探究。

艾略特的傳統觀，在〈傳統和個人的才能〉（Tradition and the Individual Talent, 1919）和《追求異神》（*After Strange Gods*,

1934）中表現得最為透徹。要言之，傳統是由古典相集形成的一種全體的精神之流，並不是靜態或固定的，而是動態的、具有發展性的。傳統雖不是可以繼承的遺產，卻是以繼承的觀念為基礎。亦即傳統是以一個時代以及後一個時代的存在為必要的，因此傳統可說是過去與現在的某種特殊的關係。傳統為「現在」所繼承，亦即構成「現在」之內容的「過去」。如此，傳統亦即既是過去的產物而又活在現代的一種精神；能夠產生這種認識的，乃是「歷史的意識」（historical sense）。

因此，傳統的成立是以不同的時代、相同精神的作家或作品之存在為必要的。只有一個個作品不能形成傳統；傳統是由一個個作品相集形成而獲得維持的。換句話說，一個個作品雖不能形成傳統，卻分享有傳統的精神。進而，傳統要是沒有過去的意識，也是不能成立的。就這層意義來說，傳統主義者確實免不了具有保守的一面。然而如果只因於過去的意識而不能踏出一步，傳統主義只是墨守舊習（conventionalism）而已，毫無創造可言。真正的傳統主義者使過去活於現在，也可說是透過現在而生存在過去之中。生活在傳統之中，而內裡感到自由，感到自己仍有活動的餘地，那是因為他在內裡感到現在的緣故。純粹的保守主義者所握有的現在，只是充滿過去的現在，並不能在過去中感到真正的現在。傳統一落到這種人的手中也就失去了發展性而成為「定型」。真正的傳統不是這樣。真正的傳統由於現在而不斷地獲得更新和成長，其中含有發展性。能夠認識到過去的精神具有發展性時，才算真正認識到過去和現在並不是完全無緣的，在過去之中生生不息的東西和僵化了的東西是判然有別的，而前者構成了現在的內容。如此，傳統的成立是以過去和現在，兩種「時

間」的意識為必要的。在這層意味上來說，一切都是有時間性的
（temporal），但是將現在看作是過去的發展時，由於過去失去
了它的過去性，因此成為超時間的（timeless）。然而，使人產
生這種看法的，是上面所說的「歷史的意識」。

　　如此，假如傳統是在「現在」之中生生不息，延綿不斷的
某種偉大的「過去」的精神，那麼傳統的維持和發展怎樣才是可
能的？前面說過，傳統是由古典相集形成的一種全體的精神之
流。青年作家在精神上開始接觸到古典時，體驗到一種血緣的親
近感。而對於一個作家的興趣，往往促使我們對於同時代作家也
抱著研究的興趣。如此我們的眼界漸廣；本身受到薰陶而逐漸發
生變化。在這種狀態下創作的作品，已不單純地只是古典的模仿
或借用，而是由古典所養育出來的另一種創作。因此，當作家以
認真的態度研究古典，將古典的精神化成自己的血肉時，他的創
作也就成為繼承傳統的作品。由於古典的研究，使一位作家知道
自己的才能、使命，以及在文學的傳統中，自己所占有的位置。
艾略特所以說「幫助拙劣詩人了解他本人能力的界限是批評家的
部分任務」，是因為批評家熟知傳統。向拙劣詩人明示，傳統使
他知道自己的才能，這是批評家的任務之一。艾略特又說：「對
於偉大作品的讚賞只不過是統御我們的一種訓練，使人留意自己
該占有什麼位置之必要的一種貴族崇拜而已。」所謂的「偉大的
作品」亦即古典，是傳統之所寄託。與艾略特認為，批評的主要
任務在於「趣味的匡正」一樣，都是由於傳統，亦即判斷標準的
存在而來的。總之，如果想成為千古不朽的作家，那麼，體會文
學大道之傳統精神是必要的；作家應該捨棄個性而歸於傳統。在
讀者方面，何嘗不然。換言之，由於批評家一再闡明傳統的存在

和意義，使得一般的趣味導向正當的方向。

　　關於傳統的維持和發展，青年作家在本質上由於對古典傑作的吸收同化而變化成長，已如上述。進而對於作家和傳統的關係試作探討，首先觸及的是「獨創性」（originality）的問題。

　　詩人在人格發展的途上，將廣泛的知識以及多樣的體驗織進自己的作品中，不能不以單純的形式表現這種複雜的內容。因此，他不得不積極地利用過去以及他那時代所有一切文化累積下來的成績。偉大的詩人由於描寫自己而描繪出他那個時代，也就是這個道理。然而，若詩人所表現的不在於矮小個性，而在於盡其吸收各時代文化的精華所形成一種新的統一體，那麼所謂的「獨創性」，是難以期待的。假如詩人有所獨創的話，不是思想或感情的獨創，而是意味著將複雜的思想感情變成一種新的統一體那種才能。艾略特認為「重要的並不在於情緒，或是構成要素，是否『偉大』或強烈，而是熔合各種要素的藝術過程的強力度，換言之，熔合時的壓力才是重要的。」即指此言。艾略特認為創作不外乎一種點鐵成金的藝術手段，亦是將舊材料給予重新組合的一種過程。鐵砂遍地而能夠點鐵成金者，唯賴以詩人的匠心；因此古今中外，一切的一切都是詩人創作的材料；詩人的獨創性，便是在於如何將這些舊有既存的材料，納入藝術的過程，加以適當的壓力，使之煥然成為新的統一體。化腐朽為神奇，才是藝術；而藝術的手法，運用之妙，存乎一心。「最可靠的判斷方法之一，在於詩人怎樣借用。不成熟的詩人模仿；成熟的詩人剽竊；拙劣的詩人毀汙所偷來的東西，而優秀的詩人使之更美好，或者至少把它變成某種別的東西。優秀的詩人將其剽竊物化成唯一無二的一團感情，與原作迥然異趣；拙劣的詩人投入於某種支離破碎之

中。優秀的詩人通常向時代隔遠的、語言迥異的，或興趣不同的作家借用。」這種融化既有的材料，創造出新作品的才能，和前面所說的感受性的統一有關。伊麗莎白時代的作家能夠藉著既有的材料創出獨有，也就是因為他們具有能夠貪吞一切，而加以消化的優秀機能。

依據艾略特的詩觀，詩人的獨創性，並非指表現出詩人獨特的個性而言。關於詩人的個性，暫不論及，但艾略特指出：「絕對獨創的詩，是絕對拙劣的；就壞的意義來說，那是『主觀的』，對於它所要求共鳴的世界毫無關係。」又說：「真正的獨創只是進展；假如那是正常的進展，這種進展可能到了最後顯得無可避免，因此我們幾乎達到否定詩人具有任何『獨創的』能力那種觀點。」因此，詩人要是極力表現出「獨創的」作品時，很可能只是表現出個人的特性或奇癖，或者只是追求新奇，陷於"perverse"（病態的不自然）而不自知。使一個作家免於這種危險的，便是傳統的意識。

如此，使作家乃至批評家免於陷入主張個性所造成的混亂，而活動於統一有秩序的世界中，那是由於傳統的意識。經常闡明傳統的意義，努力於傳統的維持和發展，亦即批評家的任務。「保存傳統——只要優良的傳統存在——是批評家的部分任務」也就是這個意思。艾略特在論英詩時，經常將「形而上詩人」和伊麗莎白時代的作家並列，且加以讚賞，極力喚起人們的注意，這只不過是實行一個批評家所義不容辭的任務而已。因為在他看來，伊麗莎白時代作家達到的完美純熟的境界，那種英詩的傳統，因密爾頓一出而陷於絕途。

然而，艾略特所主張的傳統，並不是指一國特有的傳統，

也不是限於地方性的，而是指貫穿歐洲文化的古典教養而言。亦即構成西洋文化中心的主流，在希臘、羅馬、義大利和法國等的古典之中淵遠流長，而歐洲各國文學匯於斯，脫去地方性而納入傳統的巨流。就這層意義來說，他所努力以赴的，正是阿諾德（Matthew Arnold）所謂 "intellectual confederation"（知的聯盟）的實現；就這點而言，艾略特可說是阿諾德的後繼者。甚至艾略特之所以讚賞伊麗莎白時代的劇作家或者唐恩（John Donne）一派，並不是因為他們最能發揮英國文學的特性，而是在他們的作品中到處閃現著艾略特所認為的真正的詩，而這種詩的命脈，上溯拉辛（Racine）、但丁（Dante）、辛尼加（Seneca）、魯克里修斯（Lucretius）、魏吉爾（Virgil）和荷馬（Homer），下經波特萊爾（Baudelaire）、拉法格（Laforgue）與哥比耶（Corbière）而傳至梵樂希（Paul Valèry）。

　　以上所述，不外是批評家的任務，而批評家的任務所以具有充分的意義，是因為批評家對於批評的目的具有明顯的意識。換句話說，真正的批評是由於為了達到批評的目的，其存在才獲得肯定。那麼批評的目的是什麼呢？直截地說，在於創作的經營。「真正批評的所有形態都是指向創作。」因此嚴格說來，批評的究極目的在於「創作」；詩的批評家為了創作詩而批評詩。批評的一切和創作連結在一起，隨著中間關係的程度而獲得重要性和意義。史文朋和威伯理雖然具有優秀的素質，但是艾略特把他們歸於「不完全的批評家」，理由便是因為他們對於創作這種明確的目的，是無意識地從事批評的活動。

　　對於創作所從事的批評，不單只是批評家在作家外部所做的工作，同時也是作家在本身內部所應做的。「我甚至認為一個

熟練而靈巧的作家，在本身創作時所做的批評，是最重要、最高級的批評。」艾略特在同一篇文章中又指出：「批評活動的最高表現以及真正完成，在於藝術家的苦心經營中與創作形成一體。」換句話說，創作和批評這兩種活動的關係密不可分；批評的意義實在是比向來所認為的更為重大。

將創造力和批評力兩者加以比較時，一般認為後者不如前者。可是艾略特認為越是真正卓越的天才，他的批評力越是發達。過去的批評家，例如阿諾德，往往忽略在創作過程中內在的批評活動。批評家在創作時，對於材料乃至體驗的取捨選擇，因選詞用字、結構組織，而不斷刪改與嘗試等等，都需要種種判斷。這種活動不僅是創造的，更是批評的。

如此，批評的活動在創作中，事實上是演著非常重大的角色。「有些作家在創作上比其他作家更為優異，只因為他們具有更為優異的批評能力而已。」在《聖林集》的序文中艾略特也說出同樣的意思：即「當某種創造的精神比別種更為優越時，理由往往是因為前者比後者更是批評的。」

在艾略特看來，批評是創作所不可或缺，沒有批評能力很難產生優秀作品。將這種觀點再加以引伸，那麼，作家在創作中所嘗試的批評，對於同道的人可說是最有價值的。這種參與創作過程的批評力，是為真正的創作活動作準備而從事的批評活動。總之，詩人以自己的體驗為基礎所說的詩論，對於同道人最為有益。艾略特說過：「對於詩人只有詩人的批評才是有用的。」也就是這個道理。

一如上述，在創作中的批評活動具有重大的意義，然而這並不是說創作必須以批評為基礎，也不是主張批評居於創作之

上。前面說過，批評的最高任務在於創造時和創作力協調形成一
體。事實上批評力和創作力是互相補足的作用，兩者不應混同。
創作是以本身為目的的（autotelic），而批評是關於本身以外之
物的活動。因此，批評能夠參與創作，而創作不容介入批評之中。
批評永遠是知性的，換句話說是純粹的（disinterested）知性活動；
亦即從事於「探究」（inquiry）的知性活動。

　　在批評的世界中，情緒的侵入以表現自己等等，是該極力
排斥的。如此，一個部門、一種能力，各有本來應該歸屬的領
域，以及各自應該完成的使命。批評家的重要職務便是在闡明這
點。要言之，「詩的確不是道德教誨，或是政治指導，亦非宗教
或宗教的同等物」，「而且因為詩本是一種藝術……詩應該給予
的第一印象是對於藝術感情，而詩應該引起的第一個問題是藝
術問題。」艾略特極力主張將文學當作文學，將詩當作詩這種
態度，都在〈小論詩的批評〉（A Brief Treatise on the Criticism of
Poetry, 1920）、《聖林集》再版的序文（1928）〈批評中的試驗〉
（Experiment in Criticism, 1929）、約翰遜的《倫敦》複刻本的
序文（1930）以及論卓萊頓的三篇論文集（1932）中一再強調。
這是艾略特所謂 "the integrity of poetry" 的問題。然則艾略特對於
詩的看法如何？

　　艾略特給詩下過一個定義，他說：「詩是一種高級的娛樂；
我不是說給予高級人們的娛樂。我認為那是一種娛樂，給予有教
養的人們一種娛樂」，本來這個定義是不完全的；艾略特本人也
承認，但是除此以外，要給詩下定義時，可能脫離他所認為的詩
更遠，因此他敢提出這麼一個看來很簡單的定義。總之不管這
個定義是否完全，艾略特認為詩本來的職能，在於給予特殊的

（peculiar）樂趣這點，在他的評論中到處可見。他甚至明白地指出詩的職能或作用，不是理智的，而是情緒的，因為樂趣或者愉快本來就是情緒的。

可是詩中所表現的是否也是情緒？關於他的知性的要素暫且擱置，艾略特對於詩處理情緒這點是承認的。他在論卓萊頓的 "Absalom and Achitophel" 以及波普的 "Letter to Arbuthnot" 時這麼說：「總之，他們從事偉大的詩所從事的某種事情；他們捕捉情緒將之表現在文學之中；我們可以說，在卓萊頓的情形，那是輕蔑之情，而在波普的情形，那是憎惡或者怨恨之情。」

可是，艾略特在〈傳統和個人的才能〉中卻說：「詩不是情緒的放縱，而是情緒的逃避；詩不是個性的表現，而是個性的逃避。」"Poetry is not a turning loose of emotion, but an escape from emotion; it is not the expression of personality, but an escape from personality." 這豈不是互相矛盾的嗎？

〈傳統和個人的才能〉中所說的這句經常被引用的話，需要極為慎重的吟味，否則任意加以解釋，可能和艾略特的本意相去甚遠。艾略特在這一節稍前的地方，說：「詩人的職責並不在於尋求新的情緒，而是在於運用普通的情緒；將這種情緒化鍊成詩，以表現在實際情緒中根本不存在的感受。」"The business of the poet is not to find new emotions, but to use the ordinary ones and, in working them up into poetry, to express feelings which are not in actual emotions at all." 將前後所引用這兩段話加以一看，前者所說的 "escape from emotion" 豈不是相當於後者所說的 "to express feelings which are not in actual emotions"？這豈不是說納入藝術中的並不是實踐的，我所經驗的那種活生生的情緒，而是脫離現實

性變成 impersonal 的感受？換句話說，詩中為避免情緒的表現，豈不是必須藉用某種方法，將情緒加以「轉換」（transmute）？艾略特在同一篇論文中接著說：「有許多人欣賞詩中所表現的真摯的情緒；能夠鑑賞卓絕技巧的人為數不多。但是只有寥寥無幾的人，知道什麼時候具有意味深長的情緒表現；這種情緒生命是在詩中，而不是在詩人的經歷裡。」艾略特在這裡所謂「意味深長的情緒」（significant emotion）為什麼是「意味深長的」，姑且不問，至少那不是現實感情或實踐感情，而是作品中所表現的情緒，亦即「純粹感情」"impersonal emotion" 這點是很明顯的。這種解釋，再引用兩段他的文章，可以得到更進一層的確實性：「對於詩人本身甚為重要的印象和經驗，在詩中或許並不占有任何位置，而那些在詩中成為重要的東西，或許有詩人本身即個性中只是占著極為無足輕重的位置而已。」「藝術家的修養越高，感受的個人與創作的心靈，在其內部越是完全分離，其心靈越能完全地將熱情亦即創造的素材加以消化和變質。」在這兩段文章中所謂「個性」或者「個人」，顯然不外就是「實踐的我」或者「現實的我」。

經以上的引述，我們可以知道，艾略特並不否認在詩作中表現詩人本身的感情。他所強調的是詩，並不是如實地表現活生生的現實感情，或者人生中喜怒哀樂的情緒。任何詩人創作的起點，不外是表現本身的體驗，或者情緒；假如詩人想表現在任何意味上，可說未曾「體驗」過的那種情緒，那麼，他的作品難免失去真摯性，同時缺乏深刻性。艾略特說：「每一個詩人都是以他自己的情緒為創作的出發點。」"What every poet starts from is his own emotion." 如此，我們不能因艾略特說過詩是情緒的逃避，

個性的逃避，就遽然下結論，認為他否認詩中情緒的表現，以及個性的表現。關於這點，將艾略特的立場表明得最為清楚的，是附在梵樂希（Paul Valéry）的傑作〈蟒蛇〉（Le Serpent）英譯中，他所寫的序文中下面的一節：「這個作品正像梵樂希其他所有詩作一樣是超個性的；這是就個人的情緒與個人的體驗，擴大而成為某種超個性的東西，就這層意義來說，——並不是就和個人的經驗和感情絕緣這層意義而言。沒有一種優秀的詩屬於後者；事實上，魯克里修斯作品所具有的優點，奇異，也就是他藉以將自我消滅在一種體系之中，將自我與之合而為一，以獲得比自我更偉大的某種東西的熱切行為。這種自我犧牲，需要很大的專注。但是對於希望將自己保存在有限的『個性』中，或使這些弱小的個性，所具有的情緒和觀念受到不斷反覆的阿諛，而不是由於詩人優越的素質而擴大和變形些人來說，魯克里修斯、桃樂希或其他任何優秀詩人，都永遠不會是真正可能接受以及可以了解的。」

　　艾略特這段話，可以和他在另一篇文章中說到，莎士比亞從事於「將他個人的私人的苦惱轉換為某種豐富而珍奇的，某種普遍的超個性的東西那種努力」的意思互相引證。所謂「個性」也者，越來越明顯地也就是「現實的我」。

　　要言之，在艾略特心中，創作的藝術是一種轉換過程（transmulation）。從他的評論中，可以歸納出下列幾項重要的內容：

1. 將粗雜的日常生活中的情緒，轉換為純粹的意味深常的藝術情緒，已如上述。

2. 將思想、觀念與觀察轉換為感覺、感受和心境。艾略特指出，

查普曼和唐恩等有一種特殊的感覺方式，就是「將思考根據感覺予以直接把握，或是將思考再創造為感情」。又說，「拉法格以及哥比耶的許多詩，較之近代任何一位英國詩人更接近於『唐恩派』。但是比他們更為古典的詩人們，具有與唐恩在本質上相同的性質，即將觀念轉換為感覺，將觀察變形為精神狀態。」艾略特在論 Sir John Davies 時也認為他具有那種珍奇希有的天賦，能夠將思想變成感受。

3. 將自我、個性的轉換為超個性的藝術作品。這點構成了艾略特「不具個性」"Impersonality" 的藝術觀，以下將再論及。

　　且說這種轉換過程，怎樣才是可能的？換句話說，怎樣才能獲得 "impersonal emotion"？怎樣才能脫離現實的自我 "depersonalization"，而達到純粹藝術的境界？關於這點，在前面所引用論梵樂希的序文後半中，已經有所暗示。艾略特進一步的說明，他說：「藝術的情緒是不具個性的。詩人若不為他所該從事的工作全然獻出自己，不能夠達到這種不具個性的境界。而詩人可能不知道該寫些什麼，除非他生活於不僅是現在，而是過去猶存的現在之中，除非他所意識到的不是那些已經死去的，而是那些一直活存的。」這裡所說的 "What is not merely the present"，顯然相當於前面所引用論梵樂希的序文中的 "a system"，亦即艾略特在〈傳統和個人的才能〉中屢述的「傳統」。特別值得注意的是，詩人在創作時不能不有所認識的兩個重要的條件，其履行的次序，在這節引文中明白地顯示出來。

　　根據艾略特的看法，二十五歲以後，還想繼續作詩人的人不能沒有傳統的意識。所謂的傳統，一如前面說過的，是在「現在」之中仍然繼續活動著的某種過去的生命，亦即先人有價值的

業績所連綿貫徹的統一體。因此，由於生存在傳統之中，才能認清留給自己的工作，才賦予的課題。這無非是在指示出自己能力的局限，因此使他自覺自己的使命，使他埋頭於自己所該從事的工作（to know what is to be done）。所謂不具個性，事實上是有雙重的意味。一則由於歸入傳統而失去了區區之「個性」而獲得普遍性；二則由於埋頭於創作這種純粹的活動，泯除粗雜的「情緒」而獲得純粹性。艾略特在〈葉慈論〉中指出：「不具個性有兩種形態：一種對於只是熟練的巧匠作家是天生的，另一種是由於藝術家越來越成熟而逐漸達成的。……第二種不具個性是從強烈的，個人的經驗中能夠表現出普遍真實的那種詩人；將自己經驗的特殊性全部保持下來，把它變成普遍象徵的那種詩人。」而葉慈原是屬於第一種的偉大巧匠，卻成為第二種的偉大詩人，這點倒是希奇。總之，「在這種泯除個性的過程中，藝術才可說是接近於科學的狀態。」一個藝術家所以「越來越成熟」，便是因為他不斷地努力，使自己生存在傳統之中，寄予傳統的發展，從傳統中獲得更恆久、更豐富的生命；在這種意味上說來，他的作品是「真正新的」"truly new"，其中所表現的情緒才說得上是「意味深長的」"Significant"。

　　如此，如果想成為詩人，首先必須具有傳統的觀念，自覺地經常生存在傳統之中，然後埋頭於創作。然而，他的創作不是追求個性，而是逃避個性；不是表現個性，而是超越個性。艾略特在論伊麗莎白劇作家時，就說出這個意思：「沒有任何藝術家創作出偉大的藝術，是由於努力試圖表現自己的個性。他全神貫注在某種工作而間接地表現出他的個性；那種工作在意義上正如製作有能率的機器，或者水罐或桌腳的銑床工一樣。」

　　將詩中的情緒和傳統連結在一起，這種看法關係到詩的價值判斷。要言之，艾略特所主張的是，不論創作或欣賞，我們在作品中所能發現的，必須是不具個性或超越個性的。亦即作品中不能如實地表現我們日常生活中所實際經驗的那種情緒。因此，如果我們想將這種感情表現為藝術，必須借用能夠喚起同樣或類似那種情緒的一群對象乃至一種情況；而這種喚起類似情緒的對象或情況，艾略特稱為「客觀的相關物」"objective correlative"，他說「以藝術形式表現情緒的唯一方法是藉著找出一種『客觀的相關物』；換句話說，是藉著找出該成為那種特殊情緒之公式的一組物體、一種情況、一串事件；當必須以感覺經驗結束的一些外在事實被給予時，情緒隨即被喚起的那種公式。」

　　借用「客觀的相關物」之表現方法，在艾略特的詩中俯拾即是。其中最有名的一行，表現出普魯佛洛克在社交上混日子那種無聊與空虛，最為深刻適切的是：

　　　我用咖啡匙量出了我的人生
　　　I have measured out my life with coffee spoons

　　這完全是借用「客觀的相關物」的表現方法，將咖啡匙和人生聯想在一起，造出「量盡了」的關係，其中所喚起的情緒，不需要再有其他任何說明或解釋。在某一意義上來說，這是一種象徵主義的手法，而上面所引用的句中所謂「公式」"formula"不外是意味著一群形象或象徵。

　　如此，「以藝術形式表現」的方法，主要地在於避免藝術中直接表現情緒，必須先藉著「客觀的相關物」之介入將情緒客

觀化，加以游離，使之成為「非個人的」"impersonal"。前面已經說過，詩本來是一種藝術，詩中所表現的感情是藝術感情。作品中的藝術感情，既不同於作者生活中的感情，也不同於讀者在閱讀時，偶爾聯想到的其他感情。因此，文學批評家首先必須處理的第一個問題，便是作品所給予的藝術感情的問題。艾略特所謂「文學批評家除了由藝術作品所直接喚起的那些情緒以外，不該有任何情緒」"A literary critic should have no emotions except those immediately provoked by a work of art." 也就是指這點而言。總之，將詩首先當作詩，將文學首先當作文學來處理，正是其批評論的出發點。這無非是在維護詩本來的傳統，企圖使十九世紀以來，受到其他部門侵蝕的詩的領域，回復到它本來應有的位置，所做的努力而已。

　　然而，對於一件作品，首先把它當作藝術來處理，並不是批評家唯一的最後工作。由於詩首先被當作詩看待，因此在文學批評中，研究作品的技巧，以及從技巧方面研究作家，也就具有重要的意義。艾略特在《聖林集》再版序文中說：「因此，在批評詩時，以我們所具有的感受性以及有關其他詩的知識，無妨從認為詩是最佳配列和最佳格律，所構成的最佳字句這點開始。」進而論及馬羅（Marlowe）的無韻詩，或者檢討其他作家的作品，在藝術上達到怎樣的程度等等，也都是這個理由。關於韻文和散文的區別，以及有關自由詩的考察等，也都是由於首先將詩當作藝術這個觀點而來。

　　關於詩之內容的情緒，已如上述。此外，關於其他的要素，主要是知性的要素，艾略特的看法如何？

　　艾略特在〈形而上詩人論〉中將錫特尼（Sir Sidney）的

"Look in thy heart, and write" 這一行稍為變形加以引用說：「那些反對密爾頓或卓萊頓那種『技巧造作』的人們，有時候告訴我們說：『看透心中事，我手寫我心。』但是這樣並不能看得十分透徹；拉辛或唐恩所窺視的比心還多。詩人必須窺透腦膜、神經系統以及消化管。」進而在《伊茲拉‧龐德詩選》序文中指出詩人表現為藝術的素材是「讀書和反省的結果，各種各樣的興趣、接觸與交友，以及熱情與冒險」，可見詩材不外是詩人的一切經驗和印象。詩人越是知性的，他的經驗越豐富越好。「詩人必須在不妨礙自己所必要的感受力以及所需要的怠惰範圍內，儘量獲取知識」，然後將他的經驗或知識變成詩。因此所謂哲學的詩人或者思想的詩人，不論其思想或哲學多麼深奧，並非指如實地表現那些抽象思想的詩人而言，而是指將思想情緒化。換言之，是指表現「思想的感情等價物」"the emotional equivalent of thought" 的那種詩人而言。

　　詩的材料不外是詩人的經驗和情緒等，而大詩人的任務是在表現他那時代最大強度的情緒。真摯的詩人不會只沉溺於個人的經驗；他不能不表現出普遍的東西。然而文化越進步，那個時代所含有的經驗越多樣複雜，因此所表現為詩的內容也越多樣複雜。「現代文明包含著極大的多樣性和複雜性，而這種多樣性和複雜性加之於受過洗鍊的感受性，結果自然產生出多樣而複雜的作品。為了適合自己的意思，將語言強制鑲入，必要時使其錯置轉位，因此，詩人的包容力不得不越來越廣，越富暗示性，表現上越成為間接的了。」從這幾句話中，艾略特指出了現代詩所朝著的一個方向。

　　而隨著詩之素材即經驗越來越多樣複雜且深刻，批評家的

興趣不得不也越來越擴大。由於興趣擴大，批評家對於批評的中心，亦即對於文學本來的目的，在於給予特殊的樂趣這點，不能不更進一步加以闡明。「只要文學被當作文學而存在，那麼文學批評，亦即和文學本身同立於一個基礎上的批評，也會有存在的餘地。因為只要詩和小說以及像這樣的東西有人寫作，它的第一個目的，過去一直是，將來也一定是——給予某種獨特的樂趣；這種樂趣不論我們對它的解釋怎樣困難和不同，具有經過許多時代仍然保持不變的某種東西。因此批評的工作將不只是擴展批評的疆界，同時也在弄明它的中心，而堅持後者有其必要，是隨著堅持前者有其必要而增強的。」如此，艾略特指出了文學批評的一個新傾向。

　　以上就艾略特的創作論和批評論概略地加以引述，特附於《艾略特文學評論選集》卷末作為解說。其中見解大多根據矢野禾積教授在 *Essays by T. S. Eliot* 一書中的序論。拾人牙慧，自知力有未逮；他山之石，但願有所攻錯。

（原載《艾略特文學評論選集》，田園出版社，1969 年）

試論〈荒原〉的八種中譯本

原詩：

April is the cruelest month, breeding

Lilacs out of the dead land, mixing

Memory and desire, stirring

Dull roots with spring rain.

Winter kept us warm, covering

Earth in forgetful snow, feeding

A little life with dried tubers.

趙（蘿蕤）譯：

四月是最殘忍的一個月，荒地上

長著丁香，把回憶和欲望

參合在一起，又讓春雨

催促那些遲鈍的根芽。

冬天使我們溫暖，大地

給助人遺忘的雪覆蓋著，又叫

枯乾的球根提供少許生命。

葉（維廉）譯：

四月是最殘酷的月份，迸生長

紫丁香，從死沉沉的地上，雜混著
記憶和欲望，鼓動著
呆鈍的根鬚，以春天的雨絲。
冬天令我們溫暖，覆隱著
大地，在善忘的雪花中，滋潤著
一點點生命，在乾的塊莖裡。

杜（國清）譯：

四月最是殘酷的季節
讓死寂的土原迸出紫丁香
摻雜著追憶與欲情
以春雨撩撥萎頓的根莖。
冬天令人溫暖，將大地
覆蓋著遺忘的雪泥
讓枯乾的球根滋養短暫的生命。

查（良錚）譯：

四月最殘忍，從死了的
土地滋生丁香，混雜著
回憶和欲望，讓春雨
挑動著呆鈍的根。
冬天保我們溫暖，把大地
埋在忘懷的雪裡，使乾了的
球莖得一點點生命。

趙毅衡譯：

四月是最殘酷的月份，在死地上
養育出丁香，擾混了
回憶和欲望，用春雨
驚醒遲鈍的根。
冬天使我們溫暖，用健忘的雪
把大地覆蓋，用乾癟的根莖
餵養微弱的生命。

李（俊清）譯：

四月這殘酷的季節，滋育
紫丁香於乾旱土地上，混合
記憶和希望，一陣春雨
擾亂半死根莖的平靜。
寒冬卻令人溫暖，飄灑
忘憂之雪掩飾險巇，而以
乾球根飼育少許的生氣。

裘（小龍）譯：

四月是最殘忍的月份，哺育著
丁香，在死去的土地裡，混合著
記憶和欲望，撥動著
沉悶的根芽，在一陣陣春雨裡。
冬天使我們暖和，遮蓋著
大地在健忘的雪裡，餵養著

　　一個小小的生命，在乾枯的球莖裡。

劉（象愚）譯：

　　　四月是最殘忍的月份，在死去的
　　　土地裡哺育著丁香，混和著
　　記憶和欲望，又讓春雨
　　撥動著沉悶的根芽。
　　冬天使我們溫暖，把大地
　　覆蓋在健忘的雪裡，用乾枯的
　　球莖餵養著一個小小的生命。

　　1948 年諾貝爾文學獎得主艾略特（T.S. Eliot, 1888-1965）的成名作〈荒原〉（The Waste Land），最初發表於 1922 年 10 月文學季刊《標準》（*The Criterion*）創刊號上，公認是二十世紀英美文學的一部劃時代的作品，也是西方現代詩的一個里程碑。第一個中文譯本是在十五年之後，1937 年 6 月，由「新月派」詩人陳夢家的夫人趙蘿蕤所完成。促成這件大事的是當時主持《新詩社》的戴望舒，由他策劃、約稿、仔細審閱譯稿，將這部翻譯列為《新詩社叢書》的第一種出版。在《新詩》月刊上的「出版廣告」可能出自戴望舒手筆，聲稱這部「附以三萬餘言的注釋」的翻譯，「譯筆流麗暢達，注釋精細詳明。卷首有葉公超先生序言，對作者做精密的研究，並附有作者肖像，均為此譯本增色不少。」可惜這個譯本當初只印三百五十冊，而且在 1937 年 6 月正值抗戰爆發前夕，早已絕版。趙蘿蕤四〇年代在芝加哥大學深造，四〇年代末回大陸之後就不得不與「資產階級作家」艾略特

「劃清界線」；在大陸對艾略特的介紹從此中斷。[1]

　　臺灣最早的〈荒原〉譯本，也是第二個中譯本，是 1961 年正當臺灣詩壇大力推展現代主義運動時，由詩人學者葉維廉所翻譯，發表在《創世紀》詩刊第 16 期。第三個中譯本是我翻譯的，發表在 1966 年《現代文學》第 28 期。當時在臺灣是看不到趙蘿蕤的譯本的。

　　第四個中譯本是由四〇年代「九葉詩人」之一穆旦，本名查良錚，在七〇年代後半期秘密翻譯的。查良錚於 1948 年赴美，在芝加哥大學攻讀英美文學，1953 年回國之後，致力於翻譯工作，到 1958 年五年之內，譯有普希金、雪萊、拜倫、濟慈等人的詩集十餘種。1958 年 12 月被判為「歷史反革命」，受勞動改造，且被剝奪了著譯出版的權利。1977 年 12 月病逝。他在文化大革命後期，翻譯了當時無人過問，事實上被禁的艾略特的作品十一首，一直到 1985 年才收入於《英國現代詩選》[2] 作為遺著出版。

　　〈荒原〉第五個中譯本的譯者是趙毅衡。他原任職於北京社會科學院，1985 年 5 月出版的《美國現代詩選》[3] 包括艾略特的作品〈荒原〉等十二首；序文寫於 1983 年 5 月，說明這本詩選的編譯工作前後斷斷續續地進行四年，可見大約譯於 1980 年前後，當時他到加州大學柏克萊分校攻讀比較文學博士。他後來任教於英國倫敦大學。第六個中譯本是臺灣東吳大學李俊清教

1　陳子善，〈《荒原》中譯本及其他〉，《香港文學》第 108 期，1993 年 12 月，頁 70-71。趙譯本後收入袁可嘉、董衡巽、鄭克魯選編，《外國現代派作品選》第一冊（上），上海文藝出版社。

2　查良錚譯，《英國現代詩選》，湖南人民出版社，1985 年 5 月。

3　趙毅衡編譯，《美國現代詩選》（上），北京：外國文學出版社，1985 年 5 月。

授於 1982 年 6 月在臺北出版的譯註《艾略特的荒原》[4]。第七個中譯本的譯者是裘小龍。他在 1985 年 9 月出版《四個四重奏》[5]一書，是艾略特詩的全譯本。他原在上海社會科學院工作，1988年到美國深造。第八個中譯本譯者是北京師範大學教授劉象愚，收入於陳敬容主編的《中外抒情名詩鑑賞辭典》，1988 年 8 月出版。[6]

　　受限於時間和篇幅，本文無法對〈荒原〉這八種中譯本的特色和優劣詳加評論。為了論證文學翻譯的特色和文學翻譯人才必備的幾個條件，我們只能以〈荒原〉開頭七行兩句為例，略加比較和說明。

　　艾略特在 1948 年獲得諾貝爾文學獎。授獎辭對艾略特的作品推崇備至，其中指出，〈荒原〉這部作品，當它那晦澀而嫻熟的文字形式，最後顯示出它的秘密時，沒有人不會感到這個標題的可怕含義，並認為，這篇淒涼而低沉的作品，旨在描寫現代文明的枯燥和無力，而全詩只有四百三十六行，但它的內涵大於同樣頁數的一本小說。在我看來，〈荒原〉這部作品的主旨和內涵，更是具體而微地包含在開篇這七行之中。

　　艾略特在原註中說，這首詩的題目、計畫，以及大多的象徵表現都受到韋絲頓（Jessie L. Weston）女士所著《從祭儀到傳奇》（*From Ritual to Romance*）一書，有關聖杯傳說的啟發，同時也取材於另一本人類學名著《金枝》（*The Golden Bough*）中關於豐年祭或繁殖神的崇拜儀式。有關聖杯傳說和繁殖神的文

4　李俊清譯註，《艾略特的荒原》，臺北：書林出版有限公司，1982 年 6 月。

5　裘小龍譯，《四個四重奏》，廣西：灕江出版社，1985 年 9 月。

6　陳敬容主編，《中外現代抒情名詩鑑賞辭典》，北京：學苑出版社，1989 年 8 月。

化背景，對了解〈荒原〉的題旨，至關重要。

中世紀傳說中有一位漁王（Fisher King），他的城堡坐落在河岸；他所統治的是一塊受詛咒的土地，一片乾旱不毛的荒原，而他本人也是殘廢不育的。這土地的命運和統治者的命運分不開，除非他的殘疾治癒，否則這土地永遠受詛咒；莊稼不長，百畜不生。只有當一個尋找聖杯的騎士歷經重重難關，來到漁王的宮堡，經過考驗，解答各種問題之後，聖杯顯現，詛咒才消失，漁王的病才能得治，他的國土和人民才能恢復生殖能力。聖杯原指耶穌基督被釘在十字架上時，聖徒用來承接他的血的杯子，另有一說是指基督及其門徒在最後的晚餐上用的杯子，後來丟失；中世紀騎士的最高榮譽便是找回聖杯，但須經過許多險阻，歷經各種考驗。

《金枝》中關於繁殖神崇拜的神話，主要是敘利亞、埃及、小亞細亞一帶的，有關的祭祀儀式是慶祝繁殖神死後再生，大地由枯寂凋萎中復活，恢復生機。將尋找聖杯與繁殖神崇拜結合在一起，可以說是受基督教化的原始崇拜，其象徵意義猶如生民失去繁殖神，大地失去生機變成了荒原；尋找聖杯是為了救治漁王的殘疾；慶祝繁殖神再生，為使荒原復甦；對西方現代文明而言，其救贖在於找回宗教信仰。

〈荒原〉開頭七行所描寫的便是這樣一個世界的浮影：荒廢、無能、愛死不活、雖生猶死、不生不死、非生非死、亦生亦死的生存景象或精神形象。以下讓我們逐行討論原詩的含義和各家翻譯的差異。

〈荒原〉一開頭，詩人故作驚人之筆，說：四月最是殘酷的一個月（「April is the cruelest month」）。四月正是大地回春，

草木復甦，欣欣向榮的時候，怎麼說是最殘酷的呢？對荒原外的人來說，這是有悖情理的；可是對荒原上的任何生命來說，正是如此。對於一個了無生機的荒地，或生機殘廢的生命，硬要他展示生機或萌生春心，知其不可能而強迫其所不能，這何等殘酷！這句原文，翻成「四月是最殘忍的一個月」（趙譯），或「四月是最殘酷的月份」（葉譯、衡譯），或「四月是最殘忍的月份」（裘譯、劉譯），都沒錯，「信」而且「達」，但是不夠「雅」，缺少詩的韻味。查譯翻成「四月最殘忍」，將「一個月」或「月份」略去了，不夠「信」的標準，但是有道理的——他一定也認為「一個月」或「月份」在中文的語感上太沒有詩意了。這正是杜譯認為四月代表春天，因此將它譯成「季節」的理由。此外，杜譯不將「is the cruelest」直翻成「是最殘酷的」，而翻成「最是殘酷的」，也是基於詩的感受性。有些讀者一定會聯想到李後主「最是倉皇辭廟日」，或是徐志摩在〈莎喲娜拉〉那首詩中的名句：「最是那一低頭的溫柔」。徐志摩不愧為詩人，將「那一低頭是最溫柔的」這九個字的散文，鍛鍊成一字不差的優美詩句。尤其值得一提的是，杜譯「四月／最是／殘酷的／季節」在節奏上完全呼應英文原句「April / is the / cruelest / month」重輕相間的四個音步。

　　其次，原詩以三個「－ ing」結尾的動詞斷行，說明何以四月最是殘酷，頗有欲斷還續、苟延殘喘的味道。先說「breeding / Lilacs out of the dead land」。這個片語直譯成散文的意思是：「使紫丁香從死去了的土地上長出來」。這裡「breeding」是及物動詞，除了「使繁殖」之外，也有「促使」、「導致」、「引起」的意思。四月之所以最是殘酷，在於使乾死的土地長出紫丁香。

這種不可能的強迫，勉其所難的酷使，是違反生命和自然之道的。這種不可能的強求，違反萬物本性的殘忍，在趙譯（荒地上／長著丁香），查譯（從死了的／土地滋生丁香），衡譯（在死地上／養育出丁香），裴譯（哺育著／丁香，在死去的土地裡），劉譯（在死去的／土地裡哺育著丁香），或李譯（滋育／紫丁香於乾旱土地上）中，都沒有暗示出來。葉譯（迸生長／紫丁香，從死沉沉的地上），略有勉強長出之意，而杜譯（讓死寂的土原迸出紫丁香）卻強烈地暗示這種天地不仁的殘酷性。「Lilacs」，該譯為「紫丁香」而不是「丁香」；前者屬木犀科，春季開花，可供觀賞；後者屬桃金娘科，夏季開花，大多藥用或作香料。至於將「dead land」譯為「荒地」（趙譯），不夠準確；譯為「死沉沉的土地」（葉譯），「死了的土地」（查譯），「死地」（衡譯），「乾旱土地」（李譯）或「死去的土地」（裴譯、劉譯），與杜譯「死寂的土原」比照之下，也顯出譯者對詩語的感受性的差異。

　　下一個跨行片語，「mixing / Memory and desire」各家的譯法大致一樣，將「memory」翻成「回憶」或「記憶」，將「desire」翻成「欲望」（李譯翻成「希望」諒是誤植），唯有杜譯別出心裁，翻成「追憶」和「欲情」，在語感上更有抒情詩的意味。這種帶有強烈感性的情緒也正是生命痛苦和煩惱的根源，是讓荒原人難以忍受的。

　　下一個片語，「Stirring / Dull roots with spring rain」。各家的翻譯差別較大，主要的原因還是由於對詩意的感受不同。「stir」的含意包括「攪動」、「使微動」（cause something to move slightly）、「激起」；翻成「催促」（趙譯）、「鼓動」

（葉譯）、「驚醒」（衡譯）、「擾亂」（李譯）都不夠準確，不如「撩撥」（杜譯）、「挑動」（查譯）、「撥動」（裘譯、劉譯）庶幾近之。「撩撥」和「挑動」隱含春雨撩人的誘惑，更具感情色彩。「Dull roots」翻成「遲鈍的根芽」（趙譯）、「呆鈍的根鬚」（葉譯）、「呆鈍的根」（查譯）、「遲鈍的根」（衡譯）都沒錯，只是略嫌呆鈍，不夠生動。李譯翻成「半死的根莖」，過於強解。杜譯為「萎頓的根莖」，含有性無能的暗示，尤其是在惱人春雨的撩撥之下，形成極大的反諷；這種暗示力即使超過原詩，只要不違背原詩的含意和「荒原」的主題，該是可取的。裘譯和劉譯翻成「沉悶的根芽」，是違反詩情的，因為荒原人深知追憶與欲情所帶來的痛苦，對春雨的撩撥採取否定的態度，雖然愛死不活，萎靡頹廢，但在主觀上對這種生存狀態是認同的，不該覺得沉悶。這種了無生趣、無所作為、安之若素的生命觀，在以下三行表現得更為明顯：

Winter kept us warm, covering

Earth in forgetful snow, feeding

A little life with dried tubers.

　　荒原人認為「冬天使我們溫暖」；所謂「溫暖」不僅指溫度上冷熱適中，更指心理上的溫馨舒適。正像前一句描寫對春天的反常心理，這一句對冬天的描寫也是違背常情的，而在句法上，同樣以跨行片語對這種反常的心理感覺加以說明。第一個理由：冬天「將大地覆蓋在遺忘的雪泥」。所謂「forgetful」，趙譯翻成「助人遺忘的」，葉譯翻成「善忘的」，杜譯翻成「遺

忘的」，查譯翻成「忘懷的」，李譯翻成「忘憂的」，衡譯、裘譯和劉譯翻成「健忘的」，語意不盡相同。就我的理解而言，雪本身無所謂善忘或健忘，更無所謂忘懷或忘憂，也許因趙譯翻成「助人遺忘的」，比較合乎常理。然而，英文「forgetful」也有「不掛在心上」或「不在意」（not thinking about something, or neglectful of something）的意思。亦即，雪對外界「遺而忘之」，漠不關心，不受牽掛或干擾，因而保持覆雪下與外界隔絕的寧靜。翻成「忘懷」或「忘憂」似乎顯得過於超脫和瀟灑。李譯「飄灑／忘憂之雪掩飾險巇」，過於浮誇；將「覆蓋」變成「掩飾」、「大地」變成「險巇」，語意不同，都顯得不夠信實。

最後一個片語，「feeding /A little life with dried tubers」。各家譯法大同小異，但對「A little life」的不同理解卻值得一提。趙譯翻成「少許生命」，葉譯和查譯翻成「一點點生命」，杜譯翻成「短暫的生命」，衡譯翻成「微弱的生命」，李譯翻成「少許的生氣」，裘譯和劉譯翻成「一個小小的生命」。這裡該指荒原上的一般生命現象，翻成「一個……生命」，不足取；翻成「短暫的」或「微弱的」是解釋，也不可取。「生氣」作為「飼育」的受詞，不無勉強。荒原上的生命不是朝氣蓬勃的，而是臨死前僅存的一點兒生命，因此翻成「一點兒生命」最為適當。冬天讓埋在雪地下的枯乾的球根滋養一點點兒生命，極言生存的極限狀況，而荒原人卻認為「冬天使我們溫暖」，可見他們甘於苟延殘喘，對這種奄奄一息的生存狀態並無怨言，然而只要一息尚存，應該仍然有希望獲得救贖的。

從以上的解釋中，我們可以對〈荒原〉的主旨有了較明確的了解。在荒原的世界裡，春天是殘酷的，他們規避欲望，拒絕

回憶，不願生命力的復甦，固然是逃避的心理，也是對現實的消極反抗；他們喜歡冬天半死不活的狀態，無為無欲，如果不能獲得救贖，是寧死勿活的。然而，這首詩的主題，並不在於讚揚或歌頌這種反常的生命觀。詩中涉指聖杯傳說的象徵意義，主要在於尋找聖杯以救治漁王的殘疾而使不毛之地恢復生機。因此，繁殖神崇拜的象徵意義，在這首詩中更為重要。換句話說，生與死是〈荒原〉的兩大主題，其根本意義在於，漁王的傳說象徵由生到死的頹廢，而繁殖神的崇拜象徵由死到生，乃至由死達到生的救贖。〈荒原〉開篇這七行的主旨在於前者，極言荒原世界的頹廢心態。若不能獲得救贖，這種生是不如死。這也是〈荒原〉這首詩在詩題之下那段引文的主旨：

　　「在庫瑪耶我親眼看見那位女巫被吊在甕中，每當孩童問她：女巫姑，你想怎樣？她總是回答說：我想死啊。」

　　這段題辭引自羅馬詩人佩特洛尼厄斯（Petronius, ?-86）作品。在希臘神話中，阿波羅愛上女巫西比爾，她向阿波羅要求永生，但卻忘了要求青春，因此她的生命只能老而不死，最後衰老萎縮成一個瘦小的軀殼，被吊在甕中或瓶子裡。這種老而不死的生命，簡直生不如死，因此她但求一死，以得解脫。這個題辭用來喻指荒原上的生命，奄奄一息，不死不活，其實是，這種生不如死，甚至可以說，生命荒廢到如此地步無異於死，這題旨是相當明顯的。

　　從以上的比較論述中，可以看出，翻譯不只是散文意義的傳達，尤其是翻譯詩。詩的語言，不同於散文，有特定的色調、節奏、暗示、聯想、象徵等等語言藝術的要素，也是詩之為詩的特質。能將這些要素或特質，在另一種語言中重現或再創造，才

是優越的翻譯。因此，文學作品的翻譯，包括原文語意的理解，文學特質或詩意的把握，以及以另一種語言的再創造。這是文學翻譯人才必備的三個條件，亦即，外國語文（包括文化）的理解能力，本國語文（包括文學傳統）的學養，以及文學的感受性。這三者表現在翻譯作品上，亦即，對原文語意理解的準確性，曲盡原意的表現力，以及再創造的藝術效果，也就是一般所謂的「信達雅」這三者合一的翻譯的理想境界。

　　從實踐中，我深知翻譯是一件吃力不討好的工作，要達到這種理想境界是不可能的，包括上述八種〈荒原〉的中譯本。然而，這無礙於我們在理論上探討理想的翻譯。我曾在〈談翻譯〉的一篇文章中，認為「翻譯是一種藝術，也是一門學問。理想的翻譯者應具有創作者的感受性和表現技巧，以及學者的學養和為學的態度。」優秀的翻譯必備的「信」、「達」、「雅」，也可以解釋為作學問的信實態度、語言的感受和表達能力，以及藝術效果再創造的技巧。「從事翻譯和作學問一樣，在態度上最重要的實實在在，不虛不巧……以作學問的態度從事翻譯，則尊重原作者的意思與原著的尊嚴，遇有疑難之處不致隨意增刪或出於不負責任的猜測……對原作的文學特性，藝術風貌，或者立論旨趣，典故象徵等等，經過研究有了確實了解之後，翻譯起來才能得心應手。」就語言的感受和表達能力而言，對原文的感受能力和以另一種語言的表達能力一樣重要。「詩的翻譯者應該具有詩人一樣的匠心，必須也具有詩人那種感受性和表現技巧。有了敏銳的感受性才能了解原詩中的『詩』；有了優越的表現技巧才能將原詩中的『詩』再創造出來，而達到同樣或相應的藝術效果。」「翻譯與原作該是不同語言的雙胞胎，不同國境的形與影。」就

藝術效果的再創造而言，「翻譯不外乎是以另一種語言表現原文所表達或暗示的一切；這一切在文學作品，尤其是詩中，包括語意、句法、語氣、象徵、暗示、聯想、風格，以及整體的藝術效果等等。」「由於語言的結構不同，譯詩與原詩中字句的組合方式不可能完全相同，但是不同的組合所放射的光芒應該是一樣晶瑩輝煌的。」[7]

（原發表於行政院文化建設委員會主辦「外國文學中譯國際研討會」，1994 年 7 月）

7　杜國清，〈談翻譯〉，《幼獅文藝》第 273 期，1976 年 9 月。

重探杜國清譯介〈荒原〉及其相關問題

洪淑苓

　　杜國清就讀臺大外文系期間（1960-1963），[1] 已加入白先勇創立的《現代文學》雜誌社，擔任寫稿、譯稿和編輯的工作。而譯介〈荒原〉[2] 的那段時間，他正在服兵役，也還是給雜誌寫稿。退伍之後（1964.8），他在中學教書一年，然後申請到日本留學，並在赴關西大學（1968）以前，將譯稿交給出版社。到 1969 年 3 月，田園出版社出版了他翻譯的《艾略特文學評論選集》，而 1972 年 4 月則由純文學出版社出版《詩的效用與批評的效用》。[3] 這兩本文學理論的翻譯，已成為當時以及後來的學者從事文學批評的重要參考譯著。當然，這也為杜國清與艾略特的關係作了定位，凡是提到艾略特的文論，都會注意到杜國清。

　　回顧五〇至六〇年代，臺灣文學界對於艾略特（Thomas Stearns Eliot, 1888-1956）文學理論及其長詩〈荒原〉（The Waste Land）等作品深感興趣，也有杜國清等人加以翻譯和介紹。1966

1　杜國清於 1959 年入臺大哲學系，次年（1960）轉入外文系，1963 年畢業。

2　杜國清最初發表時以〈荒地〉名之，後來也都沿用「荒原」的稱法，因此本文皆以〈荒原〉標示。

3　參見蔡欣純，〈論杜國清現代詩創作、翻譯與詩論〉，「第二章 杜國清的生平與創作歷程」及「附錄 杜國清寫作年表」（臺北：臺灣師大臺文系碩士論文，2009），頁 14-23、146-168。

年 5 月，《現代文學》雜誌刊登杜國清翻譯的〈荒地〉，此後杜國清陸續翻譯多篇艾略特的文論，並出版《艾略特文學評論選集》與《詩的效用與批評的效用》。其後，杜國清亦翻譯、研究日本學者西脇順三郎的《詩學》、法國象徵主義詩人波特萊爾的巨著《惡之華》等。

進入九〇年代，艾略特〈荒原〉在華文界的傳播與接受，重新受到重視，譬如孫玉石、張潔宇在研究中國現代主義新詩時，都特闢章節來討論艾略特〈荒原〉及其影響，[4] 可見大陸學界對這個現象的關注。但他們顯然忽略了臺灣學者的成就，因此像杜國清在六〇年代業已譯介此詩，其貢獻也應該再次探討。

華文界對〈荒原〉的譯介

艾略特於 1922 年發表的長詩〈荒原〉，以一次大戰以後的倫敦為世界的縮影，寫出了人類文明毀壞，心靈世界崩解的情形；在創作形式上，突破了以往浪漫主義的表現手法，強調知性的觀念，可說揭開了現代主義創作的旗幟，具有開創性與經典的位置，因此受到後人的注意，不僅震撼了西方世界，也很快地傳入華文世界。

最早的是 1923 年 8 月 27 日《文學周報》上茅盾發表的〈幾個消息〉，但對於艾略特僅有寥寥數語[5]。到三〇年代，《現

---

4 參見孫玉石，《中國現代主義思潮史論》（北京：北京大學出版社，1993）、張潔宇，《荒原上的丁香》（北京：中國人民大學出版社，2003）。

5 參見楊宗翰，〈艾略特，荒原與台灣文學場域〉，《自由時報》，2004 年 1 月 10 日，副刊。此文為近年來重新關注艾略特〈荒原〉譯介問題之文章，除涉及臺灣文學場域之外，有關早期對〈荒原〉的譯介，亦有述評。

代》、《新月》等刊物都曾數次譯介艾略特的詩文評論和作品，徐志摩、何其芳、卞之琳、孫大雨、廢名等，都深受其影響。[6]而葉公超更是個關鍵性的人物，他早年留學英美，在英國時即與艾略特熟識。1932 年，葉公超在〈施望尼評論四十周年〉一文（《新月》4 卷 3 期）中第一次提到艾略特，隨後在〈美國《詩刊》之呼籲〉（《新月》4 卷 5 期）又再次談起艾略特。1934 年 4 月，葉公超在《清華學報》（9 卷 2 期）發表〈愛略忒的詩〉，指出要了解艾略特的詩，也要了解艾略特對於詩的主張；葉公超並詳細分析了〈荒原〉的主題和創作技巧；當時卞之琳便說，葉公超是中國最早引進並完整闡釋〈荒原〉的人。在此前後，北平詩壇對艾略特的關注日漸強盛，有曹葆華、卞之琳等，零星譯介艾略特的詩論文論。1936 年底，清華大學研究生趙蘿蕤動手翻譯〈荒原〉，葉公超也給予她很大的幫助，並為之作序。至四〇年代，《詩創造》、《中國新詩》派下的「九葉」詩人，如鄭敏、陳敬容等，對於艾略特更是極為推崇。[7]

　　但這股「艾略特熱潮」隨著戰爭而消失殆盡，直到六〇、七〇年代以後，臺灣與大陸新詩界才有新的譯本出現。臺灣的第一本譯本是 1961 年由葉維廉翻譯，[8]不久，1966 年，杜國清也翻譯了〈荒原〉；而在大陸則是七〇年代末期由穆旦翻譯。有關〈荒

6　孫玉石，《中國現代主義思潮史論》，第六章〈現代派詩人群系的心態觀照・"荒原"的意識〉（北京：北京大學出版社，1993），頁 174-207。

7　張潔宇，《荒原上的丁香》，第二章〈荒原與古城〉（北京：中國人民大學出版社，2003），頁 86-97。

8　本文以杜國清研究為主，有關葉維廉與艾略特的關係，當另文討論；亦可參見須文蔚，〈葉維廉與臺港現代主義詩論之跨區域傳播〉，《東華漢學》15 期，2012 年 6 月，頁 249-273；有關葉維廉對艾略特及新批評的研究，見頁 262-265。

原〉的中譯本，杜國清〈從〈荒原〉的八種中譯本到文學翻譯人
才的培養與合作〉曾說，艾略特的成名作〈荒原〉發表於 1922
年，而第一個中文譯本是在十五年後，由趙蘿蕤女士所完成，於
1937 年 6 月作為戴望舒主持的《新詩社叢書》第一種出版。第
二個譯本是 1961 年在臺灣推展現代詩運動時，由葉維廉翻譯，
發表在《創世紀》詩刊。第三個譯本是由其本人所翻譯，1966
年發表在《現代文學》。第四個譯本是在七〇年代後半期，由「九
葉詩人」之一穆旦（查良錚）所譯。其他的四個譯本於八〇年代，
前後在臺灣和大陸出版，譯者是李俊清、趙毅衡、裘小龍和劉象
愚。[9] 但因為 1949 年以後，臺海兩岸分隔，所以趙蘿蕤的譯本並
未在臺灣流傳。杜國清說：

> 在台灣最早的〈荒原〉譯本，也是第二個中譯本，是在
> 一九六一年正當台灣詩壇大力推展現代主義運動時，由詩
> 人學者葉維廉所翻譯，發表在《創世紀》詩刊第十六期。
> 第三個中譯本是我翻譯的，發表在一九六六年《現代文學》
> 第二十八期。當時在台灣是看不到趙蘿蕤的譯本的。[10]

也因此，葉維廉、杜國清兩人的譯本等於另起爐灶，呈現
出戰後臺灣現代詩壇的新成果。此外，除杜國清提到的八個中譯

9　杜國清，〈從〈荒原〉的八種中譯本到文學的翻譯人才的培養與合作〉，「外國
　　文學中譯國際研討會」論文，文建會策畫，太平洋文化基金會、國立中央圖書館
　　承辦，臺北：國立中央圖書館，1984 年 7 月 8-10 日。收入杜國清，《詩論·詩評·
　　詩論詩》（臺北：臺大出版中心，2010），頁 282-296。編按：後經修訂改題為〈試
　　論〈荒原〉的八種中譯本〉，收於本書頁 482-495。

10　同上註，頁 282。

本外，七〇年代有香港出版的李達三、談德義主編的《艾略特的荒原》，[11] 臺灣出版的杜若洲譯的《荒原・四重奏》[12] 以及宋穎豪翻譯、刊載於藍星詩刊的譯文。[13]

杜國清譯介〈荒原〉的理念

　　杜國清非常重視自己的翻譯理念和成果，在上述的論文中，他還以〈荒原〉開頭的句子（"April is the cruelest month"）來說明他的譯法有何根據與獨特性。大多數譯者將此譯為「四月是最殘酷的一個月」，但杜國清特別翻譯為「四月／最是／殘酷的／季節」，不僅將 month 譯為季節，也將此句翻成四小節，以突出其韻律。杜國清的說明與比較是：

> 〈荒原〉一開頭，詩人故作驚人之筆，說：四月最是殘酷的一個月（「April is the cruelest month」）。四月正是大地回春，草木復甦，欣欣向榮的時候，怎麼說是最殘酷的呢？對荒原外的人來說，這是有悖情理的；可是對荒原上的任何生命來說，正是如此。……這句原文，翻成「四月是最殘忍的一個月」（趙譯），或「四月是最殘酷的月份」（葉譯、衡譯），或「四月是最殘忍的月份」（裘譯、劉譯），都沒錯，「信」而且「達」，但是不夠「雅」，缺少詩的韻味。查譯翻成「四月最殘忍」，將「一個月」或「月

11 李達三、談德義主編，《艾略特的荒原》（香港：新亞出版社，1976）。

12 杜若洲譯，《荒原：四重奏》（臺北：志文出版社，1985）。

13 宋穎豪，〈荒原〉，《藍星》詩刊 2 期，1985 年 1 月，臺北：九歌出版社印行。

份」略去了，不夠「信」的標準，但是有道理的——他一定也認為「一個月」或「月份」在中文的語感上太沒有詩意了。這正是杜譯認為四月代表春天，因此將它譯成「季節」的理由。此外，杜譯不將「is the cruelest」直翻成「是最殘酷的」，而翻成「最是殘酷的」，也是基於詩的感受性。有些讀者一定會聯想到徐志摩在〈莎喲娜拉〉那首詩中的名句：「最是那一低頭的溫柔」。徐志摩不愧是詩人，將「那一低頭是最溫柔的」這九個字的散文，鍛鍊成一字不差的優美詩句。尤其值得一提的是，杜譯「四月／最是／殘酷的／季節」在節奏上完全呼應英文原句「April / is the / cruelest / month」重輕相間的四個音步。[14]

文中的「杜譯」即是杜國清本人，由此可見他對翻譯所堅持的「信、達、雅」的理念，而且因為他也從事創作，故特別重視音節與韻律的問題。在內容的理解與詮釋上，杜國清亦展現了他深厚的西洋文學學識以及敏銳犀利的文學涵養：

> 從以上的解釋中，我們可以對〈荒原〉的主旨有了較明確的了解。在荒原的世界裡，春天是殘酷的，他們規避欲望，拒絕回憶，不願生命力的復甦，固然是逃避的心理，也是對現實的消極反抗；他們喜歡冬天半死不活的狀態，無為無欲，如果不能獲得救贖，是寧死勿活的。然而，這首詩的主題，並不在於讚揚或歌頌這種反常的生命觀。詩

---

14 杜國清，〈從〈荒原〉的八種中譯本到文學的翻譯人才的培養與合作〉，《詩論‧詩評‧詩論詩》，頁290。

中涉指聖杯傳說的象徵意義……換句話說，生與死是〈荒原〉的兩大主題，其根本意義在於，漁王的傳說象徵由生到死的頹廢，而繁殖神的崇拜象徵由死到生，乃至由死達到生的救贖。〈荒原〉開篇這七行的主旨在於前者，極言荒原世界的頹廢心態。……這個題辭用來喻指荒原上的生命，奄奄一息，不死不活，其實是，這種生不如死，甚至可以說，生命荒廢到如此地步無異於死，這題旨是相當明顯的。[15]

這雖只是針對開頭七行的詮釋，但已經通貫整個〈荒原〉的主題精神，讓我們充分感受到「四月」所代表的生與死的衝突性。而這樣的衝突不斷在〈荒原〉一詩中重複出現，更具體呈現了「文明毀壞、心靈崩解」的「荒原意識」。杜國清雖然僅以〈荒原〉的第一句譯文做比較，但已充分顯現他深諳信、雅、達的翻譯技巧與境界，以及身為詩人從事譯詩時的創造性。

臺灣文壇對艾略特的介紹與杜國清譯介的貢獻

臺灣文壇對艾略特的介紹，除了〈荒原〉，也包括其他詩作與詩學理論。在 1954 年，紀弦主編的《現代詩》第 8 期即刊登了方思摘譯的艾略特詩論；詩作部分，《現代詩》也曾刊登一些節譯文章，如馬朗、葉冬、柏谷曾陸續選譯〈歇斯底里亞症〉、〈晨起憑窗〉、〈風景〉、〈灰燼禮拜三〉、〈荒原〉、〈普魯

---

15 同上註，頁 293-294。

弗洛克戀歌〉、〈大教堂的謀殺〉與〈東方博士之旅〉。夏濟安
主編的《文學雜誌》上則有余光中譯的艾略特論文〈論自由詩〉
（1 卷 6 期；1957.2）、李經〈倫敦市上訪艾略忒〉（4 卷 6 期；
1958.8）。[16]

　　這些現象顯示，五〇至六〇年代，臺灣文學界對艾略特又
重新注意。除上述情形外，1961 年 1 月，《創世紀》詩刊第 16
期刊載了葉維廉翻譯的全文；此後葉維廉有多篇相關的研究論
文，今已收錄在他的《從現象到表現——葉維廉早期文集》[17]。
篇目與著作年代如下：〈焚毀的諾墩之世界〉，1959 年；〈艾
略特方法論序說〉，1960 年；〈艾略特的批評〉，1960 年；〈靜
止的中國花瓶——艾略特與中國詩的意象〉，1960 年；〈荒原
與神話的關係〉，1961 年。

　　可見，葉維廉與杜國清兩位教授都是艾略特專家，他們在
六〇年代都已經注意到艾略特的創作和理論，並且多次譯介相關
作品。而白先勇等創辦的《現代文學》雜誌，也有多篇相關的譯
介，試臚列於下：

期別	出版年月	原作者	譯者	篇名	類別
2	1960.5	Eliot. T. S.	伍希雅	〈焚毀的諾墩〉	翻譯
3	1960.7	Eliot. T. S.	銅馬	〈四首序曲〉	翻譯
13	1962.4	Eliot. T. S.	余光中[18]	〈論葉慈〉	文學評論
22	1964.10	Eliot. T. S.	杜國清	〈艾略特論文選輯〉	翻譯
24	1965.4	Eliot. T. S.	泥雨	〈JA 普魯洛克的戀歌〉	翻譯

16 參見楊宗翰，〈艾略特，荒原與台灣文學場域〉。

17 葉維廉，《從現象到表現——葉維廉早期文集》（臺北：東大圖書公司，1994）。

18 余光中也在 1960 年元月號的《文星》雜誌 27 期上發表〈創造二十世紀之新詩的
　大詩人艾略特〉。

期別	出版年月	原作者	譯者	篇名	類別
24	1965.4	Eliot. T. S.	李篤恭	〈宗教與文學〉	翻譯
27	1966.2	Eliot. T. S.	非馬	〈空心人〉	翻譯
27	1966.2	Eliot. T. S.	杜國清	〈普魯洛克與其他的觀察〉	翻譯
28	1966.5	Eliot. T. S.	杜國清	〈荒地〉	翻譯
28	1966.5	杜國清		〈關於荒地〉	文學評論
30	1966.12	Eliot. T. S.	杜國清	〈「磐石」底合唱〉	翻譯

　　從以上目錄看來，《現代文學》確實是譯介艾略特作品與詩論的一個重要園地，杜國清也因參與編撰工作，所以提供多篇譯稿與評論。而杜國清也是笠詩社發起人之一，所以在六〇年代，他也在笠詩刊發表多篇有關艾略特的譯作或評論，從最早的〈論聽覺的想像〉（《笠》2 期，1964.6），到最後的〈小論詩的批評〉（28 期，1968.12）刊登之後，《艾略特文學評論選集》也在翌年出版（1969.1）；期間總共刊登十六篇艾略特的作品或評論翻譯，[19] 可見六〇年代杜國清傾盡全力譯介艾略特的用心。

　　此外，1968 年，顏元叔在《大學》雜誌發表〈歐立德與艾略特〉，其後又發表〈論歐立德的詩〉及〈歐立德的戲劇──音響與字質的研究〉，[20] 他將艾略特改譯為歐立德，意欲凸顯艾略特的評論家身分；而顏元叔本人對艾略特的詮釋也展現了他新批評的功力。綜論六〇年代末到七〇年代初期，對於艾略特有深入引介與評論的，當屬力倡新批評的顏元叔。[21]

---

19 參見蔡欣純，〈論杜國清現代詩創作、翻譯與詩論〉（臺北：臺灣師大臺文系碩士論文，2009）。

20 收入顏元叔，《文學批評散論》（臺北：驚聲出版社，1970）。

21 參見陳芳明，〈細讀顏元叔的詩評〉，《詩與現實》（臺北：洪範書店，1977），頁 9-40。楊宗翰前揭文亦指出：「但台大外文系教授顏元叔才真正是六〇年代台灣文學場域中，影響力最大的艾略特詮釋者。這位英美『新批評』的引渡人，甚至還倡議要把文化界慣用的『艾略特』改譯為『歐立德』。」

　　五〇至六〇年代這段期間對艾略特的詩歌理論、〈荒原〉及其他作品的譯介，無疑大大地推進了臺灣現代詩進入現代主義的時期。陳芳明〈翻譯艾略特——余光中與顏元叔對新批評的接受〉一文中，對杜國清、余光中、顏元叔等人的翻譯與論述分別加以評點，同時也提出一個觀點：

> 台灣詩人對現代主義的整合，尤其是對艾略特技藝的吸收，並不是單方面的接受。艾略特的風貌，經過變貌的解釋，就不再屬於西方，而是屬於台灣現代主義的一環。[22]

　　是故，利用譯介，把艾略特「本地化」，從而建立起臺灣的現代主義文學，陳芳明亦肯定杜國清的兩點貢獻，一是透過日文文學資源以及他自己的融會貫通，將艾略特〈荒原〉及其他重要文論，推進臺灣現代文學的場域；二是，杜國清翻譯出版《艾略特文學評論選集》與《詩的效用與批評的效用》，也「開啟台灣文學對艾略特較為開闊的認識」，「確定台灣文學對艾略特的接受，在六〇年代已宣告成熟。」[23]

　　準此而言，無疑的，在當時無法一窺三〇年代學者的論著資料情況下，杜國清個人對於艾略特〈荒原〉以及其他作品、詩論的譯介，確實提供給臺灣讀者更清楚地認知艾略特之詩與詩論的成就。

---

22 陳芳明在國科會 94 年度研究計畫成果報告〈翻譯現代性的再思考：新批評在台灣現代主義文學中的引介與實踐〉中，已有相關論述，後發表為專文〈翻譯艾略特——余光中與顏元叔對新批評的接受〉，收入其《現代主義及其不滿》（臺北：聯經出版公司，2013），頁 145-174，引文見頁 161。

23 參見陳芳明，〈翻譯艾略特——余光中與顏元叔對新批評的接受〉，同上註，頁 152-154。

〈荒原〉對華文現代詩的影響

　　有關〈荒原〉對於現代派詩人的影響，孫玉石《中國現代主義詩潮史論》曾為「荒原」意識下定義：「所謂『荒原』意識，就是在 T.S. 艾略特〈荒原〉的影響下，一部分現代派詩人頭腦中產生的對於整體人類悲劇命運的現代性觀照，和對於充滿極荒謬與黑暗的現實社會的批判意識。」他認為四〇年代現代派的詩人吸收艾略特〈荒原〉的內涵和創作技巧，而轉化為荒城、荒園、古鎮、古城和荒街等意象，並且以之為題，創作出許多作品。例如戴望舒〈深閉的園子〉、卞之琳〈古鎮的夢〉、何其芳〈古城〉等，都可看得出來受到艾略特〈荒原〉的影響。[24]

　　如是，依孫玉石之說，在四〇年代的中國現代詩壇是將荒原意識轉換為古城、荒街，則在六〇年代及其後的臺灣現代詩壇是激發出什麼樣的作品呢？經筆者與杜國清討論，杜國清認為艾略特〈荒原〉對臺灣現代詩的影響有兩個，一是影響了戰爭詩的出現，因為艾略特此詩是描寫一次大戰以後的倫敦，詩中對於戰爭帶來的災害與慘狀，有深刻的描寫；二是長詩，因〈荒原〉的篇幅長、結構謹嚴而繁複，對當時還在發展中的現代詩也很大的示範作用。[25] 而筆者則初步認為，這應當與都市詩的出現有密切關係，因為倫敦是個都市，是都市的題材啟發了臺灣現代詩人的創作。可以作為佐證的是，當《文學雜誌》與《現代文學》雜誌分別介紹艾略特之後，其刊物上往往都會出現仿作、與艾略

---

24 孫玉石，《中國現代主義思潮史論》，頁 177-190。張潔宇亦持此說，見其《荒原上的丁香》，頁 86-120。

25 筆者有機會多次聆聽杜國清教授演講，曾向杜國清教授請教與討論，此為其口頭表示之意見。

特對話，或出現長篇詩作、以都市為題材的作品等，例如《文學雜誌》刊登余光中譯的艾略特論文〈論自由詩〉（1 卷 6 期；1957.2），不久即出現李經的〈倫敦市上訪艾略忒〉（4 卷 6 期；1958.8），此詩乃以倫敦這個都市為背景；而楊宗翰亦發現「最特別的是，該刊 4 卷 6 期有一首夏濟安自己刻意仿效〈荒原〉的『試作』〈香港──一九五〇〉。」[26] 此係以「香港」來仿效倫敦。而次年，《文學雜誌》則刊登了羅門〈都市〉（5 卷 5 期，1959.1），都市詩的興起已經蓄勢待發。而余光中的長詩〈天狼星〉（《現代文學》第 8 期，1961.5），也有可能受到艾略特的啟發；這類現象都可以作為進一步研究的依據。

（原載《孤獨與美：台灣現代詩九家論》，釀出版，2016）

---

26 同前註。

後記

　　艾略特對我的影響，不論是在現代詩創作上或是詩學理論的建構上，持續至今，剛好整整一甲子。那是我有志於詩創作開始接觸西方現代主義的上世紀六〇年代，1962 年開始在《現代文學》發表創作和翻譯的時候，包括〈荒原〉和〈普魯佛洛克的戀歌及其他觀察〉。作為詩人和學者，我的生涯可以說是開始於接觸艾略特，很高興終於能夠出版《艾略特詩選》，正如艾略特所說的，「在我的開始裡有我的結束」（In my beginning is my end）；有始有終，似乎是天意。

　　促成這一完美天意的是，聯經出版公司的陳逸華副總編的策劃，作為紀念《荒原》出版一百周年的獻禮。（詳見他的〈出版弁言〉一文）承他的好意，協助搜集當年在《現代文學》和《笠》發表的翻譯，並請人打成文字檔。臺大臺文所學弟涂書瑋也幫忙整理了一份有關艾略特的翻譯資料掃描。在審訂的過程中，多謝陳怡燕小姐的協助，將每一首詩的原文和翻譯並排對照，以便我逐行核對修訂。事實上，沒有她的盡心盡力幫忙整理和校對，我是無法完成審訂舊稿的。艾略特的《荒原》出版已有一百年，是公認的現代詩經典，而我的翻譯本也有半個世紀了。禁得起時間的考驗，能有再版的機會，固然感到欣慰，可是回顧當年的舊作，恍如隔世，喚起我的一個未了的心願，希望能夠翻譯艾略特的壓軸巨作，四首〈四重奏〉。因此，藉此機會我進一

步翻譯〈四重奏〉和另外兩篇重要的詩作：〈聖灰日〉和〈東方博士的行旅〉。四首〈四重奏〉是詩人的傑作，表現藝術作品的普遍主題：人與自然的關係、生死與神的宗教情懷、現實與理念的糾葛、現世與時間的抗衡、生命終於回歸先祖等等人生現象的觀察、思索、冥想和感悟，在彼此連結的四首詩中，圍繞著「氣」、「土」、「水」、「火」四大自然元素相互交響重奏。總之，這本《艾略特詩選》不是舊譯重刊，而是有相當分量的增譯，包括艾略特最重要的詩作而無遺憾。

　　除了詩作的翻譯，這本選集還收錄了我過去寫的一些有關艾略特的文章，包括〈艾略特生平〉、〈艾略特與我〉、〈艾略特的文學論〉、〈試論〈荒原〉的八種中譯本〉，以及洪淑苓教授的〈重探杜國清譯介〈荒原〉及其相關問題〉，希望能較多面地呈現艾略特的詩人風貌和對華文世界的影響。所選譯的作品，依照出版的時序安排，根據 *T. S. Eliot: The Complete Poems And Plays, 1909-1950* （HARCOURT, BRACE & WORLD, INC., NEW YORK, 1952），不是全譯，也不包括戲劇。這本英文原版書還是我大學時的同班同學、鄭恆雄知道我有意翻譯艾略特的詩特地送給我的。這本選集書名題為：「艾略特詩選：〈荒原〉、〈四重奏〉及其他觀察」，除了標示重要的內容之外，也揭示詩人創作的基本態度，在於觀察。這與艾略特的第一本詩集《普魯佛洛克及其他觀察》（*Prufrock And Other Observations*, 1917）互相呼應，反映出艾略特所主張的「不具個性」（Impersonality）的客觀詩論——以「客觀的相關物」（objective correlative）表達感情的創作手法。這一技法與即物主義（Objectivity）「以物觀物」的客觀表現，可以說是一脈相承，異曲同工。這一藝術創作的詩

觀，我在其他詩論文章中，已再三論述，也是我在創作實踐中常用的表現手法。艾略特對我的創作和詩觀的影響，我相信，值得有志藝術創作者的參考（見詩集《光射塵方・圓照萬象：杜國清的詩情世界》，臺大出版中心，2017）。

艾略特是一位高度知性的詩人。他的詩，思辨性強，相當深奧難解，耐於思考。在語言表現上，往往借助於客觀的事物或事件，描寫人物、動作、行為、對話、場景、地理景觀等，呈現戲劇性的情景，富有形象性和象徵性；同時突破固定的格律，講究自然的節奏感，使用的手法包括尾韻、頭韻、行中韻，或是跨行、斷句、並列、重複等，藉以表現自由詩的音樂性。在翻譯上，我盡力呼應原文的表達方式，而不只是詩句意義的傳達。詩的藝術創作，艾略特稱之為作者「與字句和意義難以忍受的角力」（the intolerable wrestle with words and meanings）。關於艾略特的創作藝術和評論研究，是一個專門的學術領域，不是這本詩選的重點。作為譯者，我只能根據有限的參考資料，力求了解原文。由於中文和英文在思考方式和語法習慣上的差異，譯文無法句句對應，迻譯時不得不做適當的調整，而在上下文中，力求照應。力拙之處，請讀者包涵；誤讀誤解，在所難免，也請讀者指正。

我希望這本詩選能夠增進我們對二十世紀傑出現代主義詩人艾略特的認識，體會他對現代與傳統、文學與宗教、創作與藝術、理論與實踐的觀點，有助於我們對東西現代詩的特質及其優越作品的了解和鑑賞。

杜國清

加州望月坡　2022 年 6 月 22 日

不朽
艾略特詩選：〈荒原〉、〈四重奏〉及其他觀察

2022年12月初版　　　　　　　　　　　　　　　定價：新臺幣580元
有著作權‧翻印必究
Printed in Taiwan.

著　　　者	T. S. Eliot	
譯　　　者	杜　國　清	
校　　　對	吳　美　滿	
	吳　浩　宇	
內文排版	李　偉　涵	
封面設計	謝　佳　穎	

出　版　者	聯經出版事業股份有限公司	副總編輯	陳　逸　華		
地　　　址	新北市汐止區大同路一段369號1樓	總　編　輯	涂　豐　恩		
叢書編輯電話	(02)86925588轉5319	總　經　理	陳　芝　宇		
台北聯經書房	台北市新生南路三段94號	社　　　長	羅　國　俊		
電　　　話	(02)23620308	發　行　人	林　載　爵		
台中辦事處	(04)22312023				
台中電子信箱	e-mail：linking2@ms42.hinet.net				
印　刷　者	世和印製企業有限公司				
總　經　銷	聯合發行股份有限公司				
發　行　所	新北市新店區寶橋路235巷6弄6號2樓				
電　　　話	(02)29178022				

行政院新聞局出版事業登記證局版臺業字第0130號

國家圖書館出版品預行編目資料

艾略特詩選：〈荒原〉、〈四重奏〉及其他觀察/ T. S. Eliot著．
杜國清譯．初版．新北市．聯經．2022年12月．512面．14.8×21公分
（不朽）
ISBN　978-957-08-6653-7（平裝）

873.51　　　　　　　　　　　　　　　　　　　111018827